THE COMIC LOOKING GLASS

LOOKING GLASS LIBRARY E-28

THE COMIC LOOKING GLASS

EDITED BY

HART DAY LEAVITT

LOOKING GLASS LIBRARY

DISTRIBUTED BY RANDOM HOUSE

NEW YORK

Library of Congress Catalog Card Number: 61-13201

Copyright © 1961 by Epstein and Carroll Associates, Inc.
Manufactured in the United States of America
by the Colonial Press Inc., Clinton, Mass.

ACKNOWLEDGMENTS

Much of the material contained in this volume is copyrighted and the publishers of the Looking Glass Library gratefully acknowledge the following permissions extended by the authors, publishers, authors' representatives, and other holders of the copyrights listed below.

"Ladle Rat Rotten Hut" from *Anguish Languish* by Howard Chace. Reprinted by permission of the author. Copyright 1953 by Howard Chace, Oxford, Ohio. "The Body Beautiful" from *Soap Behind the Ears,* by Cornelia Otis Skinner, Copyright 1941 by Cornelia Otis Skinner; "Ordeal for Sons" from *Nuts In May* by Cornelia Otis Skinner. Copyright 1944 by Cornelia Otis Skinner, reprinted by permission of Dodd, Mead & Company; "Who Knows It" from *Model Memoirs* by Stephen Leacock, "Sorrows of a Super Soul" and "Hannah of the Highlands" from *Nonsense Novels* by Stephen Leacock, reprinted by permission of Dodd, Mead & Company. Copyright 1938 by Dodd, Mead & Company, Inc. and The Bodley Head Ltd., London. "The Third Ingredient" from *Options* by O. Henry. Copyright 1908 by Doubleday & Company, Inc.; "The Princess and the Puma" from *Heart of the West* by O. Henry. Reprinted by permission of Doubleday & Company, Inc. Excerpts from the book *1066 and All That* by W. C. Sellar and R. J. Yeatman. Copyright 1941 by E. P. Dutton & Co., Inc., Renewal, 1959 by Robert Julian Yeatman. Dutton Everyman Paperback. Reprinted by permission of E. P. Dutton & Co., Inc., and Methuen & Co. Ltd. Excerpt from *Acres and Pains* by S. J. Perelman, copyright 1943, 1944, 1947 by S. J. Perelman, copyright 1942, 1943, by The Curtis Publishing Company. Reprinted by permission of the author. "Hun-gah" and "Beware the Brazilian Navy" from *My Sister Eileen,* copyright 1938 by Ruth McKenney. Reprinted by permission of Harcourt, Brace & World, Inc. and Rupert Hart-Davis, Ltd., London. "Mr. Kaplan and Shakespeare" from *The Education of H★Y★M★A★N K★A★P★L★A★N* by Leonard Q. Ross, copyright 1937 by Harcourt Brace & World, Inc., and reprinted with their permission and the permission of Leo Rosten. "Animal Stories" or "How Georgie Dog Gets the Rubbers on the Guest Room Bed" and "How Lillian Mosquito Projects Her

Contents

FACT

FICTION

FABLE

FOOLING

FANTASY

FARCE

CORNELIA OTIS SKINNER

Ordeal for Sons

The time approaches for me to go mortify my young son by a visit to his school again, and it's a tossup as to which of us is anticipating the event with more happy apprehension. Not that I am not eager to see him; nor is there, I trust, any lack of filial warmth on his part. But in the environment of a large and pretty impressive boarding school and the atmosphere of one of those week ends when parents, teeming with tradition, run around with their offspring, doing a great many traditional things, something seems to happen which puts us both under a considerable nervous strain. My son suddenly appears to me as an amiable but utter stranger and it's obvious that I appear to him as a complete menace. In the tender bosom of home, I smugly pride myself that he looks upon me with devotion, respect and even periodic moments of admiration. In the Spartan bosom of boarding school, he regards me with tolerance, embarrassment and moments of profound shame, mingled with the sort of pitying affection one might feel for a harmless family imbecile. That he considers me anything but bright, is evinced by his letter concerning my impending visitation and containing instructions so detailed, it surprises me he didn't at the same time write his father asking him to pin my ticket on me, tip the porter and ask him to put me off at the right place. He tells me to take the night train which goes, he says, at night, from Grand Central. "When you arrive at . . ." (and, just in case my memory needed jogging, he mentions the name of the town) . . . "get off the train." (Possibly he thought I might want to stay on for the ride.) ". . . and walk through the stashion. Go to the hotel and have breakfast allthough the dogwaggon has hamburgers but then you just take coffee. I have classes all morning so do what you like. You may want a bath. . . ." (A startling suggestion coming from a small boy so allergic to them.) "At 12, take a taxi to the Alumen" (his own basic English for Alumni) "House where I'll be waiting with severall peopel for lunch." These instructions were a replica of those he sent me prior to my previous visit and as such were superfluous, the events of that pilgrimage being indelibly impressed on my memory.

That night train which leaves at night, may do so from the Grand Central, but there are certain features of it which lead one to think it would feel more at home in the Smithsonian. It winds its way northward, stopping at all stations, signal towers and, it would seem, cattle crossings, and politely pulling off at all sidings to make way for slow freights. At Lowell, the train is dismembered and the car bound for the school town is violently clashed onto a series of other trains who will have none of it and who, the moment it is coupled to them, shake it loose in apparent fury. In between times, it is taken on a scenic tour of the yards behind a switch engine driven by a novice engineer who has a lot to learn. This goes on for three or four hours, at the end of which interlude, the brakes sigh shrilly and the car, attached at last to one train which will tolerate it, heads for the north. The school is situated in the frozen heart of New England in a climate called, by those who have survived it, "bracing." You start in bracing about two A.M. and ring for the porter in the naïve hope that he will hear the bell and bring another blanket. He does neither and you continue to brace under cover of a coat, the extra pillow and that suitcase they no longer allow you to set in the aisle. By morning, you are permanently braced in a manner which, when you manage to emerge from between the icy Pullman curtains, becomes a semicrouching position.

This trip, the weather will, blessedly, be not so bracing. But the other features will be the same. Early morning in the ladies' room there will be the same jam session of females in various states of dishevelment . . . myself in the worst state of the lot . . . lurching against one another and politely fighting for a chance at the tooth-brushing basin. This is a rude introduction to the sisterhood with whom one will be rubbing elbows for

13

the next forty-eight hours. Last trip, my child had neglected to mention the fact that it was to be a gala week
end and that a good many other parents were also coming, and I remember regarding these ladies with sentiments not untinged with venom, until, with remorseful
chagrin, it occurred to me that they might be somebody's mothers, and my glare of resentment melted into
a weak leer of tentative friendliness to which some re-
sponded wanly and some not at all.

This time also, I shall try to feel more charitably inclined toward whoever is in the drawing-room. Occupants of a drawing-room, unless I am one of them,
rouse in me sentiments of proletarian resentment. I fix
them with a Madame DeFarge stare and look about for
a copy of *The Daily Worker* to brandish in their faces.
The injustice of this attitude was proved by the fact that
the room on this occasion was filled to bursting point by
a genial family also bound for the school—mother,
father, small brother entered for the year 1953, little
sister profoundly bored by everything and a slap-
happy Sealyham dog. The boy they were visiting turned
out to be a friend of my son's . . . a fact which
endeared them to me only a few degrees less than the
happy moment before dinner when the father, sensing
my need for such encouragement, poured me out a generous hooker of Scotch.

This time, too, I am going to know how to dress. The
first trip, under the impression that I was a lone mother
going quietly to visit her child at a country school, I
dressed the part, as I thought, to perfection, in a tweed

suit, flat shoes and an ancient coat which, after years of exposure, is beginning to look less like beaver than cocker-spaniel. With a rapidly increasing sense of inferiority, I watched the disheveled ladies of the washroom emerge from the night-in-a-Pullman chrysalis into visions of mink-coated smartness. In June, mink coats will hardly be worn, but I'm asking a friend to lend me a sable scarf in case of an emergency.

At the station, there will, I suppose, be the absence of a porter and the scramble for a taxi which is eventually shared by five beaming mothers and one lone father, anything but beaming. On the way to the hotel, there is a good deal of strained merriment. Everybody asks everybody else if they have enough room, and everybody assures everybody else that they have, although nobody has any. Then everybody asks everybody else what form their boy is in and somebody who is in the know recounts the athletic events for the day and everybody says doesn't that sound grand and everybody else says yes, doesn't it. The lone father says nothing until the taxi approaches the hotel when he comes forth with the consoling statement that he hears the school has two cases of scarlet fever.

The hotel is one of those New England hostelries that must have been in its prime about the time of Rutherford B. Hayes. It may not be aquiver with Statler efficiency, but I find in it a good deal of pristine charm and it is perfectly comfortable. A morning spent there quietly reading a book, writing a letter or even taking that suggested bath, is restful and pleasant. Then the village clock strikes the hour of noon and I take a conveyance to the school and the "Alumen House."

Previous experience has resigned me to the deflating fact that my small boy who, at home, hurtles to meet me after an absence of only half a day, with demonstrations of rapture, will now, after an absence of several months, greet me with a formal "Hi" and a bare handshake. I know better than to try to kiss him. Last time, when I leaned forward to do so, he ducked in mortification and left me smacking the air. As before, he will be waiting for me outside the front door and will conduct me inside in the manner of someone at Tattersall's bringing in a horse, the behavior of which is uncertain. The weather being milder, he will be spared the humiliation of watching me, in the process of taking off my galoshes, remove my shoes at the same time and have to stand stocking-footed for some moments in the crowded hallway. I suppose the "severall peopel" will again be three or four of his classmates to whom he will be reluctant to exhibit me and concerning whom, albeit I have never before laid eyes on them, he will expect me to know every detail. The prospect of that luncheon reminds me to reserve a table. Last time, being a novice in such matters, we found the dining room looking like Saturday noon at Sardi's, with every table overflowing and a line-up at the door. A gracious and rather pretty lady asked us if we had reserved a table and I said why no, and my son said why hadn't I, and I countered why hadn't *he*, to which his reply was an exasper-

16

ated "Really, Mother!" Our distress was evident and the
gracious lady consoled us by setting us up a special fes-
tive board in an alcove of the library . . . which was
all right by my son who, after the episode of the
galoshes, thought it safest to keep me quietly out of
sight. Lunch was nervous but pleasant. My child's bud-
dies impressed me as being very nice and I thought,
somewhat fatuously, that we all got along amazingly
well; although at one point, my boy hissed at me that I
didn't have to laugh so loud. If I did, it was due to a certain amount of strain which I imagine they too shared.
There is a technique to carrying on social chit-chat with
little boys which I am slow at mastering. All of them
were on their best behavior, which meant that most of
the time, they maintained complete silence while I
searched wildly about in my mind for topics of possible
interest. With much too eager brightness, I asked the
usual routine questions . . . where each of them came
from, what colleges they were going to . . . how they
liked school. I even ventured a few remarks concerning
athletics, which, coming from me, was the equivalent of
Betty Grable discussing Relativity. They answered each
question politely and then lapsed into polite silence.
Once or twice I managed to come forth with something
in the nature of a quip at which they would burst out
in a chorus of deafening guffaws which ceased as
abruptly as they started, and there would then ensue
further stretches of that polite silence. All through the
meal, my son regarded me with a look which was sof-

17

tened by momentary gleams of appreciation, but which for the most part indicated that he thought I might at any minute start dancing a Samba on the table.

Lunch ended with no greater mishap than that I forgot to pay for it, which made him again say, "Really, Mother!" He never calls me Mother unless he is particularly ashamed of me and that week end he never called me anything else.

Lunch safely over, he pulled off the first of a series of disappearing acts which he performed at intervals during the next twenty-four hours. The school is a large one, with many buildings and vast grounds. Emerging from some hall or dormitory, he would suddenly announce that now we would go to some place with a cryptic name like Big Upper or Down Lower and, before I'd have time to ask him what he meant, he'd be gone, leaving me to wander about like a derelict until he'd appear as suddenly as he had vanished, to ask impatiently why I hadn't come along. Having some extra studying to do, he then deposited me on a settee in a sort of parents' social hall, told me not to move till he got back, and, seemingly, evaporated. My time, for the most part, was beguiled by another mother . . . an imposing woman who looked like a combination of Demeter and Susan B. Anthony. She was knitting a seaboot with such a zealous efficiency, she gave the impression of doing two at the same time.

"What form's your boy in?" came from her in a clarion tone, and I realized she was addressing me.

"The First," I replied, then, noticing the slight lift to

18

her eyebrow added, vindicatingly, "He's only just thirteen."

"Same form as my youngest," she said. Then, doubtless to put me at ease, "He's eleven."

"A Quiz Kid!" was what I wanted to say, but being a lady, merely inquired if he were her only child.

"Mercy no," she retorted. "I have five. All boys. All of them went here."

"How wonderful," I murmured.

"Their father went here before them," she continued and, being stuck for another reply, I came out with another "How wonderful."

She then started a dissertation on the subject of the school. Did I think Mr. So-and-So in the Whatsis Department was as good as old Mr. Whosis had been, and, to my mind, did Dr. X preach as good a sermon as Dr. Y? I had to confess my ignorance on such matters and the horrid fact that this was my first visit to the place. If I had admitted to never having known about the Fourth of July, she could not have looked more horrified. But she proved to be a kindly sort, and after her initial shock, she launched forth in a detailed narrative history of the school and its traditions in the simple language of a missionary telling a heathen child the story of Christmas. This hour of instruction was cut short by the arrival of my son who said it was time for hockey practice and would I care to watch. Thanking the Mother of Men for her enlightening information, I set forth with my child who, the moment we got to territory totally unfamiliar to me, again disappeared. I wandered on aimlessly, passing stray professors and groups of boys who looked at me as if they wondered if my attendant knew I was loose. Some of the mink-coat mothers also passed and we bestowed on one another that sickly smile which can be taken for recognition or pure imbecility. After a time, my offspring hove in sight armed with skates and a stick and told me to follow him. Hockey was being played on a pond some hundred yards beyond us and the people I had passed were all heading for the barrier, which seemed to be the vantage place for watching the game. Once arrived at the pond, however, my son started leading me off in an oblique direction. When I shyly asked the reason, he said he didn't want me near the barrier . . . that I might get in the way, or fall down or otherwise make myself conspicuous. His method of making me inconspicuous was to station me off on a remote and windy promontory. A strange, solitary figure, silhouetted against the snow, I felt like that picture of Napoleon overlooking Moscow. I could hardly see what was going on, much less make out which of the distant swirling figures was my child, which, perhaps, was just as well as it saved me the anguish of seeing him make a goal on his own side which counted some sort of colossal penalty and made him a pariah for the remainder of the game. On my forthcoming visit I am told the sport will be boat racing and I suppose by way of making me inconspicuous, I shall be placed in a tree.

After hockey, we made a brief sojourn to his room, which isn't a room but a sort of cubicle in a long dormitory. It looked like the East Coast of Florida after a hurricane and I offered to neat it up a bit for him. But he said no, if I did, he'd never find anything in it. So, with a shuddering glance at a mud-caked shoe reposing on a pillow and a toothbrush handle jammed into a jar of peanut butter, we left.

Next morning was Chapel, a very charming and moving ceremony which takes place at eleven. My son, although he knows I am the soul of punctuality, told me it was at ten-fifteen, but that I'd better get there by ten. I did, and found the place locked and deserted. Nor was there any sign of my child. After a time of sitting like Leah the Forsaken on the chapel steps, waiting for the doors to open, he appeared, greeted me with one of those ardent "Hi's" and said "Come on, I'll take you to your place." He sings in the choir and I was hoping for a good view of him. However, he led me to the visitors' gallery where he placed me in a far corner of the back row. When I inquired why I couldn't sit in the front row he replied, "Because" . . . an irrefutable answer I myself have resorted to so often with him, I hadn't the nerve to pursue the matter further. Perhaps he was right in putting me off in a corner. Little boys in white surplices marching down the nave of a chapel, their clear young voices raised in song, make me cry quite badly and I was glad, for his sake, nobody could see me.

After Chapel, came the ordeal of interviewing certain terrifying powers that were, concerning his work. My boy is not of the stuff that Phi Beta Kappas are made of and his marks have been a source of anguish for him, his family and, I suspect, his instructors. I had forced him into making an appointment for me with the assistant headmaster who acted as sort of dean, holding jurisdiction over the students' academic welfare . . . or, in our case, ill-fare. He seldom, they said, came into direct contact with the boys but ruled their destinies from an Olympian distance. He sounded extremely awesome and I pictured him as something between Erasmus and Zeus, hurling down on the student body thunderbolts or diplomas as he saw fit. At the prospect of my impending interview, my child was in a panic which I shared with equal acuteness. I was convinced that he would expel my son and me along with him and my knees buckled as I neared his office, at the threshold of which my offspring turned tail and beat it. The cause of our panic proved to be a delightful, mild-mannered gentleman who with great courtesy asked me to be seated and plunged right into the matter at hand by remarking that my son's marks were not over-satisfactory . . . to which triumph of understatement I acquiesced with sorrow. Then and there we both dismissed the painful subject and there passed a charming half hour in which we talked about Katharine Hepburn's Rosalind. At the end of this I remembered that my scholar was quaking outside and excused myself, relieved that neither of us had as yet been expelled. My scholar met me with gloomy foreboding. It was apparent that he was afraid to hear the verdict.

"What did he say?" he finally managed to ask.

"He said for you to work harder," I answered. After that we then went off to lunch, just the two of us, in the hotel where, under the influence of steak, mashed potatoes and three helpings of ice cream, his formal manner relaxed and, there being nobody he knew around, I detected a gleam of the filial affection I had feared was dead.

Time came for my train. I dropped him in front of his dormitory, where was gathered a group of upper classmen. He tried to say good-by in the frozen style of his previous greeting, but in the language of departing there is no equivalent of "Hi," so he murmured an awkward "Be careful." Then he turned to leave, rushed back as if he'd forgotten something and, flinging his arms about me in a sudden tackle, smacked me shamelessly on the cheek.

I guess this impending trip will be quite similar. I shall ask the wrong questions, say the wrong things and generally shame him. In conversing with upper classmen, I shall again adopt that hearty tone of voice which, according to my son, sounds as if I were on a quarterdeck in a stiff gale. I shall again be deserted in unfamiliar portions of the grounds, I and the mink-coat mothers, now in summer prints, will again leer sheepishly at one another and I shall again weep profusely over Chapel. Some long-suffering master will again discuss with me my child's mental progress . . . or lack of it. And it will all be quite charming and rather awful. But I'm going to do it. And I guess the reason is, I wouldn't miss it for anything.

JOSEPH WECHSBERG

The Sleepy Piano-Player

The laziest man I have ever known was Sebastiano, a Spanish pianist from Algeciras, who joined our four-man orchestra aboard *La Bourdonnais* for one voyage. On sailing day, Dimitrij, our regular piano-player, explained in a laconic radiogram addressed to Maurice that "for personal reasons" he was unable to leave Paris. The personal reasons were, as we found out later, a vendeuse from the Galeries La Fayette, fourth floor, *caleçons*, *peignoirs*, ladies' underwear. Fortunately, Maurice ran into Sebastiano at the Café des Quat'z' Arts three hours before the departure of our train for Bordeaux, and hired him at once.

Maurice had worked with Sebastiano at the Rendezvous des Américains, a tiny, permanently overcrowded boîte in a side street off the Boulevard Raspail on Montparnasse, where the customers literally sat on one another's laps and the lights were so dim that no one was able to read the bill. In the Rendezvous, Sebastiano sat behind an upright Pleyel piano in a corner, concealed from the rest of the boîte by a heavy velvet curtain, his job being to create what Monsieur Boniface, the proprietor, referred to as *"l'atmosphère—c'est tout."* He played soft, subdued, intimate piano music, *en sourdine.* On Saturdays, he would be joined by a violinist and a 'cellist, and it was on such an occasion that he met Maurice.

The atmosphere at the Rendezvous des Américains was anything but American, Monsieur Boniface having never seen more of America than the United States Treasury building on the back of a ten-dollar bill. The bartender was from Rouen and the headwaiter from Corsica, and Sebastiano, a pupil of Albéniz, played mostly Spanish music—Granados, de Falla, Albéniz. He was a short fellow with thin shoulders. He had beautiful dark hair, always uncombed and falling down over his forehead; prominent cheekbones, black eyes, and a colorless complexion.

Sebastiano was unbelievably lazy. He said he could sleep twenty-four hours a day for four days in a row, and I think he did not exaggerate. He liked to point out, however, that in Algeciras he was not known as an especially lazy type. "You should see my father," he once told me. "Never gets out of bed. On Easter Sunday, Mother, my eleven brothers and sisters, and I have to work for an hour before we get him dressed and drag him all the way to church. There he falls asleep at once. *C'est la vie.*" Sebastiano shrugged and fell asleep himself.

Sebastiano had a tiny room at a little hotel near the Panthéon. The room was on the fourth floor and Sebastiano hated climbing up the narrow, winding stairway. Often he would sit down on the stairs between the second and third floors and fall asleep. Mademoiselle Renée, a pretty, dark-haired girl, who lived next to him, would go down and call the proprietor and his wife, and the three of them would drag Sebastiano up to his room. Renée was crazy about Sebastiano, but he was indifferent and resented her hanging up her washed panties and stockings on a string across her window. "She's frivolous," he used to say. "Most girls are. *C'est la vie.*"

He got so tired of climbing the four flights that one day he decided that from then on he would stay at the Rendezvous and sleep under a piano. He took two plush seat covers and placed them on the floor in front of the piano. He hung his tuxedo across a chair and slipped into his pajamas, which he had brought from his room, and slept all day long. The place was being cleaned, and Monsieur Boniface carried on noisy discussions with wine salesmen, and once the headwaiter from Corsica almost stabbed the cook to death with a fruit knife, but Sebastiano slept peacefully and undisturbed. Around eight-thirty that evening, the headwaiter, aided by the entire staff, started to wake up Sebastiano. By nine-thirty the pianist was ready to get up. He changed into his tuxedo, had a glass of dry sherry, and sat down at the piano. His fingers worked automatically, though his mind was still in a deep trance.

One day Sebastiano's tuxedo was stolen while he was sleeping under the piano. That night he had to play in his pajamas. He did not mind. He hated to dress and the place was always overheated, and he was safe, anyway, behind the velvet curtain. At two in the morning, two American tourists discovered him in his odd attire. They pushed him out onto the floor, where he was an instant success. Everybody agreed that wearing nothing but pajamas was a great idea. The two Americans jumped into a taxicab, went to their hotel, and came back in their pajamas. Everybody bought drinks for everybody else. The idea caught on, and three or four evenings later all habitués of the Rendezvous des Américains arrived at the place in their pajamas, over which they had put on their overcoats and furs. Monsieur Boniface, a man of sound business principles, increased the prices of liquor fifty per cent and put out more lights. The son of the Corsican headwaiter was posted as guard in front of the entrance, and a small sign, "MEMBERS ONLY," printed in English, was hung on the door. Only people dressed properly—that is, in pajamas—were allowed to come in.

Sebastiano, never given to loose talk, was particularly reticent about the weeks that followed. That epoch was, he indicated, characterized by cheerful abandon and wonderfully large tips. Then the cook, who was carrying on a vendetta with the Corsican headwaiter, got fired and went to the police. The agents raided the place, and that was the end. *"C'est la vie,"* Sebastiano concluded gloomily.

The police tactfully suggested that Sebastiano find himself employment outside of France or they would have to ship him back to Algeciras. Sebastiano hopefully went to the Café des Quat'z' Arts and happened on the job aboard *La Bourdonnais*.

Sebastiano began his career as ship's musician promisingly by missing the nine o'clock train which he had been ordered to take with the rest of us. He told us later that he took a taxi to the station and fell asleep. The cabdriver, unable to wake him up, took him to the nearest police station, where they managed to shake him out of his trance, but by that time our train had left. He took the midnight train and came aboard the following morning with the last group of first-class passengers. He had on his tuxedo, a yellow camel's-hair overcoat, and no hat. He had no baggage whatsoever and looked so bored and genuinely expensive that the maître d'hôtel, who took pride in his infallible judgment of his fellow men, made his de-luxe bow and asked him for the number of his stateroom on A Deck. Two smart, tall Vassar girls, returning from their European vacation, gave him a wistful look, and a vivacious divorcée from Boston, reclining in a deck chair, put down her Michael Arlen story and stared at him in fascination.

Sebastiano was much too sleepy to return her stare. I took him down to the two connecting staterooms where the orchestra slept. Maurice started a noisy tirade. Sebastiano, his eyes half-closed, dreamily inquired which of the four berths was his. He took off his over-coat, lay down in his tuxedo, and in four seconds was sound asleep. Baggage porters bumped into the door and uttered pungent oaths, women came into our state-room looking for their husbands and husbands came in looking for their wives, a steward swung his bell ("Visitors ashore, all visitors ashore"), the siren wailed, but Sebastiano slept peacefully through all the excitement that preceded the sailing and we had to pour half a glass of ice water into his open mouth to get him up on deck in time for the national anthems, which were always played as the ship was being towed away from the pier. After the last note of the "Marseillaise," he went back to bed again.

The eleven days that followed, en route to New York, were a nightmare. Sebastiano kept the three other musicians—Maurice, Lucien, who was our French first violinist, and myself, the second violin—in a perpetual state of nervous tension. We had fairly easy working hours aboard *La Bourdonnais*. There was an apéritif concert on deck, between eleven and noon; a concert in the tourist-class dining-saloon from three to four, which was merely a rehearsal for the afternoon concert in the first-class saloon from four to five; and a concert, after dinner, from eight-thirty to nine-thirty, either in the saloon or outside on deck, depending on the weather. From ten to eleven, we played dance music. All in all, it was only five hours' work a day.

From the very first day, Sebastiano never showed up in time for work. As long as he was asleep in our rooms, we did not mind so much. You could always go down, pour some ice water into his mouth, and drag him up-stairs. But he got tired of drinking ice water and began to hide. Twenty minutes before concert time, someone would discover that Sebastiano had vanished and there would be a mad scramble for our piano-player. You can play without your second violinist or your 'cellist, but you have to have your pianist. The first few days, we found him in fairly accessible places: lifeboats, heaps of rope on deck, the benches on the sun deck, the hospital, the tourist-class saloon. As the days went on, however, Sebastiano became more ingenious. He vanished be-hind stacks of breakfast-food boxes in the kitchen, in a corner of the wireless room, in the engine-room. We had ingenious helpers in all departments of the ship and so we always found him, though sometimes rather late.

Things started to get really tough when Sebastiano be-gan to vanish in the staterooms of the passengers. First he vanished under the bed of Mr. Wayne, a real-estate broker from New Jersey, who had Cabin Number 7 and spent all his days on deck playing shuffleboard. Fortu-nately, the cabin steward discovered him before Mr. Wayne, a tough character with a top kick's voice, could raise hell. Next, Sebastiano was found hiding in Cabin Number 4, which belonged to a Mr. Rhys Price, Mr. Wayne's English shuffleboard partner and an outdoor man too. One evening Sebastiano went into Cabin Num-ber 35B, where the two Vassar girls lived. It was din-ner-time for the first-class passengers and Sebastiano thought the young ladies were in the dining-saloon, but they were in their stateroom, and not by themselves either, and they had forgotten to lock the door. Sebastiano's face was still red as he tried to reconstruct the scene for us. "I said I was sorry, but the two men looked at me as though they were thinking of murder." He thought for a minute and then added, "And they were, I'm sure. They had that look in their eyes. I was frightened to death. I turned around and ran. *C'est la vie, mes amis.* All you want is some sleep and what do you get? Murder."

On the day before we reached Halifax, *La Bourdonnais* ran into bad weather and many passengers became seasick. Some stayed in their rooms, but the majority spent the day on deck, lying in their chairs, their faces the color of long-dead halibut. The deck stewards hustled back and forth, carrying trays with consommé and crackers, taking care to keep the door to the dining-saloon closed because the smell of food made some of the passengers wish they were dead. Mrs. Sloan, the divorcée from Boston, was the sickest of all. She remained on deck until midnight, and the following day she was carried up there again early in the morning. Sebastiano had his own intelligence system among the deck personnel. That afternoon he was gone. We looked for him everywhere but did not find him.

We knocked at all the cabin doors and stammered foolish excuses when the occupants opened up and we glanced over their shoulders, trying to discover Sebastiano under a bed or behind a curtain. Some passengers got very angry, and Mr. Wayne spoke his mind in unmistakable terms. We did not find Sebastiano. There was no tourist-class concert that afternoon and no concert in the first-class saloon. We were reported to the captain and he ordered a methodical search of the steamer.

They found Sebastiano at seven o'clock. He was sleeping peacefully in Mrs. Sloan's bed. He was in his underwear, his shoes were placed beside the bed, and his tuxedo was hung carefully over a chair. He explained that he did not want to get the bed dirty. The captain had us all summoned to the bridge. He was angry as never before, but Sebastiano was his old, dreamy self. "It must be a sort of hypnosis, my captain," he said. "It overwhelms you. There's nothing you can do but lie down. It is stronger than you are."

Maurice said: "Maybe he has sleeping sickness without knowing it. Were you ever in the Belgian Congo, Sebastiano?" Maurice always tried to help us out when we got in a jam.

"What the hell has the Belgian Congo got to do with this?" the captain shouted. We fell silent and looked at Sebastiano, who was standing in front of the captain. The pianist's eyes were half-closed and he was swaying back and forth, like a tall pine in a wind. Soon, I knew, he would be asleep.

The captain stared at Sebastiano, opened his mouth, shut it again, and shrugged. "Get out of here," he said. "All of you. . . . No, wait, you!" He called Sebastiano back and ordered him to apologize to Mrs. Sloan for using her bed. Sebastiano went down from the bridge to the windy, isolated place on deck where Mrs. Sloan was

lying in her deck chair. He kissed her hand with all his
inborn Algeciras grand manner, pulled up another chair,
and sat down next to her.

The following evening, Sebastiano did not take his
customary nap before the concert. He came down to our
cabins for a moment, put on his camel's-hair overcoat
and pulled up the collar, and went out again. At eight-
fifteen, I found him in the chair beside Mrs. Sloan. I said
I was sorry, but it was time for the evening concert. He
nodded and helped Mrs. Sloan out of her covers and gal-
lantly escorted her to the music saloon. I walked behind
them. They called one another "Sebbie" and "Kathie."
The lady from Boston was still pale and somewhat weak,
but there was a light in her eyes as she sat down in the
music saloon not far from the piano. She was a pretty
woman, dark-haired and a little taller than Sebastiano.
She seemed restless and excited. She watched Sebastiano. He played very well that evening. He asked Maurice to let him play a few solo numbers, and he played
two Chopin études, a piece by Debussy, and a Brahms
waltz. After every piece he turned around and smiled
at Mrs. Sloan. It was the first time I had seen him make
a movement that was not absolutely necessary. I looked
at Maurice and Maurice looked at me, and we must have
had the same thought because we both forgot to close
our mouths.

After the concert, Mrs. Sloan invited the members of
the orchestra to the bar for a drink. It was cool and she
shivered, so Sebastiano volunteered to go for her mink
coat. "Sebbie is such a dear boy," she said when he had

33

gone. "He sits next to me and I talk and he just listens." She sighed and looked down at her fingernails. "My husband never did that. He never listened to me. He wasn't interested in anything I said."

There was a pause, then Maurice said, "Sebastiano is a quiet man. Very quiet."

Mrs. Sloan sighed again. "He's so understanding," she said. "Doctor Wellman, my nerve specialist, always told me, 'It's hard to find an understanding person. A man who will listen to you and——'"

Sebastiano came back with her mink coat and she stopped in the middle of her sentence. That night, after the dance, Mrs. Sloan and Sebastiano sat in the bar. She talked all the time and Sebastiano listened, motionless and rigid, like a Brahmin on the shore of the Ganges who has vowed never to move.

Sebastiano did not make the return trip with us to Europe. Two days after our arrival in New York, he vanished again. We looked in all the staterooms, including the captain's, but there was no trace of our piano-player. The next morning, Maurice got a telegram from Sebastiano. Our pianist was not coming back. He was up in Boston and he had decided to stay there for good. There was one particular sentence in Sebastiano's telegram which I remember: "Boston is a nice, quiet place," he wired, "colder than Algeciras, but a good place to sleep."

STEPHEN LEACOCK

Who Knows It?

OUR PASSION FOR INFORMATION

The other night I heard the radio in my living room asking who was King George's great-grandmother. I felt terribly pleased—because I knew the answer—Queen Victoria! In fact I remember her quite well. Then it asked how high is Mount Popocatepetl, and I was clean out of it. In all these years I had never stopped to inquire. When the machine went on to ask how many gallons there are in a cubic foot, and who fought the battle of Actium, I had to shut it off.

Odd, isn't it, this sudden new passion for information that seems to have swept over us like a wave. Questionnaires, intelligence tests, quiz classes held by Professor Knowit, puzzles, problems—anything that can stand for information given and received, knowledge checked up and proved. And even when we are listening to other people being questioned, it's really ourselves that we

35

are checking up on. "Who was the bosom friend of Damon?" asks the radio—and we *know* it; Pythias, eh, what? Where was Napoleon born? Corsica!—we got it the first time—ask us another.

The wave of questions sweeps the whole coast of human knowledge. Sometimes it's history: "Where was General Burgoyne defeated?" That's just a sort of come-along, made easy, to coax us into the water. "In what year was America discovered?" That gets us right in up to the neck; and then, "Who was John Wilkes?" "Who was Vasco da Gama?" "Who defeated Hannibal?" "Who were the Sumerians?" We're swamped and drowned.

Often the questions branch into poetry: "The curfew tolls the knell"—of what? "The boy stood on the burning deck"—what boy? "Father, dear father, come home with me now"—home from where? "The shades of night"—were doing what?

A person who stands up to questions like that feels that he's getting a grip on literature.

Sometimes we drop into straight mathematics, which has the same attraction as playing with fire; for example:

If a frog falls into a sand pit 20 feet deep and gets up the side in jumps 2 feet at a time, but slips back 1 foot on the sand while taking his breath after each jump, how many jumps would it take him to get out of the pit?

There, be careful with it. Don't say you can do it by algebra—that's cheap stuff—and anyway you can't.

A side line of this new question-and-answer craze is

the "information-questionnaire" as used in business. The idea of it is to find out all about a person by reducing him to a set of questions and answers. As a recommendation of a candidate for a job we no longer want a few words of glowing praise, but something by which we can "measure him up" on a scale. Perhaps as the light of the spirit grows dim, we turn on the artificial lamp of science.

Fifty years ago, if a business house wrote to a college for a recommendation of a young man seeking a job, they merely asked in general terms what sort of young man he was. They received in reply from a dean, or other academic authority, a letter which said that Mr. Jones was a "young man of high Christian character who had earned the esteem of his teachers, both for his assiduity and his intelligence." But nowadays, that kind of recommendation wouldn't get the young man very far. The business house wants him "measured." So they send out a printed form of questions. It says:

"We understand that Mr. Jones was at your college. Kindly fill up the data as requested in the questions below:

(1) What percent of character has he got?

(2) What is his percentage of Christianity?

(3) How is his assiduity (state how many hours he can sit still).

(4) How would you class his intelligence: (a) normal? (b) supernormal? (c) subnormal? Compare him with a higher ape."

The college of course meets the situation on its own terms. It keeps books like ledgers in which Mr. Jones is reduced to credits, merits, hours per week, and weeks per year. They can fill him out in five minutes as sixty percent Christian, forty-five percent normal, assiduity guaranteed up to fourteen hours a day—saturation point —and intelligence tested five times under high pressure and never burst.

Some of the question sheets (I've filled in dozens of them) go further. They want to know not only what Mr. Jones is and does, but what he would be and do under circumstances that haven't happened yet. Such questions as:

(1) How would Mr. Jones measure up in an emergency?

(2) If we left a hundred dollars on our office table would he steal it?

(3) If not a hundred, at what sum would he reach the stealing point?

(4) If burglars entered our office and shot at him, how would he react?

(5) If they hit him, what then?

As a natural result of this "questionnaire" system, once it got started, there arose the "intelligence test," as applied direct to an applicant, the last word in the attempt at quantitative measurement of human capacity. It has since run riot. It proved a godsend to college psychology just at the time when the lamp of the old metaphysics burnt dim. It overspread business. It invaded the army. There was no end to it.

It works like this: you want to know what a piece of steel is like. Test it. You want to know what a young man is like—test him. Here, for example, is a young man who wants to marry your daughter. All right—have him tested. Send him up to the college psychological laboratory and let the professor test him. Don't send your daughter up, though—just the young man.

To test him they find out whether he can remember how many windows there are in the corridor he passed through—how many steps he came up to get in—and what kind of trees he passed by in the campus. In reality, anybody who remembers windows and trees and steps has a mind as empty as a dried nut. What he needs is furniture. A hen, which can see but can't think, would pass an intelligence test in Class One . . . Isaac Newton couldn't touch it. To my mind an "intelligence test," if it means anything more than talking to a person as a way of getting to know him, is just a piece of pretentious non-sense, as ineffective as it is ancient.

But what does all this mean, this everlasting searching of our brains, testing our knowledge of fact, this passion of information, this desire for accurate measurement? Does it mean that there's something going wrong with us? "Is civilization a failure, and is the Caucasian played out?" asked the Truthful James of Bret Harte seventy years ago. Indeed, every nation is always asking itself if it is getting played out. The Greeks complained of it. The Romans talked of it so much that at last they got it. Every nation likes to hark back to the "men of old" and pity themselves as degenerate descendants. Just now we are running through a phase of pretending that Western civilization—the name we give ourselves—is playing out; that presently it will "crash"—a new metaphor brought down from the air—and when it "crashes" we'll pass into a form of nebula called "world-chaos."

Seen in this light, the present craze for "questions," for "facts" means that earlier faith having gone, the mind runs to seed in meaningless intellectuality; what "purpose" is being replaced by purposeless capacity, just as the "helmsman" is replaced by the gyro compass, and machines with steel fingers replace the human agent.

There's no end to it. People can get as mournful as ever they like about it, but if you come to the reality of things you will find that the present puzzle-quiz-and-fact craze has no particular meaning and no particular novelty. It's the kind of thing that comes and goes and always has come and gone. The trouble with humanity is not that it changes so much but that it changes so little. The "men of old" never existed, or, when they did, were pretty much like ourselves. Later on, we'll be the "men of old"—rugged, honest, but all dead.

So what I am saying is that the new question-and-answer mentality is just a passing phase, not so new as it seems, and, in one form or the other, often in the world before.

Let me start at some of the simpler phases of it. There

are people, and always have been, who have a weakness for *facts* rather than *fancies;* and others who prefer fancies to fact. Some people read romances, and others prefer an almanac. Some lose themselves in a poem, others bury themselves in a railway folder. But the motive is one and the same, the desire to "escape" from the little prison of our consciousness in which we are compelled to dwell. Some attempt to fly out on the wings of the imagination, blown up as light as helium, and others make an aeroplane of the solid metal of facts.

But it was always so. The biggest encyclopædia ever written was compiled in China several thousand years ago: the romances of the troubadours took a week to sing. Archimedes was as deeply buried in thought as Omar Khayyam was lost in imagination. Fact and fancy have always divided us.

Personally, I am willing to plead guilty, along with thousands of other people, to this passion for facts. Say what you will against statistics, I must admit that I like them. I can open a guide book or a compendium or a digest at any time and get absorbed in it; absorbed, for instance, in that marvellous and vivid description of the United States (who hasn't read it with delight) which says:

The United States has a continental area of 3,026,-789 square miles with a non-contiguous territory of 711,606 square miles, making a total area of 3,738,-395—think of that! Just by adding them together, the continental population at the census of 1930 was 122,-775,046. The national wealth was $361,800,000,000 or $2,977 per capita.

Everyone had a share. That's great stuff: it's vivid—and with it are mixed streaks of higher colour such as:

The number of children enrolled in the public schools in 1934 was 27,157,601 (that one boy may have left since); the number of mules in the United States was 4,925,000. There were on July 1, 1933, fifty thousand miles of natural gas pipe lines.

After you've read an account like that you feel you know the country. So too with its people; what you want is their actual statistical measure. The old-fashioned way of talking about them was in such general terms as: "The average American is a volatile individual, restless, energetic and with a passion for novelty and experiment." How much superior is the newer method: "The average adult American is five feet seven and one-half inches high; he weighs one hundred thirty-eight pounds, with a chest measure of thirty inches. He has (approximately) two ears, one on each side of his face. He has 2.1 children and dies at fifty-one." There—with that you feel you know the fellow! Or at least lots like him.

But certain statistical figures appeal not so much by their exactness as by their size, by their very magnitude. People like to be staggered with huge figures, just as they like exaggeration in humor and in romance. The little child who reads of the dog with eyes as big as the round tower of Copenhagen (see under Hans Andersen) will grow into the man who reads that the estimated orginal natural stock of coal in the United States was 3,214,898,000,000 tons!

But if you want to get a real stagger you have to turn to Astronomy. That's where you get the real stuff! How's this: "The diameter of the star Betelgeuse is estimated at 240,000,000 miles." How's that for size! Almost difficult to visualize, isn't it? Or take this one: "The beams of light from the great nebula, the constellation Something-or-other, which started during the Trojan War and have been moving ever since at the rate of 187,000 miles a second, are not here yet." It makes you feel like going out and watching for them to come.

But what I am saying is that this passion for big figures is as old as humanity. In earlier times they had no statistics and so they had to fall back on lies. Hence the huge exaggerations of primitive literature, giants, miracles, wonders! It's the size that counts. They did it with lies and we do it with statistics: but it's all the same line.

In the same way our present passion for puzzles and puzzle-questions is nothing new. The puzzle man is probably a type as old as humanity. They must have had him in Babylon and on the Nile.

Everybody knows him as we see him with us today— never happy unless he is working out a puzzle. He carries it round with him, as men used to carry a chew of tobacco. You see him sitting in a railway train gazing fixedly out the window. But he sees nothing. He doesn't know whether he's going through the Adirondacks or over the Susquehanna. He's got a puzzle inside him: he's trying to think how a farmer with a ten gallon can and a three gallon can and a two gallon can, manages to measure out six gallons of milk.

These puzzle men, when you understand them, are singularly easy to entertain if you have them on your hands in your house. Just throw them a puzzle. All you do is to say, to such a man, "Bentley, I saw a good puzzle the other day but I couldn't work it. It said, 'A shop-man has a piece of linoleum twelve feet by twelve feet and a customer wants a piece sixteen feet by nine feet—same number of square yards but different shape. The shop-man says, "All you need to do is to cut this twelve by twelve piece into two parts and place them together." "Only two parts?" asks the perplexed customer. "Only two," says the shop-man.' Now how could he do that, Bentley?"

And with that Bentley is off. You don't need to think of him any more all evening. He'll just sit round and murmur, "Sixteen feet by nine, eh?" Then he won't speak for a long time, till he says, "Linoleum, eh?" You don't need to talk to him, or amuse him or to let him cut in at bridge. Just turn from the card table now and then to say, "Linoleum, that's right, Bentley." If he gets restless, give him a Scotch and soda and let him walk up and down, and mutter, "Twelve by twelve." He's all set for the evening.

But be sure to tell him the answer before he goes home. Even if he protests, tell it to him. Otherwise he'll call you up by phone at two in the morning, jubilant, to say he got it. He thinks you'll be too glad to sleep.

But this puzzle stuff, as I say, is as old as human thought. As soon as mankind began to have brains they must have loved to exercise them for exercise's sake. The "jig-saw" puzzles come from China, where they had them four thousand years ago. So did the famous "sixteen puzzle" (fifteen movable squares and one empty space) over which we racked our brains in the middle eighties. The mathematical puzzles come from the Greeks who left some behind them never yet solved. For example: If Achilles is chasing a tortoise and moves at such a rate that he catches up half the distance in the first minute, and half the remaining distance in the second minute, then, as he is always moving faster than the tortoise is, he must sooner or later catch up with it. But as there is always half the distance left at the end of each minute, it is equally certain that he will never catch up with it. The Greeks died without knowing the answer.

Or take all the "crossword," "catchword" stuff. That carries back to the Middle Ages, otherwise the Muddled Ages, when all life was one big puzzle. The Monks and the few who could read used to divert themselves with "acrostics," "anagrams," and "magic squares."

Even the word *puzzle* is so old that nobody knows what it's derived from, and the thing puzzle must go back to the twilight beginnings of human thought. Most people know, by reproduction in pictures, the wonderful statue of a primitive man, made by the French sculptor Rodin, and called *Le Penseur*—The Thinker.

That figure is that of a huge creature, just emerged above the ape—seated—the narrow head bent on the hands—the rude face immobile and furrowed with a fierce attempt at constructive thought. In looking at it one realizes that the man is probably muttering—"Linoleum, eh? Twelve by twelve."

As to the intelligence test, ask anybody old enough to recall the Spanish American War of 1898 to tell you the famous story of the Message to Garcia. Then work from that to the story of King Solomon and the undistributed baby—and you'll realize that tests are as old as intelligence.

No, no—it's all old stuff come back in a new form that suits our ideas. Let's turn on the radio and hear Professor Knowit asking about Christopher Columbus.

JAMES THURBER

The Dog That Bit People

Probably no one man should have as many dogs in his life as I have had, but there was more pleasure than distress in them for me except in the case of an Airedale named Muggs. He gave me more trouble than all the other fifty-four or -five put together, although my moment of keenest embarrassment was the time a Scotch terrier named Jeannie, who had just had six puppies in the clothes closet of a fourth floor apartment in New York, had the unexpected seventh and last at the corner of Eleventh Street and Fifth Avenue during a walk she had insisted on taking. Then, too, there was the prize-winning French poodle, a great big black poodle—none of your little, untroublesome white miniatures—who got sick riding in the rumble seat of a car with me on her way to the Greenwich Dog Show. She had a red rubber bib tucked around her throat and, since a rain storm

47

came up when we were half way through the Bronx, I had to hold over her a small green umbrella, really more of a parasol. The rain beat down fearfully and suddenly the driver of the car drove into a big garage, filled with mechanics. It happened so quickly that I forgot to put the umbrella down and I will always remember, with sickening distress, the look of incredulity mixed with hatred that came over the face of the particular hardened garage man that came over to see what we wanted, when he took a look at me and the poodle. All garage men, and people of that intolerant stripe, hate poodles with their curious haircut, especially the pom-poms that you got to leave on their hips if you expect the dogs to win a prize.

But the Airedale, as I have said, was the worst of all my dogs. He really wasn't my dog, as a matter of fact: I came home from a vacation one summer to find that my brother Roy had bought him while I was away. A big, burly, choleric dog, he always acted as if he thought I wasn't one of the family. There was a slight advantage in being one of the family, for he didn't bite the family as often as he bit strangers. Still, in the years that we had him he bit everybody but mother, and he made a pass at her once but missed. That was during the month when we suddenly had mice, and Muggs refused to do anything about them. Nobody ever had mice exactly like the mice we had that month. They acted like pet mice, almost like mice somebody had trained. They were so friendly that one night when mother entertained at dinner the Friraliras, a club she and my father had be-

longed to for twenty years, she put down a lot of little
dishes with food in them on the pantry floor so that the
mice would be satisfied with that and wouldn't come
into the dining room. Muggs stayed out in the pantry
with the mice, lying on the floor, growling to himself—
not at the mice, but about all the people in the next room
that he would have liked to get at. Mother slipped out
into the pantry once to see how everything was going.
Everything was going fine. It made her so mad to see
Muggs lying there, oblivious of the mice—they came
running up to her—that she slapped him and he slashed
at her, but didn't make it. He was sorry immediately,
mother said. He was always sorry, she said, after he bit
someone, but we could not understand how she figured
this out. He didn't act sorry.

Mother used to send a box of candy every Christmas
to the people the Airedale bit. The list finally contained
forty or more names. Nobody could understand why
we didn't get rid of the dog. I didn't understand it very
well myself, but we didn't get rid of him. I think that
one or two people tried to poison Muggs—he acted poisoned once in a while—and old Major Moberly fired at
him once with his service revolver near the Seneca Hotel
in East Broad Street—but Muggs lived to be almost
eleven years old and even when he could hardly get
around he bit a Congressman who had called to see my
father on business. My mother had never liked the Congressman—she said the signs of his horoscope showed he
couldn't be trusted (he was Saturn with the moon in
Virgo)—but she sent him a box of candy that Christmas.

He sent it right back, probably because he suspected it was trick candy. Mother persuaded herself it was all for the best that the dog had bitten him, even though father lost an important business association because of it. "I wouldn't be associated with such a man," mother said. "Muggs could read him like a book."

We used to take turns feeding Muggs to be on his good side, but that didn't always work. He was never in a very good humor, even after a meal. Nobody knew exactly what was the matter with him, but whatever it was it made him irascible, especially in the mornings. Roy never felt very well in the morning, either, especially before breakfast, and once when he came downstairs and found that Muggs had moodily chewed up the morning paper he hit him in the face with a grapefruit and then jumped up on the dining room table, scattering dishes and silverware and spilling the coffee. Muggs' first free leap carried him all the way across the table and into a brass fire screen in front of the gas grate but he was back on his feet in a moment and in the end he got Roy and gave him a pretty vicious bite in the leg. Then he was all over it; he never bit anyone more than once at a time. Mother always mentioned that as an argument in his favor; she said he had a quick temper but that he didn't hold a grudge. She was forever defending him. I think she liked him because he wasn't well. "He's not strong," she would say, pityingly, but that was inaccurate; he may not have been well but he was terribly strong.

One time my mother went to the Chittenden Hotel to

call on a woman mental healer who was lecturing in Columbus on the subject of "Harmonious Vibrations." She wanted to find out if it was possible to get harmonious vibrations into a dog. "He's a large tan-colored Airedale," mother explained. The woman said that she had never treated a dog but she advised my mother to hold the thought that he did not bite and would not bite. Mother was holding the thought the very next morning when Muggs got the iceman but she blamed that slip-up on the iceman. "If you didn't think he would bite you, he wouldn't," mother told him. He stomped out of the house in a terrible jangle of vibrations.

One morning when Muggs bit me slightly, more or less in passing, I reached down and grabbed his short stumpy tail and hoisted him into the air. It was a foolhardy thing to do and the last time I saw my mother, about six months ago, she said she didn't know what possessed me. I don't either, except that I was pretty mad. As long as I held the dog off the floor by his tail he couldn't get at me, but he twisted and jerked so, snarling all the time, that I realized I couldn't hold him that way very long. I carried him to the kitchen and flung him onto the floor and shut the door on him just as he crashed against it. But I forgot about the backstairs. Muggs went up the backstairs and down the frontstairs and had me cornered in the living room. I managed to get up onto the mantelpiece above the fireplace, but it gave way and came down with a tremendous crash throwing a large marble clock, several vases, and myself heavily to the floor. Muggs was so alarmed by the racket that when I picked myself up he had disappeared. We couldn't find him anywhere, although we whistled and shouted, until old Mrs. Detweiler called after dinner that night. Muggs had bitten her once, in the leg, and she came into the living room only after we assured her that Muggs had run away. She had just seated herself when, with a great growling and scratching of claws, Muggs emerged from under a davenport where he had been quietly hiding all the time, and bit her again. Mother examined the bite and put arnica on it and told Mrs. Detweiler that it was only a bruise. "He just bumped you," she said. But Mrs. Detweiler left the house in a nasty state of mind.

Lots of people reported our Airedale to the police but my father held a municipal office at the time and was on friendly terms with the police. Even so, the cops had been out a couple times—once when Muggs bit Mrs. Rufus Sturtevant and again when he bit Lieutenant-Governor Malloy—but mother told them that it hadn't been Muggs' fault but the fault of the people who were bit. "When he starts for them, they scream," she explained, "and that excites him." The cops suggested that it might be a good idea to tie the dog up, but mother said that it mortified him to be tied up and that he wouldn't eat when he was tied up.

Muggs at his meals was an unusual sight. Because of the fact that if you reached toward the floor he would bite you, we usually put his food plate on top of an old kitchen table with a bench alongside the table. Muggs would stand on the bench and eat. I remember that my mother's Uncle Horatio, who boasted that he was the third man up Missionary Ridge, was splutteringly indignant when he found out that we fed the dog on a table because we were afraid to put his plate on the floor. He said he wasn't afraid of any dog that ever lived and that he would put the dog's plate on the floor if we would give it to him. Roy said that if Uncle Horatio had fed Muggs on the ground just before the battle he would have been the first man up Missionary Ridge. Uncle Horatio was furious. "Bring him in! Bring him in now!" he shouted. "I'll feed the——on the floor!" Roy was all for giving him a chance, but my father wouldn't hear of it. He said that Muggs had already been fed. "I'll feed him again!" bawled Uncle Horatio. We had quite a time quieting him.

In his last year Muggs used to spend practically all of his time outdoors. He didn't like to stay in the house for some reason or other—perhaps it held too many unpleasant memories for him. Anyway, it was hard to get him to come in and as a result the garbage man, the iceman, and the laundryman wouldn't come near the house. We had to haul the garbage down to the corner, take the laundry out and bring it back, and meet the iceman a block from home. After this had gone on for some time we hit on an ingenious arrangement for getting the dog in the house so that we could lock him up while the gas meter was read, and so on. Muggs was afraid of only one thing, an electrical storm. Thunder and lightning frightened him out of his senses (I think he thought a storm had broken the day the mantelpiece fell). He would rush into the house and hide under a bed or in a clothes closet. So we fixed up a thunder machine out of a long narrow piece of sheet iron with a wooden handle on one end. Mother would shake this vigorously when she wanted to get Muggs into the house. It made an excellent imitation of thunder, but I suppose it was the most roundabout system for running a household that was ever devised. It took a lot out of mother.

A few months before Muggs died, he got to "seeing things." He would rise slowly from the floor, growling low, and stalk stiff-legged and menacing toward nothing at all. Sometimes the Thing would be just a little to the right or left of a visitor. Once a Fuller Brush salesman got hysterics. Muggs came wandering into the room like Hamlet following his father's ghost. His eyes were fixed on a spot just to the left of the Fuller Brush man, who stood it until Muggs was about three slow, creeping paces from him. Then he shouted. Muggs wavered on past him into the hallway grumbling to himself but the Fuller man went on shouting. I think mother had to throw a pan of cold water on him before he stopped. That was the way she used to stop us boys when we got into fights.

Muggs died quite suddenly one night. Mother wanted to bury him in the family lot under a marble stone with some such inscription as "Flights of angels sing thee to thy rest" but we persuaded her it was against the law. In the end we just put up a smooth board above his grave along a lonely road. On the board I wrote with an indelible pencil "Cave Canem." Mother was quite pleased with the simple classic dignity of the old Latin epitaph.

CORNELIA OTIS SKINNER

The Body Beautiful

At least three times a year the average woman tries on dresses in a shop. She finds herself standing before one of those fitting-room mirrors with movable side-panels suggestive of a primitive triptych . . . that is, if she has sufficient imagination to turn the triple reflection of herself in a pink slip into a trio of medieval saints. Such mirrors afford one a lot of seldom beheld angles of one's self and the sudden sight of them comes in the nature of a shock. You find you're staring at yourself rather than at the clothes you're buying; at your profile which somehow isn't at all the way you'd remembered it; at that curious three-quarter view when your face appears to be the shape of a Jordan almond, and at that alarming, almost indecent exposure of the back of your neck. When, furthermore, your eye travels earthward from the nape and is suddenly arrested, not without horror, by the re-

56

flection of that portion of the anatomy of which you catch a good glimpse only on these sartorial occasions, and which since the last shopping trip appears to have taken on distressing prominence, you reach the grim conclusion that it's almost too late for clothes to matter.

A recently beheld panorama of myself in the clear, cold light of Bloomingdale's most relentless mirror filled me with such panic, I felt I must do something immediately. Recalling the ads of those numerous "slimming salons" which assure you that within a few weeks and for a price unnamed they can change you from a model for Helen Hokinson into a stand-in for Katherine Hepburn, I decided to take my troubles and my protuberances to one of them. Ever since the days of boarding-school, when I used to send for every free sample from henna rinses to stove-polish, I have always fallen for ads. The sweetheart of J. Walter Thompson, I have a peasant-like belief in whatever miracle they profess to effect.

I made inquiries among my better-shaped acquaintances and was told that an establishment in the East Fifties was among the best. The place, though small, was impressive. The façade was what is known as "moderne." Instead of the usual show window, it had sort of portholes in which terracotta dryads (they might even have been hamadryads) danced amid bottles of perfume. On the ground floor was a sales and reception room where were displayed cosmetics, evening bags and (although a blizzard was raging outside) dark glasses and suntan oil. The place, decorated in Louis something style, had such an air of luxe and "parfum" about it you felt that, instead of streamlining you, they ought to turn you out looking like a Boucher. (Why didn't I live at that time, anyway?) A marquise disguised as a saleswoman was sitting behind the sort of table at which de Sévigné must have written her letters. It now held an enormous appointment book, some atomizer bottles and a very pure white phone. She asked if there were anything she could do for me and I said, "Yes. Reduce my rear," which shocked her very much; but, being of the aristocracy, she managed to smile politely. "Have you made an appointment for a consultation with Mme. Alberta?" "Mme. Alberta?" I echoed. "I'm afraid I haven't heard about her." From the expression of the marquise I might have said I hadn't heard about the Duchess of Windsor.

"I don't think I need any consultation," I said. "I just want to reduce my . . ." Her eyebrows flickered ever so slightly and I ended lamely, "I just want to lose a few inches."

"All our clients have a consultation first with Mme. Alberta," was her reply. "She happens to be disengaged at the moment. If you'll please go upstairs I'll phone her you're coming." I climbed a mauve-carpeted stair, wondering what sort of consultation lay in store for me. Would Mme. Alberta greet me with a stethoscope or would she be discovered gazing into a crystal? A pretty woman, youngish and frighteningly smart, was seated at another period table. I gathered she was Mme. Alberta for she said "How do you do?" She had a very strenuous smile and her accent was so determined to be English it broadened every "a" . . . even in the case of such words as *hand* and *ankle*. It was hard to know how to address her. "Mme. Alberta" sounded embarrassing. She didn't look much like an Alberta and to call her plain *Madam* was unthinkable. She was one of those women who are so well-groomed they are positively "soignée" . . . In their immaculate presence you feel as if you had several runs in your stockings. She motioned me to a chair and listened to the story of my proportions as if it were a case history. She then quoted me prices and after accepting my check took out a card resembling a hospital chart. On it she wrote my name and address and some things that struck me as being singularly irrelevant in the matter of hip reduction . . . when my child was born, what sicknesses I'd ever had, the current lie about my age, and my blood-pressure which, like my Social Security number, is something I can never remember.

"Now, then, we'll see about your weight."

"I know what I weigh," I said, and added recklessly, "and I don't care. All I'm after is to reduce my . . ."

"Weight and measurements must be taken every treatment." Her tone, though polite, implied she didn't think I was quite bright. "There's the dressing room. Will you disrobe kindly?" I went to what seemed to be a daintily furnished sentry box and disrobed kindly. I felt somehow I was up for a woman's branch of the Army. A trim mulatto brought me a sheet and a pair of paper slippers that were the shape and texture of peanut bags. I tried to drape the sheet so I'd look like a Tanagra figure but it wouldn't work, so I arranged it along the more simple

59

lines of a Navajo blanket and emerged with caution. Mme. Alberta, who was waiting, told me to "come this way" and I followed her down a corridor, not without a vague apprehension that at the finish of the trip I might find myself confronted by an anæsthetist. She led me behind a screen, whisked off my sheet in the manner of a mayor unveiling a statue and placed me on a scale, naked as Lot's wife . . . nakeder, because that lady could at least boast of a good coating of salt.

"But I tell you, I *know* what I weigh," I protested weakly and told her. She shed on me the indulgent smile a night nurse might give a psychopathic patient, took my weight which turned out to be exactly what I'd said and then told *me*. "Now for those measurements," she said. "Miss Jones, will you please come here?" Miss Jones proved to be a lovely young thing in a wisp of sky blue tunic. She was of such bodily perfection one had the suspicion that "Miss Jones" was incognito for "Miss America." We were formally introduced . . . Miss Jones in her bright blue suit, I in my bright pink skin. She handed Mme. Alberta a tape measure in exchange for which Mme. Alberta gave her a pencil and my hospital chart.

"Please mark as I call them, Miss Jones," and as if she hadn't already sufficiently humiliated me, Mme. Alberta began calling out my measurements to the world at large. She measured everything. She even measured my neck, my ankle and the length of my arm. I began to wonder if a suit of acrobat fleshings were thrown in with the course.

"I hardly think you need go to all that trouble," I interposed. "It's just my . . ."

"We take all measurements," Mme. Alberta said somewhat acidly and continued to encompass me with the tape measure which was a flexible metal affair . . . very cold and with a tendency to tickle. She accompanied her work with a flow of exclamations that might be taken any way. "Well, *well!*" she'd murmur, or "I *thought* so!" and at times shook her pretty head and went "Tsk! Tsk!"

Having completed her survey, she turned me over to Miss Jones, who had me don a baggy little lemon colored suit . . . the sort of thing that in my girlhood was known as an Annette Kellerman. It contrasted cruelly with her own trim tunic, and I felt more humble than I had in my recent nakedness. She led the way to an exercise room that contained a mat, a gramophone and far too many mirrors, ordered me onto the mat and proceeded to put me through twenty minutes of hard labor. I rolled and thumped. I stretched and kicked. I jumped and pranced. I also puffed and panted. I stood on my shoulders with my feet in the air; that is, Miss Jones hoisted my feet into the air while I rose up onto a fast-breaking neck and screamed. She never paused to allow me to catch a breath which by now was of such weakened quality it hardly seemed worth while trying to catch it. I tried to take time out . . . to divert her with harmless chatter. But Miss Jones is very strict. Now and then when total collapse seemed imminent, using the therapy of the brass band spurring on exhausted troops, she'd play a lively record on the gramophone calling out "one *and* two *and* three *and* four" as if it were a battle cry. She herself was tireless. She'd do awful things such as picking up her ankle with one hand and holding her foot above her head like a semaphore, and expected me to do likewise. I'm one of those rigid types who, since early childhood, has never been able to lean over and touch my toes—not that I've ever wanted to especially. Moreover, I not only can't raise my foot above my head, I can't even bend far enough to get my hand anywhere near my ankle. Miss Jones tells me I'm seriously hamstrung . . . a nasty expression that makes me feel they've been keeping me in the smoke-house all these years.

It's hard to feel cozy with Miss Jones. She is not only strict, she's exceptionally refined. What I call "middle" she calls *diaphragm,* what I call *stomach* with her goes whimsey and becomes *tummy,* and what I call something else she refers with averted eyes to as *derrière.*

The time dragged almost as heavily as my limbs. Finally Miss Jones said I was a good girl and had done enough for the day (the dear Lord knows the day had done enough for me!) and I might go have my massage. I staggered out and into the capable arms of a Miss Svenson who looked like Flagstad dressed up as a nurse. She took me into a small room, flung me onto a hard table and for forty-five minutes went to work on me as if I were material for a taffy-pulling contest. She kneaded me, she rolled me with a hot rolling pin, she did to me what she called "cupping" which is just a beauty-parlor term for good old orthodox spanking. After she'd gotten me in shape for the oven she took me into a shower-room and finished me up with that same hose treatment by which they subdue the recalcitrant inmates of penitentiaries.

I was then permitted to return to my sentry-box and my clothes. Once I'd recaptured my breath I felt extraordinarily full of radiant health and rugged appetite. It was time for lunch and visions of beefsteak danced in my head. But Mme. Alberta was lying in wait for me outside. "Here is your diet," she said, handing me an ominous little slip of paper which I fully expected to be marked ℞.

"I don't really care about a diet," I stammered. "You see, it isn't my weight, it's just my . . ."

"We'd like you to try it," she said.

It was a tasty little menu with the usual well done dab of chop-meat, a few fruit juices and some lettuce garnished by a rousing dressing made with mineral oil. I was to dine at the Colony that evening and could just imagine Eugene's expression if I were to ask him to bring me an order of green salad mixed with Nujol. However, I pocketed the darn thing and used the back of it for a shopping list.

Part of the system at Mme. Alberta's consists in doing quite a lot of extra curricula work. Employing the honor system, Miss Jones expects one to go through a daily routine of prescribed gymnastics at home. For this end (that end I've been referring to) she has tried to lure me

into purchasing a mat of purple satin but with Jefferso-
nian simplicity I maintain that I can gyrate just as un-
successfully on the moth-honored surface of my old college blanket. Exercise in the privacy of one's domicile is
a brisk and splendid idea provided one has any amount
of domicile and any modicum of privacy. Space in my
apartment is by no means magnificent and the only reasonable expanse of it is in the living-room which in lieu
of a door has an open archway and is exposed in every
portion to the hall. Having no yellow Annette Kellerman
at home I generally gird myself for my exertions in nothing more confining than a pair of old pink rayon bloom-
ers. This means that whenever the door-bell rings I am
obliged to leap for sanctuary behind the sofa and I don't
always hear the bell—which makes it pretty fascinating
for whoever comes to the door. Once, in all innocence
and semi-nudity, I gave a private performance for the
window-cleaner; since then, on the occasions of his
monthly visit, if we have the misfortune to meet, we pass
each other with lowered eyes.

A problem that confronts me more, perhaps, than
most people is that much of my time is spent in travel.
The rooms in the newer of what are known as the "leading" hotels are often of dimensions akin to those of a
Pullman roomette. To find a sufficient number of square
feet in which to spread out one's blanket and one's self
becomes a problem in engineering. Often as not I have
to lie with head and shoulders under the bed, one arm
beneath the bureau and the other half-way across the

sill of the bathroom—a pretty picture indeed for the chambermaid or house detective, should they take the notion to enter with their pass-keys. The over-shadowing proximity of furniture is a constant menace. During the course of leg-flinging, rolling upside-down, bicycling, and the rest of Miss Jones' required antics, I have cracked shins on the corners of tables, dislocated digits on the rockers of chairs, stunned myself into momentary insensibility against radiators and kicked cuspidors about like medicine balls. An important feature in reducing the— well, you know—is the thump—double thump, single thump and just plain boops-a-daisy. When executed with sufficient enthusiasm, thumping can produce considerable strain on the structure of the room and there is always the fear that the plaster in the ceiling underneath will start falling and prove fatal to some distinguished traveler like Mrs. Roosevelt or Nelson Eddy.

Reducing, if one goes by the doctrines of the Mme. Alberta school, is a twenty-four-hour job. Aside from the list of more or less stereotyped exercises, one is shown any number of everyday contortions that can, supposedly, be indulged in anywhere, any time. You can, for example, improve your posture by straightening out your spine along the edge of the nearest available door even if, to the casual observer, you appear to be scratching an itching back. You can also, while standing, do those thumps against the handiest walls—say those of the elevator, thereby bringing a moment of diversion into the monotonous life of the operator. Then there are a few less inconspicuous numbers such as standing on tiptoe and stretching up the hands ("Reaching for cherries" is Miss Jones' pretty term for it), leaning over sideways from the waist, deep-knee bending and a movement dignified by the name of "abdominal control" that curiously resembles the beginnings of the *danse du ventre.*" These you are expected to burst forth with at odd hours of the day and night even at the risk of starting the grim rumor that you're coming down with St. Vitus. Then one must walk. "Walk like a goddess" is Miss Jones' advice. So I do. I walk like mad if not particularly like a goddess. Walking in New York is a simple pursuit but in strange towns it leads to any number of surprises. Setting out for the residential section, I suddenly find myself in the thick of the colored population; or, aiming for a public park, discover that, with the unerring instinct of the homing pigeon, I'm back at the railroad yards. At other times I realize I'm striding enthusiastically down one of those streets of a nature that isn't even questionable. There remains nothing to do but hasten back to the hotel and walk round and round the block until the local policeman begins to grow suspicious.

However, all things come to she who weighs and I discover that I'm tipping the scales to a much lesser degree. Thanks to Miss Jones and Miss Svenson and my own shining determination, the last time Mme. Alberta encircled me with that glacial little measuring tape she found signs of considerable shrinkage and told me she was pleased with me—which made me glow with pride. I doubt if anyone viewing me from the neck down

66

would as yet mistake me for Hedy Lamarr but I'm no longer so horrified by the reflection of myself in a triple mirror and what is more satisfying my clothes are beginning to look like the hand-me-downs of an older and fatter sister. And that is *déjà quelque chose.*

GEORGE AND HELEN PAPASHVILY

To Be Happy Married

Naturally when I engaged myself for marriage with Helena Gerbertovna I went right away with heartful of happiness to carry the good news to my friends.

But seemed like they weren't so pleased. Vactangi showed long horse face. Challico sat dark blue in a corner. Even Illarion, practically American himself now, didn't give me any support. Only Dzea shaked my hand and that sadly. "You take a big chance, Bijo, to marry with an American girl." All he said.

"First place," Vactangi pointed out, "American young ladies don't like foreigner names. Now you have to change yours. One Russian, I knew him well, immediately he married American young lady she made him go in court take the name of Gerbert Goover. For honor. Next election Gerbert Goover don't wins. How he feels then, that Russian fellow? Be same with you."

"Main thing," Illarion said, "the American girls I met so far can only cook out of books."

"See. Something else you didn't know," Vactangi said. "Lose the book. Ph-i-i-i-t-t. No eat. You'll starve."

"I can buy another book," I said.

"And what's more," Challico had his turn, "Americans cooking every day just enough. Two peoples, two steaks. Three peoples, three steaks. Never cooking one extra piece for the pot's good luck. Company comes unexpected they gonna sit hungry. You'll die from shame before you're six months married."

"Yes," Vactangi said, "and after your funeral there won't be any table either. Maybe a cup a tea for who carries your burial box. I won't come."

"Never enjoy the pleasure at mealtime to call in strangers passing on the road to share your table." Challico shook his head. "Won't even be any use to get rich. You'll have a shiny white five-hundred-dollar, pull-a-button, push-a-button refrigerator and not one extra piece of baloney to keep inside."

"But you don't know the worst thing that's gonna happen in your house," Vactangi warned. "American young ladies all keep bodguts."

"Helena Gerbertovna has dog," I said. "Irishman setter named Veleike Kneeaz. Comes 'Duke' in English. But that's all."

"Bodguts means writing down moneys before you spending," Vactangi explained. "Suppose you not feeling good, we take for example. You want to stop in Russian

Club drink glass of vodka, eat piece herring maybe, for your stomach. You have to write down in bodguts first:

I'm drinking whiskys..............35c
Eating piece herring, too..........10c

"Where you ever knew American young lady to find out such informations?" I asked him.

"That's enough, boys," Dzea said. "If they promised to each other can't help now. Damage is done." He shook my hand again. "Never mind, I stood your friend twenty years, Bijo Gogio, and I don't stop now."

Well, I didn't pay attentions to them and everything was fine. First time in my life I had a family—best mother a man could want, a sister with a sweet face that smiled, even a grandmother. Should have everybody a grandmother to make a dignified ornament for the house.

So I lived under a bright blue sky in my shining world until the day came the ladies was planning for the wedding company.

"If you want to invite ten or eleven people," My Mother said to me, "and fifteen more here—we'd better count on about thirty, I suppose. Patty shells, three, no, four chickens, mushrooms——"

Four chickens. This was a terrible situation. But better I tell now what kind of countrymen I have than they find it out at the table. "Dzea Vanno can eat two chickens alone by himself, "I said, "when he's in good appetite."

70

My Mother looked surprised. "Goodness, doesn't it give him high blood pressure?"

"Seems healthy enough," I said, "for man eighty-five anyway."

"Well, more chickens then and French peas, those *petits pois*, and tiny hot biscuits. Then a mousse——"

"Moose be O.K.," I said, "can make *shashlik* from haunches and boil up the shoulders—" I saw Helena Gerbertovna was laughing.

"Mousse is like ice cream," Sister whispered to me.

Just showed you never can tell. For me is like elk. But I didn't say anything.

"Look, dear," My Mother suggested. "Suppose we do it this way. You tell us about a wedding breakfast in Georgia and then we'll see what we can manage."

"They never stop at breakfast," I said. "They eat all day."

"Well, what do they have?"

"First is fishes," I said, "maybe white sturgeon smoked over hickory and mountain trout fried crispy in sweet butter and *zootki*, that's like bass, with a sauce of carrot and dill and bay and then *satules* and sprats and *oragueli*, a *kalmaki*, he's a big fish baked with a slice of lemon in his mouth. Then little caviar for anybody likes it dusted over with chopped chives and let's see——"

"Sounds like real good shore dinner back to hum in the state of Maine," The Grandmother said. "You folks ever eat lobster?"

"Not usually," I told her, "but wouldn't do any harm

71

to put three or four on the table. Maybe somebody likes to try them. I guess that be enough for the fish."

"What comes next?" Sister asked. She was writing it all down with pencil."

"*Satskali Katzis-Kzilala* means 'poor man's caviar,' " I said. "We always have that. It's easy. Scoop whole baked eggplants out of their skins and mash up with fine, fine chopped green baby onions, lemon juice, oil, tarragon, and parsleys."

"Oil, tarragon, eggplant," My Mother was repeating faintly, "sturgeon, caviar——"

"The soup we can skip," I said, "so next comes meats. First the roast turkeys with *t'sat t'sivi* sauce. Is Dzea Vanno's speciality, *t'sat t'sivi* sauce and—wait—" That gave me idea. "With your kind permission how would it be if I asked Uncle John to come few days early and he can manage everything?"

"You mean he's a cook?" My Mother said.

"He had restaurant for years and years, " I said. "Don't worry more."

"Well," My Mother breathed a big sigh, "that will be just fine. He'll tell us what to order and Helen can watch him and learn some dishes for you. It doesn't make any difference how much he charges. A caterer. We should have thought of that before."

What means caterer? Should I ask? No. If it's about food Dzea will manage it.

So I made the arrangements and few days before the wedding I went to the station to take Dzea Vanno off the train. He's so surrounded with packages and cartons

72

and suitcases I told him he looks like mother hen with chicks.

"Well, I couldn't decide which my *cherkasskas* to bring, boy," he said. "My black one with the sable hat or my white one with the astrakhan. So I finally made a choice and bringed both. Then there's my soup kettle and some herbs probably can't get in place like this and—" Named over a dozen articles he can't live without.

I picked everything up and stowed in car. Everything, that is, except the velvet portfolio where Uncle John carried his big desperate butcher knives, the wicked-bladed slicers, his curved-edged corers, the choppers, and little fancy cutters, sharp as a razor. This nobody was ever allowed to touch except Dzea himself. Artist's tools.

We drove home and I took him in hall.

"Is that the man to cook?" My Mother said.

Dzea was sorting his luggages and taking out this and that, but soon he heard lady's voice he looked in mirror gave last pull to his coat and made an entrance. First he bowed to room, then he kissed hands all around, next he presented bouquet of red roses to The Grandmother, offered satin box of fruit glacé to My Mother, gave Sister a bottle of perfume tied with bow, and made a speech in Georgian. When he finished that he found small jeweler's box in his pocket for Helena Gerbertovna, kissed me on both cheeks and sat down.

The Grandmother got her breath back first. "Much obliged. But what did he say?"

"He thanks you for the honor of your invitation," I said, "and he wishes a long life in a happy family together for us all. He regrets I don't have no mother, and my father is so far away but he will be pleased to act my nearest relative in all ceremonies necessary."

"Thank him for us, please," My Mother said. "Express our appreciation."

Uncle John spoke again.

"He says," I explained, "that to save the ladies the trouble of writing long lists for the party he gives himself the pleasure of accompanying you to the market tomorrow. He helps you choose everything."

"Can't we talk with him?" Sister asked.

Uncle John had himself pretty well collected together by this time and he understood the question. He rose. "I luff you," he said in English. "I luff you all," and sat down again.

So for next few days the house was full of party, and from early morning you couldn't hear anything but the sound of chopping, stirring, rolling, pounding, oven doors snapping open and shut, tops of pots dancing with steam. And Dzea was having grand time—peeking in bins and counting silverwares and popping in and out of pantry to look over each new dishes came down off the shelf and twirling empty wineglass in his fingers while he thought up next new dish he could surprise us with.

First day Dzea and The Grandmother had some sharp words over what makes right brine for pickled peppers, but like many quarrels they was the better friends after-

ward, especially when it came out they was both great
believers in the principle of the bean, baked, boiled,
fried, in soup, and in salad, as man's best friend.

Then there was ladies that came to call and Uncle
John was always having long tête-à-têtes with them
about best way to candy quinces or hearing confidential details about a certain angel cake recipe they knew.
For his spare minutes house was full of cooking gadgets
he never tried before—slicer for making dried apples,
carved butter mold, and if you can imagine it he even
proposed I take apart some kind of special coffee grinder,
almost heirloom, came around the Horn with Helena Gerbertovna's great-grandfather, just so he can see how it
pulverizes coffee so fine.

Naturally I had no time for foolishness like this. I
needed my whole days to memorize the wedding service
so I don't disgrace my friends and my country in the
critical moment.

At last the great day came; the ceremony was over
and I'm a married man. And after all the congratulations
were said and we got enough good wishes to furnish our
life for a century it came time to sit down at the beautiful table where candles shone and roses bloomed and
the food—well maybe some of the American guests were
little surprised and shocked to see this different kind of
wedding refreshment. But not so surprised they couldn't
eat with brisk appetite and not so shocked they didn't
come back for second, and might as well tell the truth,
third and fourth helpings.

As for my friends, when they saw table Challico was

man enough to make me apology and even Vactangi admitted he didn't see any better since his uncle's daughter got married. So everybody was happy.

Meantime Uncle John was sitting in midst of American ladies humming like a buzzlebee in a bouquet of flowers and darting his head this way and that. "So we pound nuts to paste," I heard him say, "then we mix with chopped onions——"

"Raw onion?" Ladies was leaning forward with all attention.

"Yes, madame, but don't be alarmed. We cut his claws, because next comes lemon juices and then a pepper——"

"Sweet pepper?"

"Sweet as lady's smile." Uncle John bowed. "Sweet green bell pepper. Then parsleys and kinsey, our special herb, and we mash it all with fresh young green beans——"

"Delightful," lady with piled up curls sang, "perfectly delightful."

"And that's our *m'tswane lobeo.*"

So time passed. There were some toasts and some tears and lots of laughing and at last came hour we had to leave because we were going on a trip. Then, of course, everybody remembered one last thing they forgot to say before and Helena Gerbertovna had another costume to put on and after that she must cut few more slices of wedding cake and throw her bouquet. And the tickets? Where's my train tickets?

"Where you put the train tickets? Illarion. Quick!" He said, "In your wallet."

76

What kind of place was that to hide train tickets? But Thank God, I found.

And now just before we were ready to leave Uncle John made an excuse to find Helena Gerbertovna in the hall and he told her a long secret. It was so important he must have repeated it over twice, because through the archway I could see her nod yes. And again, yes.

But at last we were on our way. Person can enjoy to have one wedding but for my part I don't think I could ever live through two.

"So now," I said to Helena Gerbertovna, we were in the train, "let's don't start our home by keeping secrets from each other. What Uncle John told you?"

She's laughing. "Another recipe."

"My God," I said, "what was this one for?"

"'If you want to be happy married,' he whispered in my ear, 'at least once a day say to your husband, "I love you!" And whenever you set a table for Georgians, remember—only too much is ever enough.'"

GEORGE AND HELEN PAPASHVILY

The Good Neighbor

"Good mail." Helena Gerbertovna came in from the box
one afternoon just as Chalvah and me were ready to sit
down to lunch. "Kathleen's coming. She found the chintz.
And Emilia Jacalevna and Eliko and Besso and Piotr,
they'll start about five on Saturday. And this one is from
Uncle John."

I read his words. "He's coming, too," I said.

"And Chancho?"

"I guess."

"You can't live in this place no longer without electric-
ity," Chalvah said all of a sudden. "Got to have elec-
tricity." He jumped up and started to tap the walls.

"I lived twenty years in Georgia without it," I said.
"And so did you, as far as that goes."

"You didn't have no American ladies visiting you
there," Chalvah said. "Entirely different situation now.

What Helena Gerbertovna's friends think when they come and find you keeping her in place without the electric? What kind impression that gives of Georgians?"

"I don't know how to make the wires," I told him.

"I show you."

"But after this you can only come out on Sundays."

"I start everything now. Then I draw you pictures on the walls how goes the wires and where the connections come and you be working on that until I come the next week. Then I make you more pictures again."

"I don't know," Helena Gerbertovna poured him coffee. "Are you sure——?"

"Don't worry," Chalvah said. "I know ladies is very particular, but you gonna paint the walls anyway, so whatever marks I make won't show."

"I mean wouldn't it short-circuit us when we turned on the bathtub or something," Helena Gerbertovna asked.

"Certainly not." Chalvah refused the cream to show he's offended. "But if you don't trust me——"

No. No. We said we had full confidence in him. So we went down and got the cables and the switches and the tape and all the things he needed and the same time we stopped at the station to meet Helena's friend, Kathleen Patrickovna.

"I have something wonderful," she said soon as she got in the door. "For you, George. And I made it myself. Boilo."

"Boilo? Sounds like a bleach," Helena Gerbertovna said. "'Boilo washes briter.'"

Kathleen Patrickovna opened her suitcase and took

out a bottle full of honey-colored something. "Boilo. It's
a drink. Wonderful."

"Well, let's try," I said.

"Certainly." Chalvah got a corkscrew. "What can we
lose but our health?"

"Fill up the glasses first with cracked ice," Kathleen
said, "and after pour enough Boilo in to come to the
top."

Chalvah like a brave man took the first sip. "Excellent.
I kiss the hands that made it." He gave a bow to Kathleen.

I tried a sip. Really was something interesting. Smooth
as cream and with a faraway taste—like orange blossoms
smell. "What's in it?"

"Luscious," Helena said. We had another all around.
"Let's save a glass for the others tonight."

"No. I'll make some more this afternoon," Kathleen
said. "It's easy. You take three oranges and a lemon and
you chop them fine and roll them in honey. Do you have
a percolator?"

"Yes."

"Then you put the chopped fruit in where the coffee
grounds would go——"

"Yes?"

"And you fill the pot up with corn whisky, plug it in
and let it perk."

"My God!" Chalvah said.

"And when it's done you strain it and let it get cold
and that's Boilo. Who's coming tonight?"

"A lot of the Georgians."

"What are the neighbors around here like?"

"Didn't any come to see us yet," I said.

"Stop worrying about it," Helena told me.

"But I like to be good friends to my neighbors."

"Boilo," Chalvah said to himself. "My God!"

"Nobody that knows anything comes to call until you have your curtains up," Helena Gerbertovna said. "That means you've got the cake ready and the lemons sliced thin——"

"How do you do," Kathleen shook hands with the air. "But a pleasure."

"Is this a general rule," I said, "or is it one that you made up?"

"No," Helena said. "This time it's true. Isn't it, Kathy?"

"Let's have another glass of Boilo," Kathleen said. "And next time I'm going to try how it comes out with tangerines and a grapefruit."

But it seems like Mrs. Cleevendon, the lady from the big place two farms over, and Helena Gerbertovna wasn't running on the same track at all because the next Sunday, the hottest day in sixty-seven years, she came visiting. Not only curtains wasn't up; neither was the ceiling.

I was in my swimming trunks working in the living room feeding cable up through the beams to Chalvah. I heard a knock. I heard a voice introducing itself. My God! A lady! And I'm over seventy-five percent naked. I dropped the cable and stepped into the nearest place handy. Happened to be an old grampa clock Helena Gerbertovna bought at an auction few weeks before.

Besso escorted in a lady. "Be pleased to take a seat,"

GEORGE AND HELEN PAPASHVILY

he said. "For the moment our hostess is absent walking in the woods. But I call her." I could see them through a crack. He went to the table and poured a small glass of sherry and brought a plate of crackers. "You will do my friend the honor," he said, "to drink this little glass and I hope he often has the pleasure to see you in his house."

"I thank you," Mrs. Cleevendon said, "but I do not indulge."

"Excuse me just a minute." Besso edged toward door. "I don't speak English so good. But the friend of our hostess is here. I call her." He went in the hall. "Kathleen Patrickovna?"

"What do you want, Besso?" she answered from the kitchen. "I'm terribly busy."

"Guest."

"Oh. Right away."

Besso closed the door and had the sense to stay on the other side of it.

All this time Chalvah keeps pulling up lengths of cable. "Not the end yet, Giorgi?" he calls. I hear the cable sliding across the floor. "End?"

I'm quiet in my clock like a mouse.

Chalvah crawls through the hole in the upstairs floor and starts working himself across the living room beams. "Giorgi?"

He's about out to his waist and true he didn't have no clothes on so far, but there was no need for Mrs. Cleevendon to scream. She ought to have known the pants was coming.

"Oh," Chalvah said. He's laying between the ceiling beams. "I beg your pardon. You wasn't who I expected to see. I mean I'll call somebody." He started to slide back. "Please be so kind to take a chair. You'll have to excuse me, I can't offer you any refreshments. If you please help yourself to a glass of wine. On the table."

"Thank you," Mrs. Cleevendon said. "I do not take spirits. I wear the white ribbon. Band of Hope."

"Well," Chalvah said philosophically, "in this world if we don't got hope what do we got? Be so kind to pour a glass and whatever you hope is I give myself the pleasure to wish you have it."

Helena Gerbertovna came in. At last. They began to have lady conversation. Maybe is gonna be O.K. everything, I thought to myself. Only too bad they don't make clocks with a place to sit down.

Mrs. Cleevendon was describing her antiques.

"—luster pitcher for a dollar," Helena said.

"I paid thirty cents for mine."

"—and a cherry cupboard."

"If it's the original hardware?" Mrs. Cleevendon said. "And your clock?"

"—is signed inside." Helena came across the room and threw open the door.

"How do you do," I said. I came out. "Happened as I was going swimming I noticed this clock was running slow. About five minutes. Little adjustment. Be all right."

Helena Gerbertovna made introductions.

"Oh," Mrs. Cleevendon said soon she heard our name.

83

GEORGE AND HELEN PAPASHVILY

"You would seem to be"—she gave little cough like people do before they say a dirty word—"foreigners. Are you Russian?"

"I'm a Georgian, madame."

"Oh. Then you must be a prince. They all seem to be princes."

"No, madame. My father was a peasant."

"You're too modest, I'm sure. One never hears of anything but princes."

"And my great-grandfather was a peasant," I said. "And before that my great-great-grandfather. As a matter of fact we go straight back to Noah."

"To Noah?"

"He landed on Ararat. I guess you read that. Later on he moved where we live now. Drier location."

"Oh," she said. "I see. Noah. Well. And now tell me," she went on, "do you like this little place?"

We said we did. Helena began to describe what we were doing and I made excuse to get upstairs and put my clothes on. When I came down again Helena was just taking Mrs. Cleevendon into the dining room. I went after them. Table is all set and cake is on the plates and coffeepot makes happy bubbling. "How nice of Kathy," Helena Gerbertovna said. "Everything ready. Will you sit here, Mrs. Cleevendon?"

But must be Helena Gerbertovna was more nervous then she looked. Otherwise before she poured Mrs. Cleevendon a steaming hot cup of corn whisky she would have noticed Kathy was making Boilo.

Mrs. Cleevendon turned green. "I'm afraid," she said,

84

"I must go." She got up. "I—I must be somewhere. Another time——" She gathered her gloves.

We had to follow her to the door. "I'm sorry you can't stay," I said, "but please come again. And next time I hope to have pleasure to meet your husband."

"I lost Mr. Cleevendon three years ago."

"I'm very sorry," I said. "I hope you find again." In my experience husbands that get lost usually do it on purpose, but I had to say something cheerful.

"Good-by. Good-by."

Helena could hardly wait for her to get in the car. "He's dead, her husband. My God! You hope she finds again."

Kathy rolled out the swing where she was hiding herself. "I'm glad that's over," she said.

"Why you don't tell me?" I told them. "Why you don't say a widow?"

"The old——" Kathy kicked the trellis.

"I'll have the same," Helena said.

"Easy for you girls to talk," I said. "Suppose you be left to fight the world alone, you be worse than her." I ran out to car.

She was just pulling out. "Excuse me." I put my head through the window. "I didn't know you was a widow. What day you like me to come and bring in your wood?"

"Wood?"

"Or if somebody has that duty, to plow? Whatever you need."

"Plow?"

"Excuse me. I don't know just how you make the arrangements here. I never lived on farm before. We have habit to work for widows one regular day, but if you have some other system," I said, "I be glad to do my share, however it comes."

"Why, thank you. Thank you very much." I see she can even smile, a thing I would never have suspected. "But so far I can manage. By the way, would you and your wife be free to have dinner with me one day next week?"

So we went and after we got to be good friends and good neighbors to each other and we used to visit often. And once after we knew each other a long, long time she said to me, "You know I didn't quite understand you first day we met I——"

"Perfectly all right, Mrs. Cleevendon," I said. "Don't apologize. You thought we was drunkards and we thought you was the crossest patch we ever saw. After all, everybody can make mistakes."

HENRY A. SHUTE

The Real Diary of a Real Boy

[EXCERPTS]

INTRODUCTION

In the winter of 1901-02, while rummaging an old closet in the shed-chamber of my father's house, I unearthed a salt-box which had been equipped with leather hinges at the expense of considerable ingenuity, and at a very remote period. In addition to this, a hasp of the same material, firmly fastened by carpet-tacks and a catch of bent wire, bade defiance to burglars, mid-night marauders, and safe-breakers.

With the aid of a tack-hammer the combination was readily solved, and an eager examination of the contents of the box disclosed:—

1. Fish-line of braided shoemaker's thread, with perch hook, to which adhered the mummied remains of a

worm that lived and flourished many, many years ago.

2. Popgun of pith elder and hoop-skirt wire.

3. Horse-chestnut bolas, calculated to revolve in opposite directions with great velocity, by an up-and-down motion of the holder's wrist; also extensively used for the adornment of telegraph-wires,—there were no telephones in those days,—and the cause of great profanity amongst linemen.

4. More fish-hooks of the ring variety, now obsolete.

5. One blood alley, two chinees, a parti-colored glass agate, three pewees, and unnumbered drab-colored marbles.

6. Small bow of whalebone, with two arrows.

7. Six-inch bean-blower, for school use—a weapon of considerable range and great precision when used with judgment behind a Guyot's Common School Geography.

8. Unexpended ammunition for same, consisting of putty pellets.

9. Frog's hind leg, extra dry.

10. Wing of bluejay, very ditto.

11. Letter from "Beany," postmarked "Biddeford, Me.," and expressing great indignation because "Pewt" "hasent wrote."

12. Copy-book inscribed "Diry."

The examination of this copy-book lasted the rest of the day, and it was read with the peculiar pleasure one experiences in reviewing some of the events of a happy boyhood.

With the earnest hope that others may experience a

little of the pleasure I gained from the reading, I submit the "Diry" to the public.

HENRY A. SHUTE

Exeter, N. H., Sept. 23, 1902

Father thot i aught to keep a diry, but i sed i dident want to, because i coodent wright well enuf, but he sed he wood give $1000 dolars if he had kept a diry when he was a boy.

Mother said she gessed nobody wood dass to read it, but father said everybody would tumble over each other to read it, anyhow he wood give $1000 dolars if he had kept it. i told him i wood keep one regular if he wood give me a quarter of a dolar a week, but he said i had got to keep it anyhow and i woodent get no quarter for it neither, but he woodent ask to read it for a year, and i know he will forget it before that, so i am going to wright just what i want to in it. Father always forgets everything but my lickins. he remembers them every time you bet.

So i have got to keep it, but it seems to me that my diry is worth a quarter of a dolar a week if fathers is worth $1000 dolars, everybody says father was a buster when he was a boy and went round with Gim Melcher and Charles Talor. my grandmother says i am the best boy she ever see, if i dident go with Beany Watson and Pewter Purinton, it was Beany and Pewt made me tuf.

there dos'nt seem to be much to put into a diry only

89

fites and who got licked at school and if it ranes or snows, so i will begin today.

December 1, 186– brite and fair, late to brekfast, but mother dident say nothing. father goes to boston and works in the custum house so i can get up as late as i want to. father says he works like time, but i went to boston once and father dident do anything but tell stories about what he and Gim Melcher usted to do when he was a boy. once or twice when a man came in they would all be wrighting fast, when the man came in again i sed why do you all wright so fast when he comes in and stop when he goes out, and the man sort of laffed and went out laffing, and the men were mad and told father not to bring that dam little fool again.

December 2. Skinny Bruce got licked in school today. I told my granmother about it and she said she was glad i dident do enything to get punnished for and she felt sure i never wood. i dident tell her i had to stay in the wood box all the morning with the cover down. i dident tell father either you bet.

December 2. rany. i forgot to say it raned yesterday too. i got cold and have a red rag round my gozzle.

December 2. pretty near had a fite in schol today. Skinny Bruce and Frank Elliot got rite up with there fists up when the bell rung. it was two bad, it wood have been a buly fite. i bet on Skinny.

December 3, 186– brite and fair. went to church to-day. Me and Pewt and Beany go to the Unitarial church. we all joined sunday school to get into the Crismas festerval. they have it in the town hall and have two trees and supper and presents for the scholars. so we are going to stay til after crismas anyway the unitarials have jest built a new church. Pewt and Beany's fathers painted it and so they go there. i don't know why we go there xcept because they don't have any church in the afternoon. Nipper Brown and Micky Gould go there. we all went into the same class. our teacher is Mister Winsor a student. we call them stewdcats. after we had said our lesson we all skinned out with Mr. Winsor. when we went down Maple street we saw 2 roosters fiting in Dany Wingates yard, and we stoped to see it. i knew more about fiting roosters than any of the fellers, because me and Ed Towle had fit roosters lots. Mr. Winsor said i was a sport, well while the roosters were fiting, sunday school let out and he skipped acros the street and walked off with one of the girls and we hollered for him to come and see the fite out, and he turned red and looked mad. the leghorn squorked and stuck his head into a corner. when a rooster squorks he wont fite any more.

December 7, 186– Got sent to bed last nite for smoking hayseed cigars and can't go with Beany enny more. It is funny, my father wont let me go with Beany becaus he is tuf, and Pewts father wont let Pewt go with me becaus im tuf, and Beanys father says if he catches me or Pewt in his yard he will lick time out of us. Rany today.

December 8. Skinny Bruce got licked in school today. Skipy Moses was in the wood box all the morning.

December 9. brite and fair, speaking in school today. missed in Horatius at the brige.

December 15. Fite at resess today, Gran Miller and

91

Ben Rundlet. Ben licked him easy. the fellers got to stumping each other to fite. Micky Gould said he cood lick me and i said he want man enuf and he said if i wood come out behind the school house after school he wood show me and i said i wood and all the fellers hollered and said they wood be there. But after school i thaught i aught to go home and split my kindlings and so i went home. a feller aught to do something for his family ennyway. i cood have licked him if i had wanted to. . . .

December 19. Cold as time. Went to a sosiable tonite at the Unitarial Vestry. cant go agin because Keene[1] told mother i was impident to the people. i want impident. you see they was making poetry and all sitting around the vestry. they wanted to play copenhagin and post office and clap in and clap out, but Mister Erl woodent let them because it was in church. so they had to play poetry. one person wood give a word and then the oppisite person wood give a word that rimed with it. it was auful silly. a girl wood give the word direxion and then a stewdcat wood say affexion and waul his eyes towards the girl. and then another wood say miss, and another stewdcat wood say kiss and then he wood waul his eyes, and when it came my turn i said what rimes with jellycake, and the girls turned red and the stewdcats looked funny, and Mister Burley said if i coodent behave i had better go home. Keene needent have told mother anyway. You jest wait Keene, and see what will happen some day.

Note: "Keene" was the sister of the boy who wrote the diary.

December 26. Crismas tree at the town hall. had supper and got a bag of candy and a long string of pop corn. Mr. Lovel took off the presents and his whiskers caught fire, and he hollered o hell right out. that was pretty good for a sunday school teacher, wasent it. Jimmy Gad et too much and was sick.

December 27. Beany has got a new striped shirt not a false bosom but a whole shirt. Beany wont speak to me now. Lucy Watson has got a new blew hat with a fether. she wont speak to Keene and Cele eether. you jest wait Beany and Lucy and see. . . .

Jan. 1, 186– Had an awful time in school today. me and Cawcaw Harding set together. when we came in from resess Cawcaw reached over and hit me a bat, and i lent him one in the snoot, and he hit me back. we was jest fooling, but old Francis called Cawcaw up front to lick him. i thought if i went up and told him he wood say, noble boy go to your seat, i wont lick neether of you. anyway i knew that Cawcaw wood tell on me, and so i told old Francis i hit Cawcaw first, and old Francis said Harry i have had my eye on you for a long time, and he jest took us up and slammed us together, and then he wood put me down and shake Cawcaw and then he wood put Cawcaw down and shake me till my head wabbled and he turned me upside down and all the fellers looked upside down and went round and round and somehow i felt silly like and kind of like laffin. i dident want to laff but coodent help it. and then he talked to us and sent us to our seats and told us to study, and i tried to but all the words in the book went round and round and i felt awful funny and kind of wabbly, and when i went home mother said something was the matter and i told her and then i cried, i don't know what i cried for, becaus i dident ake any. father said he wood lick me at home when i got licked at school and perhaps that was why i cried. ennyway when father come home i asked him if he was a going to lick me and he said not by a dam sight, and he gave me ten cents and when i went to bed i got laffin and crying all to once, and coodent stop, and mother set in my room and kept her hand on my forred until i went to sleep. i drempt i was fiting all the time. when i get big enuf there is going to be a fite between me and old Francis, you see if there aint. . . .

Jan. 3. brite and fair. Went down to Pewts tonite to make hayseed cigars. We made 5 kinds, hayseed, sweet firn, cornsilk, mullin leeves, and grape vine. my mouth taisted aufuly all nite.

Jan. 4. brite and fair. Pewt dident come to school today. i gess he was sick. my mouth taisted aufuly all day. . . .

Jan. 10. rany. Nipper Brown is the best scolar in my class. i am the wirst. i can lick Nipper easy. . . .

Jan. 12. nobody got licked in school today, gess why, becaus there wassent enny school. old Francis was sick, i went skating.

Jan. 13. brite and—no it was rany. had a speling mach today in school. Cele and Genny Morrison staid up til the last and then Cele missed and set down balling, and Genny beat. . . .

Jan. 15. i am all spekled over. mother says she is

afrade i have got chicken pocks. i gess i have been in the hen koop to mutch.

Jan. 16. the speckles have all gone of. doctor Perry says i et to many donuts.

Jan. 18. brite and fair. yesterday to and day before yesterday i have forgot.

Jan. 19. snowed all day. Me and Beany is mad.

Jan. 20. father is sick becaus he et to mutch salt fish and potato and pork. he is auful cross and hit me a bat today becaus i left the door open. i gess he will be sorry when i am ded. . . .

Jan. 22. i had to stay in the woodbox today for whispering to Whacker with the cover down. i like it becaus they is a peep hole in the box and you can see the fellers and they cant see you. by and by Gimmy Fitsgerald whispered and old Francis put him in to and we took turns peeping. . . .

Jan. 25. brite and fair. everything was covered with ice and when father started for the depot he tumbled down the front steps from the top to the botom. mother says he went bumpity bump and his hat went one way and his dinner box went the other. i herd him swaring aufuly about that dam boy, and i guess he wood have com up and licked time out of me, but he had to hurry to get the train. . . .

Jan. 27. i coodent go out of the yard this afternoon becaus i dident put ashes on the front steps before father fell down and so Pewt and Beany and Whacker and Nibby Hartwell and Diddly Colket and Nipper and Prisilla and Gim Wingit and lots of the fellers came over and we had a snowball fite. mother says she hops father wont keep me at home anuther afternoon.

Jan. 28. brite and fair. it never ranes sundays so a feller cant go to church.

Jan. 29. Nothing puticular today. it always seams harder to go to school mundays, more fellers gets licked mundays than enny day in the weak. i got stood on the platform with my head in the corner for looking of my book today. . . .

Feb. 15. Got to the head in spelling today. old Francis makes us all stand up in the ile and gives us a lot of words to spell and then we wright them down on our slates and then the head feller or girl changes slates with the foot feller or girl and so on and then old Francis wrights the words on the blackboard and then we mark each others slates. John Flanygin was the foot feller and had my slate. well most of Johns words was wrong. but John marked mine all write. i gess John dident know it, but ther was 4 or 5 of my words speled wrong. i set out to tell old Francis but dident dass to becaus he licked me for teling that i paisted Cawcaw Harding that time. so i kept still and kept at the head and John kept at the foot. i hope John will do it again tomorrow.

Feb. 16. Beat in speling today.

Feb. 17. beat in speling today.

Feb. 19. Beat in speling today. old Francis is a going to give a prise tomorrow. i told father i was pretty sure to get it and he said it will be the first one. Aunt Sarah asked him if he took many prises. and he said he dident get much of a prise when he got me. i gess he wont say that tomorrow when i bring my prise home.

Feb. 20. i dident get the prise. you see yesterday John Flanygin spelt more words write than Gimmy Fitsgerald and Gimmy went to the foot. when we marked slates Gimmy marked 9 of my words wrong out of 20, and i had to go down most to where John Flannygin was. old Francis said he dident beleave i had aught to have staid at the head so long as i did and i was afraid he wood lick me and John but he dident. he said he was ashamed and disapointed in me but i gess he was not the only one who was disapointed. i had told Pewt and Beany i wood treat on what father wood give me for getting the prise. Pewt and Beany was both mad, and are going to lay for Gimmy. . . .

Feb. 24, Beany and Pewt got punching today in school and old Francis made them stand on the platform with their arms round each others neck all the forenoon, i bet they felt pretty cheep. Brite and fair. . . .

Mar. 10. plesent day. old Si Smiths big white dog and a bull dog had an awful fite today. neether licked and they had to squert water on them to seperate them. they dident make no noise, only jest hung write on to each others gozzles. my aunt Sarah said it was dredful, and she staid to the window to see how dredful it was.

Mar. 11, 186– Went to church in the morning. . . . Mister Lennard preeched about loving our ennymies, and told every one if he had any angry feelings towards ennyone to go to him and shake hands and see how

much better you wood feel. i know how it is becaus
when me and Beany are mad we dont have eny fun and
when we make up the one who is to blam always wants
to treet. why when Beany was mad with me becaus i went
home from Gil Steels surprise party with Lizzie Towle,
Ed Towles sister, he woodent speak to me for 2 days,
and when we made up he treated me to ice cream
with 2 spoons and he let me dip twice to his once. he
took pretty big dips to make up. Beany is mad if enny
of the fellers go with Lizzie Towle. she likes Beany better than she does enny of the fellers and Beany ought to
be satisfied, but sometimes he acks mad when i go down
there to fite roosters with Ed. i gess he needent worry
much, no feller isnt going to leave of fiting roosters to go
with no girls. well i most forgot what i was going to say,
but after church i went up to Micky Gould who was
going to fite me behind the school house, and said Micky
lets be friends and Micky said, huh old Skinny, i can lick
you in 2 minits and i said you ain't man enuf and
he called me a nockneed puke, and i called him a wall
eyed lummix and he give me a paist in the eye and i
gave him a good one in the mouth, and then we rassled
and Micky threw me and i turned him, and he got hold
of my new false bosom and i got hold of his hair, and the
fellers all hollered hit him Micky, paist him Skinny, and
Mister Purington, Pewts father pulled us apart and i had
Mickys paper collar and necktie and some of his hair
and he had my false bosom and when i got home father
made me go to bed and stay there all the afternoon for
fiting, but i gess he dident like my losing my false bosom.

ennyway he asked me how many times i hit Micky and which licked. he let me get up at supper time. next time i try to love my ennymy i am a going to lick him first. . . .

Mar. 29, 186– The toads has come out. fine warm day. me and Potter Gorham have been ketching toads this afternoon. they sit in the puddles and peep. folks think it is frogs but most of it is toads. Potter got 23 and i got 18. tonite i put my toads in a box in the kitchen after the folks went to bed. in the night they all got out of the box and began to hop round and peep mother heard it and waked father and they lissened. when i waked up father was coming threw my room with a big cane and a little tin lamp. he had put on his britches and was in his shirt tale, and i said, what are you going to lick me for now i havent done nothing and he said, keep still there is some one down stairs and mother said dont go down George and father said, lissen i can hear him giving a whistle for his confedrit, i will jump in and give him a whack on the cokonut. i had forgot all about the toads and you bet i was scart. well father he crep down easy and blowed out his lite and opened the door quick and jest lammed round with his club. then i heard him say what in hell have i stepped on, bring a lite here. then i thought of the toads and you bet i was scarter than before. mother went down with a lite and then i heard him say, i will be cussed the whole place is full of toads. then mother said did you ever and father said he never did, and it was some more of that dam boys works and he yelled upstairs for me to come down and ketch them. so i went down and caught them and put them out all but 2 that father had stepped on and they had to be swep up. then all the folks came down in their nitegounds and i went up stairs lively and got into bed and pulled the clothes round me tite, but it dident do enny good for father came up and licked me. he dident lick me very hard becaus i gess he was glad it wasent a berglar and if it hadent been for me it might have been berglars insted of toads. . . .

May 5, 186– Saw a bully fite today. Cris Staples and Charlie Clark. Charlie is visiting his uncle J. Albert Clark, the feller that we sassed. that is he said we did but we dident. Charlie is a city feller, he lives in Chelsy and think he knows a pile about things and gets mad if we call him names. now every feller who amounts to anything has a nickname, and some of them have 2 or 3. my nicknames are Plupy and Skinny and Polelegs, and Beany is called Bullethead and sometimes Fatty. i told Charlie that if i called him Charlie the fellers would call him sissy or Mary and he better agree to let me call him bulldog or tomcat or diddly or gobbler or some nickname whitch wood mean something. but he said he would lam the head off of enny feller which called him names.

Well you jest see what trouble he got into for not having a nickname. he would have knowed better than that if he hadent lived in Chelsy.

Well today me and Charlie was setting on his steps. Beany was mad because i was going with Charlie and he had gone riding with his father and he felt pretty big be-

THE REAL DIARY OF A REAL BOY

cause his father let him drive. well while we were setting
there along came Cris Staples who carries papers for
Lane and Rollins store, and Cris hollered over, hullo
Polelegs. Charlie hadent heard enyone call me Polelegs.
and i said, i woodent stand that if i was you Charlie,
now less see you lam the head off of him, and Charlie
he started across the road and walked up to Cris and
said who in time are you calling Polelegs and Cris
wasent going to back down and said, you, and Charlie
said jest drop them papers and i will nock your face rite
off, and Cris dropped his papers and they went at it. it
was the best fite i have seen this year. they fit from Mr.
Head's down to Gim Ellisons corner, and Cris licked
time out of Charlie, and Charlie began to yell and give
up and then Cris let go of his hair and told him he was
to smart, and that it was me he was calling Polelegs and
not him, and he better not be so smart another time, and
Cris he picked up his papers and went off with a great
slit in his jacket and his necktie way round on one side,
and Charlie came home howling and Aunt Clark,
Charlie's grandmother came out and said, that is what
you get Charlie for quareling. see how much better Harry
feels, and i said, yes mam. Charlie is never going to
speak to me again. . . .

May 21. erly this afternoon me and Fatty Melcher got
some real segars at Henry Simsons store and went
down behind old man Churchills store and smoked them.
we were both auful sick and laid there all the afternoon. when i went home i walked wobbly and mother
asked me if i was sick and she put me to bed and was

going to send for the docter, but father came in and when he found out what aled me he laffed and said it served me rite. then after supper he set out on the steps rite under my window and smoked a old pipe and i cood smell it and i thought i shood die. then mother asked him to go away and he laffed and said all rite, but he gessed i had enuf for one day and she said she gessed so and i gess so too. he said if it hadent made me sick he wood have licked me.

i dont see why it is so, father swears sometimes when he hits his thum with a hammer and once when he was in the dark he was walking towards the door with his arms out to feel for the door, one arm went on one side of the door and the other arm on the other side and he hit his nose a fearful bump rite on the ege of the door, and i wish you cood have heard him swear, well if i swear he licks me, and he smokes and if i do he says he will lick me and he dont go to church and if i dont go he says he will lick me. O dear i gess i wont smoke enny more. . . .

June 2. Rany. Beany is mad with me. i dont care.

June 3. went to church today. . . .

June 5. brite and fair. Beany is still mad.

June 6. brite and fair. i know what Beany is mad about. he thinks i told about his getting a licking. i dident tell. he can stay mad if he wants to. . . .

July 25. i got a fishhook in my leg today. me and Fatty Melcher was a fishing when we got our lines tangled. i hollered first cut, but i dident have enny nife and Fatty woodent let me have his nife. So we got jerking our lines kinder mad like and all of a suddin the hook got into my leg. gosh you bet it hurt. me and Fatty got the hook out but it bled some. the worst of it was there was a wirm on the hook and when we got the hook out they wasent enny wirm there. Fatty says people sometimes dies from having wirms in them. i bet this one has crawled way in. it may grow inside of me. something is always hapening to me. when i got home i went down to docter Derborns store and bought some wirm medicine and swalowed sum. it was auful bitter. it cost 20 cents out of my cornet money.

July 26. brite and fair. i was all rite today except my leg was stiff. mother asked what made me lame and she put on a peace of pork. i told her about the wirm and she said the pork wood draw him out if he was there but she gessed he dident go in. when i told her about the wirm medecine she jest set down and laffed. so i gess i needent wory about having wirms. i went down to docter Derborns and tride to get him to take the medicine back but he said he woodent. i think he is pretty mean not to. . . .

Aug. 21, 186– Gosh, we are having fun now. what do you think. they is going to be a big mass meeting this fall. Ben Butler and Jake Ely and lots of old pelters are going to be here, and they is going to be 4 or 5 bands and lots of fun well before that comes they is going to be lots of political meetings and the first one is to be next week, and father is going to make a speach. Gim Luverin and Bil Morrill and General Marsten and Tom Levitt, and he is a ripper to holler. and they want father to make a speach. father says he must work for the party and perhaps he can get his salery rased. so he has been a riting every nite and mumbling it over to hisself and last nite he said he had got it. tonight he is a going to speak it to us.

Aug. 22. last nite father studed his speach over and let us stay up to hear it. he stood up and looked auful stirn and put one hand in the buzum of his shert. i coodent help laffin, but he told me to shet up or i cood go to bed and so i shet up. i tell you it was fine. It begun Mister Moddirator had i supposed, or for 1 moment drempt that i a humble offis holder under this glorious government, wood have been called upon to speak, i shood have remained at home with my wife and my children.

i said, if you dont want to make a speach why dont you stay at home that nite, and he said 1 more word from you sir and you go to bed. so i dident yip again.

then he went on like this, were it not that a crool axident in my erly youth, in my far away boyhood days prevented me from voluntearing and desecrating my life to my countrys welfare, in the strugle jest ended i wood have poared out evry drop of my blud to have maintaned her owner and the owner of her flag. mother began to laff and said George how can you tell such feerful stories, you know you were scart most to deth becaus you was afraid you wood be drafted.

father said they was a lot of old fellows traveling round the country and talking that way who coodent have been drug into the war with a ox chane. then he stood on the other leg a while and said, it is peculiarly appropriate that Exeter, the berth place of Lewis Cas, the educater of Webster, the home of Amos Tuck, of General Marston shood be fourmost in the party strife, and as for me i wirk only for my partys good, my countrys good, without feer or hope of reward. they was a lot more to it, and some of it you cood hear about a mile he hollered so.

Aug. 23. We are all going the nite of the rally. mother says she wont go for she wood be ashamed to hear father tell such dredful stories. Aunt Sarah dont want to go because she is afraid father will brake down. but she has got to go with me and Keene and Cele and Georgie.

Aug. 24. father practised his speach tonite and we all hollered and claped at the fine parts. he has got a new pair of boots. they hurt like time and he only wears them nites when he is practising his speach.

Aug. 25. father licked me tonite becaus i spoke some of his speach to Beany. he was auful mad and said i was the bigest fool he ever see. . . .

Aug. 26. father called me and Beany out behind the barn tonite and gave us 10 cents apeace if we woodent say anything about his speach. after supper father practised again but he dident holler so loud because he was afraid some body wood hear him and mother dident want him to wake up the baby, and it was sunday too. . . .

Aug. 27. father went down to General Marstons office tonite to arrange about the rally. he came home and practised about an hour. i gess he wood have practised all nite if the baby hadent waked up an hollered.

Aug. 28. we are all getting ready for the rally. Keene and Cele and Georgie have got some new plad dresses. father has got a pair of gray britches and a black coat. mother said the rally was a good thing becaus it was the first time she had seen father dressed up since he was married. . . .

Aug. 30. we had the last practise tonite, father put on his best close and new boots and the girls had on their plad dresses and i had on a new paper coller. we all set down and father came in and stood up. i tell you he looked fine. well he begun, mister modderater had i supposed or for 1 moment dremp, and then he forgot the rest. i tell you he was mad. i wanted to laff but dident dass to. well after a while he remembered and went through it all rite, and then he went over it 2 times more. gosh what if he shood forget it tomorrow nite. he is going to wright some of it on his cufs and he practised tonite making jestures so as to bring his cufs up so that he cood read it.

Aug. 31. the rally is tonite. father woke us all up last nite hollering in his sleep. he dremp about the speach. this morning he went to Boston without eating his brekfast. i gess he is begining to be scart. i am a going to make his boots shine today. gosh what if he shood brake down. i gess i am getting a little scart too. brite and fair.

Sept. 1. Last nite father came home and the first thing he did was to send me down to miss Pratts for his shert. it was all pollished and shone like glass. then he asked if i had blacked his boots and then he et supper. he dident eat much though. he said Mr. Tuck came down from Boston with him. Mr. Tuck was a going to make a speach first and then he was going to introduce Gim Loverin as chairman and then Gim Loverin was a going to call on father. father said he bet 5 dollars he wood call him Gim instead of mister moderater. father was pretty cross at supper. i gess he was getting scart. the baby began to cry and father asked mother why she dident choak the squawling brat and mother sorter laffed and put the baby into fathers lap and said i gess you had better choak him. father laffed and began to toss the baby up and down. he likes the baby and while he was playing with it he was all rite. but after supper he was cross and said he hed a auful headake. then he went practising his speach again so as not to call the modderater Gim. well we got ready and went down erly to get some good seats so as to hear father and see him come in with them that was to set on the platform. we wanted to go down with father but he said he coodent bother with us. but before we went he came down stairs with his new close on and he looked fine but his face looked auful white. he said he had a headake but as soon as he got started to speak it wood all go off. so we went down. Cele had her hair curled and Keene had a new red silk ribbon on her hair becaus her hair wont curl and Aunt Sarah had on a new dolman with beeds on it and some long coral earrings and they all looked fine. Aunt Sarah took Georgie by the hand becaus she was the littlest and me and Keene and Cele followed on.

When we got there the band was playing in front of the town hall and aunt Sarah said i cood stay out and

hear it and then said i cood sit with Gim Wingit
and Willy Swet if i wood behave. i said i wood and we
lissened and after the band went in we went too. most
all the seats were taken and we got some bully seats way
up in front. i looked for father but coodent see him becaus the speakers hadent come in. well jest as soon as
we got in the policeman was up in front and he said they
has been to much whisling and stamping and the
next one that whisles or stamps will get put out. . . .
after a few minits the band began to play hale to the
chief and the speakers came marching up the middle
ile. i looked for father but he wasn't there. evrybody began to clap and stamp and Gim and Willy asked
me where my old man was. i stood up to see if he was
there and jest then i saw the policeman a rushing at me.
he grabed me by the collar and shook me round till I
dident know which end my head was on and he
draged me down the ile and threw me out. as we were
going down the ile i saw Aunt Sarah running down the
other ile as fast as she cood go with her bonnet on the
back of her head and Keene and Cele and Georgie following along all bawling. she got out in the entry jest as
he was going to put me out of the front door and she
grabed me away from him and said you misable cow-
ardly retch to treat a boy that way. he said i whisled and
she said he dident and you knew it only you dident dass
take ennyone else.

Then she told us to come home and we went home as
fast as we cood all bawling. when we got home mother
was sitting up alone and aunt Sarah started to tell her

and Keene and Cele and Georgie all bawled and you never heard such a noise, and father was in bed with a headake and hollered out what in time is the matter. and she told him and i heard him jump out of bed and in a minit he came out buttoning up his suspenders. Mother said where in the world are you going George, and he said things is come to a pretty pass if a boy cant go and hear his father make a speach without being banged round by a policeman. i am going down to knock the heads off every policeman there. and he reeched for his vest. mother said George, dont you go near the hall, and father said he cood lick anny 2 men on the police force easy and he would show them how to slam people round and he reeched for his coat, and Keene and Cele and Georgie began to bawl again to think he wood get hurt and aunt Sarah and mother said you had better not go George, and father said he wood give them more fun in 5 minits than they had seen in a political rally in 5 years and he reeched for his boots and mother said what will they think of you after you have sent word that you are too sick to make a speach, to see you come rushing into the hall and go punching the policemen and father had got on 1 boot and when she said that he began to look kinder sick and said, thunder that is so. and then his headake got wirse and he gave me a twenty five cent scrip and Keene and Cele and Georgie ten cents each and he went to bed and so did we.

i wonder if his head aked really so he coodent make a speach or if he was scart. i bet he was scart.

school commences monday. father hasent asked once about my diry, so i aint going to wright enny more.

RUTH MC KENNEY

Hun-gah

EILEEN LEARNS TO PLAY THE PIANO AND I TAKE
ELOCUTION LESSONS

When my sister and I were ten and eleven, our six aunts
on the lace-curtain-Irish, or Farrel, side of the family
got up a little fund to make their nieces cultured.

In their dreams, they could see, these amiable ladies
who loved us so dearly, Eileen at the piano bringing
tears to the eyes of her relatives with a splendid performance of "Narcissus," the selection where you cross your
hands on the keyboard. They could see me, too, in their
affectionate musings, spreading a fluffy organdie skirt for
a polite curtsy to a parlor full of admiring Farrels and
Murphys and Flannigans, and then launching into a
moving recitation of "Trees."

After all, our second cousins, the Murphy children,
aged only eleven and twelve, could already recite
"Trees" and play "The Rose of No Man's Land," not to

speak of "Humoresque," on the piano. If the Murphys could be cultured, so, my aunts said grimly, could the McKenneys. If they had secret misgivings, they never said so. They started off the big culture program by getting Eileen a music teacher, a nervous, angular lady who wore her eyeglasses on a black ribbon and sniffled.

"One," she used to say, "two, three," and then a long sniffle, "four. One, two," then another short, ladylike sniffle, "three, four."

The sniffles and the black ribbon for the eyeglasses fascinated my sister. She used to keep time to the sniffles instead of the counting, and as a result her scales went from bad to worse. Eventually, though, she learned to read simple sheet music. She also learned a bass which consisted mostly of fearful thumping and a rolling sound like kettledrums, all in the lowest octave of the keyboard. With this equipment, she was able to play "Chloe," a popular song of the early nineteen-twenties. She was never able to play anything except "Chloe," but she certainly could play that.

She used to stalk to the piano and seat herself firmly, with quite a thump, at the bench. Then, swaying largely from the waist, she picked up the melody, not without some difficulty. Finally, when the preliminaries were over, she burst into song, accompanying herself as she went along.

"Thr—ooo the bu-la-ck of NIGHT," Eileen used to intone in a deep bass growl, "I got-tuh go wheah yew ARE."

The climax of the song, where the melody goes up, always used to baffle my poor sister, who, like myself, is absolutely tone-deaf and has never been able to carry a tune, even the simplest one, in her whole life. She solved the difficulty by simply pounding so hard in the bass that she drowned herself out. Her voice emerged triumphantly just at the end: "I GOT-TUH go wheah yew ARE."

While Eileen was learning to play a bayou chant, I, too, was busy with culture. I was taking what my aunts thought were elocution lessons. These thoughtful ladies, after a solemn family conclave, had decided I should study public speaking because I stuttered over the telephone. I still do. It is very humiliating.

How my conservative, respectable aunts fell afoul of Madame DuLak and her Studio of the Voice I cannot imagine. Certainly she was not the teacher they thought she was. They hoped that I would learn how to recite "Trees." Madame DuLak told me the first time I met her that Joyce Kilmer "stank." That was the word she used. I was eleven years old, and I certainly was surprised to hear that about Joyce Kilmer.

Madame DuLak had studied in Paris. She said so often. She had picked up a lot of fancy notions in gay old Paris, I gathered, not only about Joyce Kilmer but also about "recitations" and "elocution lessons."

"We are going," Madame DuLak intoned, in a rich, deep voice full of culture, that first morning our little class of six assembled, "to undertake the study of a litt-tul play which I rather" (she said "rawther," of course) "like. I shall assign and read the parts this morning. By next week you will have memorized your lines, and then we shall settle down for a winter's work."

I memorized my lines easily. My part consisted of the word "hunger." But do not imagine that I was a mere walk-on in this little play of Madame DuLak's. On the contrary, I was one of the leading characters. I was, in spite of my rotund figure, a hungry old beggar. I sat on the steps of what was supposed to be a cathedral. From the time the curtain went up until at last it went down, I sat on those steps, chanting the word "hunger" more or less at one-minute intervals. Sometimes I said it very loudly, drowning out the rest of the cast, and sometimes I was supposed to whisper it very softly, as background. It was a Greek-chorus idea.

The play was exceedingly symbolical. I was not supposed to be physically hungry, which was a good thing, considering my appearance; I was just supposed to be spiritually hungry. Madame DuLak used to urge me to put this difference into the reading of my lines, or, rather, line. I was a big girl for my eleven years, and I was often hungry in the good old-fashioned sense of wanting another piece of chocolate cake or second helping of chocolate pie. So when Madame DuLak would urge me on Saturday mornings to "Put some *feeling* into your part, Ruth," I would concentrate hard on something chocolate and howl, "Hun-gah!" with a fine frenzied note in my voice. Madame DuLak thought I was pretty good, on the whole. Of course sometimes I forgot and said, "Hunger," and then Madame DuLak used to denounce me as a boor.

The rest of the pupils were also symbolical. The only other girl in the class, Betty Chippendale, was Vice. I

RUTH MC KENNEY

wanted to be Vice myself; I got pretty tired of being a
dirty old beggar yelling, "Hun-gah!" all the time. Vice
was a nice, rich part. There weren't any lines in the part,
to be sure, not even a one-word chant like my "Hun-
gah," but Vice got to stroll up and down the stage, wig-
gling her hips, brushing against other characters with
lewd gestures, and such like. Of course Betty was only
thirteen years old, and although she wanted to be an
actress when she grew up, her life had been rather re-
stricted so far. So she had some difficulty in making her
character study of Vice symbolical enough to suit
Madame DuLak.

"No, no, Betty," Madame DuLak would say in her
cultured voice, "you represent the dregs of humanity,
you are the symbol of lust and ugliness. You must make
your audience feel that as you move across the stage,
you must put that into every gesture of your little finger."

"Yes, Ma'am," Betty would say. She took her work
very seriously, and never got tired of walking up and
down and being the symbol of lust and ugliness.

The boys were, variously, Greed and Power and
Truth and Loving Kindness. Since this was a pretty modern morality play, Loving Kindness and Truth got
licked to a frazzle at the curtain. Greed and Power beat
them up and dragged them off bodily every Saturday
morning. Vice tagged along to get in on the kill, and that
left me still sitting on the cathedral steps. I had the last
lines. "Hun-gah!" I bellowed. "Hun-gah! Hun-gah!" Curtain.

114

I think now that Madame DuLak must have written that remarkable play herself. Of course it had certain resemblances to other dramas of its genre, but that smashing finish—that was pure DuLak.

After the first three weeks, Madame DuLak decided we must have costumes for our rehearsals. The costumes, she said, would help us get into the feeling of our roles. My costume was wonderful. I made it myself, and it certainly was realistic. I wore an old, ragged, burlap sack with holes cut out for the arms. My legs were bare, and I had a pair of Father's old bedroom slippers tied on my feet with rope. This was only the beginning, however. I took off my hair ribbon, unbraided my pigtails, and systematically, with a comb, snarled and matted my long hair. Then I covered my face, arms, and legs with artistic smatterings of coal dust. The first time Madame DuLak saw me emerge from my dressing room in her little studio, she gave me the highest praise a make-up artist can get.

"Awk!" she said, blasted out of her usual cultured calm.

With the first soft breezes of spring, with the first robin, my aunts began to question me rather sharply about my elocution lessons. I explained as well as I could about the play, but I could see that they rejected my story as the simple fantasy of an imaginative child. They urged me to recite my part for them, but some inner instinct warned me off.

Finally, though, one of the Farrel family reunions came along. The Farrels had family reunions at the drop of a hat, and the Murphys, the Flannigans, the McKenneys, Aunt Susan Maloney with her brood, and assorted other in-laws turned up, ate prodigiously, and argued about politics. Our aunts felt that it was practically certain that the Murphy girls would play "The Rose of No Man's Land" and recite "Trees."

"This time," Aunt Molly said, with a dangerous glitter in her eye, "we'll show them that the Murphy girls aren't the only ones in the family who take lessons."

Eileen and I turned up at the family reunion bearing our stage properties. I brought my costume in a box, with a neat bag of coal dust, and Eileen brought the sheet music of "Chloe." We weren't nervous in the least. After dinner we retired upstairs to prepare for what we felt would be our triumph. Eileen gargled, and I repeated "Hun-gah, hun-gah" several times, to get in voice.

Downstairs we could hear Margaret Murphy playing "The Rose of No Man's Land," and very badly, too. She had to start over again several times. The applause, however, was generous.

When Cousin Rita Murphy began to recite "Trees," Uncle Wally went out to the kitchen, and we heard him say, "There is a limit to everything, Katie. Where do they keep the whiskey bottle around here?" Katie was the cook. We bridled. Uncle Wally would never walk out on *our* performances, we felt sure.

He didn't. Nobody did. They were frozen to their seats. We got, in fact, the most flattering kind of attention. Even Uncle Wally's jaws fell ajar.

Eileen played and sang first. Just as the final notes of

her bass monotone chant, "I GOT-TUH go wheah yew ARE," and the final rumble of the piano died away, I burst dramatically through the door, shouting "Hun-gah! Hun-gah!" and shaking my matted and snarled locks at my assembled relatives. My grandmother Farrel, who always takes everything seriously, let out a piercing scream.

Ignoring the awed comments of the rest of the audience, I paced slowly over to the fireplace. "This," I said in stately tones, while my aunts stared at my coal-dust-streaked face, "is a cathedral. I am sitting on the cathedral steps." I sat down. There was a long pause. Then I put up my arms to the heavens.

"Hun-gah!" I shrieked. Grandma jumped and said audibly, "Mercy!"

I let another impressive silence fall. The Murphys, mother and father and the two accomplished child Murphys, breathed heavily. Suddenly I plopped down on the floor, my face turned to the horrified audience.

"Hun-gah," I barely breathed. Eileen struck a soft chord in the bass.

"God!" Uncle Wally said. In the silence, everybody heard him, but they were too engrossed in my performance to be shocked. I rolled over, one limp hand trailing on the carpet.

"Hun-gah!" I whined. I lay on the floor several seconds, letting it sink in. Then I began to drag myself to my feet. My knee joints always cracked, and in the silence you could hear them clearly all over the room. Nobody said anything. Finally I was all the way up, and panting. I was supposed to pant. I was supposed to have some kind of a terrible disease, like leprosy. I lowered my head, inch by inch. In those days I had a double chin, and I couldn't get my head down very far, unfortunately. I sighed, heavily.

Then in a flat, sad voice I said, "Hun-gah."

Eileen struck a minor chord. I bowed. I stalked toward the door. Eileen rose gravely and followed me. At the door we bowed together.

"Well, for God's sake!" my Uncle Wally said, quite loudly. We waited for the burst of applause, but our relatives sat glued to their seats, staring at us. Finally Aunt Molly pulled herself together and started to clap. Everybody else clapped too, dutifully, and we retired with the sweet sound of applause in our ears.

There never was another family reunion like that one. We knew perfectly well we had electrified our dear relatives. As Eileen put it, "It was about time somebody stuck a pin in them." Anyway, Uncle Wally told us afterward that he liked us better than "Trees." He thought that we had done it on purpose, and maybe, as I look back on it, we did. Our approach to life was somewhat confused at ten and eleven.

After that, the Murphy girls had the field of culture, in our family, to themselves. It never did them any good, either.

RUTH MC KENNEY

Beware the Brazilian Navy

ALMOST THE WORST THING THAT EVER HAPPENED TO US

I once had a perfectly frightful experience with the Brazilian Navy which has made me very shy of navies, especially South American navies. It was just an example of the kind of thing that often happened to me while I earned my living as a newspaper reporter, but *l'affaire Brazil* (which is the term by which Eileen always grumpily refers to the frightful incident) was rather more spectacular than most of my professional troubles.

My relations with the Brazilian Navy began under the worst possible circumstances. The gallant boys from our neighbor land on the equator came whooping into New York during one of those heat waves when people were keeling over right and left in subways. On the third day of it, when everybody in town simply began to go to pieces, the Brazilian Navy arrived in Brooklyn, expecting to be greeted by little children throwing flowers, by

mayors, men in silk hats, and bevies of flashing-eyed
American peacherinos. The little children, of course,
were home with the heat rash, the Mayor was in Washington, the Deputy Consul got lost in Brooklyn and was
four hours even finding his countrymen. To cap the dis-
mal climax, all available American peacherinos, like admirals' daughters and such, refused point-blank to abandon Newport and Southampton for Brooklyn to do any
welcoming of the flower of Brazilian manhood.

You can imagine, then, the distress and disappoint-
ment of the brave lads of the Brazilian Navy when it
got to be eleven o'clock on their first morning in New
York and no mayors, no little tots with bouquets, and
especially no beautiful girls who were heiresses to rub-
ber-goods fortunes, had turned up to gladden their
South American hearts.

Just as annoyance was beginning to develop into definite pique, a taxicab drove up on the pier and I clambered out, panting like a dog in the heat.

"Whee!" shouted a manly little ensign, in what I was
just able to recognize as rich Portuguese. "A dame!"

Instantly a throaty cheer went up from more than half
a hundred sturdy South American throats. Scores of
brand-clean white hats went sailing recklessly in the
air. A dense crowd gathered at the side rail of the boat,
the better to see the approaching lady. Merry cries
went up from the thick clusters of brave Navy lads.

My first move was to dig a crumpled piece of paper
from my pocketbook and, standing sullenly in the blazing sun, read it carefully through. This baffled the gen-

tlemen hanging over the rail. The piece of paper was a City News "Note to all City Editors," giving the glad tidings that a Brazilian training ship had come to Brooklyn on a world tour. "The crew," said City News enthusiastically, "is entirely composed of Brazil's future admirals and many of the young men now scrubbing decks on this sailing ship are heirs to great coffee fortunes."

Just as I finished reading this interesting document, four gorgeous future admirals marched down the gangplank to the pier, right-faced, removed their glistening white hats, and bowed in solemn unison. The leader of this little band then began a long speech in that lovely romantic language of the coffee country. At intervals during the speech, the men on the rail of the ship cheered and threw their hats in the air. I began to wish vaguely that I were clad in one of those long, fluttery dresses the girls always wear in the newsreels for Daisy Day at Annapolis. Finally the man who was making the speech rose to a terrific climax, all hands cheered again, and a pregnant silence fell.

I dug my battered press card from my pocketbook, took a deep breath, and handed it to the orator, saying nervously, "I'm afraid you've got me wrong. I'm only a newspaper reporter." The orator examined the press card with great interest, then he handed it to the resplendent future admiral beside him, who also examined it with careful eye, and finally all four of the boys were crowded around it, shaking their heads with anxious curiosity. At last they handed it back, smiled in happy unison, and bowed.

The orator then made another speech, and the boys at the rail cheered again. At the end of this speech two future admirals drew up on my left flank, two on my right, and we all began to march smartly toward the gangplank. I kept looking over my shoulder for somebody from another newspaper or even from the A.P. to show up, but nobody did, of course.

"No speakee Portugee," I said desperately to the orator, who was piloting me up the gangplank by careful pressure on my perspiring left elbow. It was certainly hot that day.

"*Je ne parle pas français ou portugee,*" I said to the handsome creature on my right. He winked, odiously. There seemed to be nothing further to add, so I marched onto the ship in dreary silence.

Upstairs, or above decks, as they say in the Navy, the boys were all waiting for our little party. Cheers broke out as I clambered up the stairs, wiping my perspiring face with a limp handkerchief. Quite a lot of coffee heirs tried to horn in on the orator, and several succeeded. The press was terrific.

"Hot!" I barked desperately, making gestures of fanning myself. Instantly great activity broke out. I was led to a patch of shade under an awning. I was lowered into a chair. Three handsome lads turned up with tall glasses of some liquid with ice in it. In front of my chair several score Brazilians lined up, natty as anything in their fresh white uniforms, and stared at me. Several score more stood in back of my chair and fanned me with their white hats. They made quite a little wind.

Just as I was getting ready to enjoy the breeze, the orator began to talk to me, softly and earnestly, with a gleam in his eyes.

"No understando," I kept saying. "*Nicht verstehe, ne parle pas français.*" The orator kept talking. The men standing in front of me stared with lustrous black eyes, and several of them grinned—wickedly, I thought.

I could feel a blush getting up under my sunburn. Finally the orator took my pocketbook.

"Hey!" I said earnestly.

He opened the pocketbook, extracted the press card, bowed, took out a little silver pencil and a neat little notebook, and began to copy the information on the card. Hordes of other future admirals crowded around him, but he beat them back with angry gestures. At this point I decided to leave.

"Go!" I said earnestly. "Leave, good-by!" They got the good-by. All hands began to shout, "Goot bee, goot bee," or something like that, and I was marched off in great style.

I was sitting at my desk in the newspaper office, quietly drinking a chocolate soda and waiting for it to be five-thirty, when the lad who prevents process-servers and people who have a plan to end war from entering the city room approached me with what is called a worried mien.

"Say," the lad asked earnestly, "where did you meet the Navy?"

A chill spread through my heart. At that very moment there was a stir in the city room, for five strong, in perfect order, dressed in gleaming, spotless white, the Brazilian Navy was marching down the city-room aisle.

"Cheese it! The cops!" cried the political reporter, an Irishman of ready wit.

While men stood on chairs to get a better view and printers rushed in from the composing room to see what was up, the five future admirals marched to my desk, removed their caps, held them over their hearts, and bowed from the waist. A man in the financial section, far off, whistled between his teeth. Otherwise there was breathless silence.

"Hello," I said.

All five future admirals bowed again and grinned. Their black eyes sparkled and the man in the middle winked.

"No speakee Portugee," I said firmly.

The Brazilian Navy smiled pleasantly.

The night city editor came over and said, "Wow!"

The situation had now grown intolerable. Even the moving-picture critic had been summoned from his of-fice on the third floor to get a load of the Brazilian Navy paying ardent court to the lady reporter. Whistles were rife all over the city room, and I thought them in very poor taste. I would have to get rid of the Navy even if I took them out myself.

I seized my hat, said "Go!" to the Brazilians, and started for the door. A Brazilian immediately seized each of my arms, and three more Brazilians marched proudly and happily behind.

"Have a nice time," the copy editor shrieked in a horrid falsetto.

"Whee!" screamed the moving-picture critic.

Outside the office, I said "Good-by" firmly, and started for home. But the Navy didn't get the idea. We progressed, my Brazilians and I, majestically up to Sheridan Square, creating a sensation of the first water on the West Side Seventh Avenue local, not to mention the excitement we caused strolling along Christopher Street. Grocery-store keepers kept running to their doors crying, "Parade!"

Finally we reached the door of the modest apartment where my sister and I lived. "Goot bee," I said desperately. The Navy bowed, smiled, lifted their white hats. I unlocked the door and they followed me in, stepping briskly.

My sister, who is a very, very pretty girl, was lying on a daybed, her arms stretched out, her hat on the pillow beside her. Her eyes were closed, but as she heard my familiar step, she said, "Boy, the heat's got me! I'm too done-in to stagger into a shower."

"Hey!" I said.

She opened her eyes to see the five future admirals regarding her with open admiration. Her jaw dropped and she sat up.

"They're Brazilians," I said, waving my arm at the Navy.

"Brazilians?" Eileen repeated blankly. The five gentlemen, holding their hats over their hearts, bowed and smiled at my sister.

"They don't speak a word of English," I said, dropping into a chair and pushing back my hat wearily. The five Brazilians now sat down in a happy row on the other daybed, staring with five pairs of gleaming black eyes at my pretty sister.

There was a long silence. Finally Eileen said, "They're winking at me."

"I know," I murmured. "They do that a lot. They think it is the universal language."

"Hmm," my sister replied.

"I'm so hot I could die," I said faintly. "I've had a terrible day. I had to go to Brooklyn, and Brooklyn is the hottest place in the world."

"Listen," my sister said in a very grim voice, "don't sit there full of idle chatter about the weather. Get rid of the Navy."

"Go away, boys," I said without much conviction. The Brazilians smiled.

Eileen stormed into the bathroom muttering.

When she emerged, all fresh from her shower and with her second-best dress on, she said, firmly, "I'm starving. Let's go to the nearest air-cooled eatery, with or without the Navy."

"Eat!" I said to the Navy, grinding my teeth ferociously. The future admirals looked startled.

"You're scaring them," Eileen objected. In the end, we drew a picture of what we felt looked like a restaurant.

"Be careful," Eileen said anxiously as I sketched. "For God's sake, don't let them get any wrong ideas."

We waltzed along Eighth Street, white uniforms to

the right and left of us, until we came to a large sign that said "Village Barn. Air-Cooled."

The Brazilian Navy never quite got over the overpowering effects of the Village Barn, and neither did we, for that matter. For one thing, twenty large, fat, oldish women were having a paper-hat birthday dinner as we came in, and their pretty screams of joy and laughter nearly drowned out the orchestra. Then, all the waiters were dressed in overalls and large straw hats, and there was a real stream of water and a real Old Mill quite near our table.

Our little party got off to a sullen start. Eileen kept saying that she never thought she would end up at a place like the Village Barn with a good section of a South American navy. My sister is an anti-militarist. As for the Navy, they were very cold and miserable. They kept making piteous gestures indicating that their necks were getting stiff. I guess you have to build up resistance to modern air-cooling.

Finally, however, the Navy began on their fourth round of rum punches and the orchestra played a rumba. I suppose you might say this was the high point of the Brazilian shore expedition. The little admirals from the far southland were, to our surprise, copiously supplied with American dollar bills, which they kept giving to the waiter, who put them in the pants pocket of his overalls, and to the orchestra, so they would play more rumbas.

Once I retired behind what was labeled a haymow to repair the ravages of several rumbas with Number Three, and when I returned a hideous sight struck my eye. All the jolly patrons of the Village Barn, which apparently gets a lot of out-of-town trade besides Brazilians, were lined up around the dance floor, three deep, jaws agape. In the center of the floor, in lonely magnificence, my sister and the Number One boy from Brazil were prowling around each other while the orchestra played a sneaky, sinister rumba. I was struck dumb by the horrid sight of my only sister doubling for the floor show.

The final blow came when Brazilian Number Two, watching from the sidelines, tossed Number One his natty white hat. Number One caught the hat with practiced gesture, threw it on the floor, and the next thing I knew Eileen and the future hero of Brazil were snake-hipping around that hat, forehead to forehead. It was spectacular. When the music stopped, even the orchestra cheered.

Everybody in our little party brightened up after that except me.

What seemed to me hours later, Eileen and I conferred on how to draw a picture of the fact that we wanted to go home because we had to work the next morning. If you will reflect on this a moment, you will see that it was a delicate situation. Pictures of home and the like can lead to fearful misunderstandings.

In the end, we just marched smartly home, the five brave sea dogs singing some little Portuguese sea chanty in tango time and trotting along beside us.

At the door of the apartment Eileen stopped, stretched out her arm, as Isolde does in the first act, and shouted "Go!" The Brazilians all looked in the direction to which she was pointing and, seeing nothing, giggled fatuously. Eileen said grimly, "They can't be that dumb."

"They aren't," I replied bitterly. "This is what comes of dancing around hats. They have got the wrong idea."

There was a long pause. Eileen nervously played with the front-door key. The five Brazilians wore eager, alert expressions.

"They're watching me like a rat in a trap," Eileen snapped.

"You open the door," I whispered, "and I'll slip in and hold it for you."

"You open the door," Eileen countered, "and *I'll* slip in."

So I did. Eileen slipped in successfully but left me outside with the Navy. The Brazilians did not look downcast, only determined.

It was four minutes before the Navy lads fell for the "Oh, look!" gag, where you point in one direction and run like hell in the other. After we were both inside, the Brazilians got mad and rattled the door and carried on generally. Several people stuck their heads out their doors and roared "Quiet!" and "Stop the noise!"

Eileen finally went to bed with her shoes on, and the eggbeater beside her pillow. We slept but fitfully, however, for the Brazilians resorted to serenades about 4 A.M. and there seemed to be a fight in the hall about 4:30. Things quieted down after that.

When we finally woke up in the heat of the bright

morning sun, we opened the door a crack and looked
out. The Brazilian Navy were gone—forever, as it
turned out. I guess they were pretty disappointed in
American girls.

ROBERT BENCHLEY

Family Life in America

The naturalistic literature of this country has reached such a state that no family of characters is considered true to life which does not include at least two hypochondriacs, one sadist, and one old man who spills food down the front of his vest. If this school progresses, the following is what we may expect in our national literature in a year or so.

PART 1

The living-room in the Twillys' house was so damp that thick, soppy moss grew all over the walls. It dripped on the picture of Grandfather Twilly that hung over the melodeon, making streaks down the dirty glass like sweat on the old man's face. It was a mean face. Grandfather Twilly had been a mean man and had little spots of soup on the lapel of his coat. All his children were mean and had soup spots on their clothes.

Grandma Twilly sat in the rocker over by the window, and as she rocked the chair snapped. It sounded like Grandma Twilly's knees snapping as they did whenever she stooped over to pull the wings off a fly. She was a mean old thing. Her knuckles were grimy and she chewed crumbs that she found in the bottom of her reticule. You would have hated her. She hated herself. But most of all she hated Grandfather Twilly.

"I certainly hope you're frying good," she muttered as she looked up at his picture.

"Hasn't the undertaker come yet, Ma?" asked young Mrs. Wilbur Twilly petulantly. She was boiling water on the oil-heater and every now and again would spill a little of the steaming liquid on the baby who was playing on the floor. She hated the baby because it looked like her father. The hot water raised little white blisters on the baby's red neck and Mabel Twilly felt short, sharp twinges of pleasure at the sight. It was the only pleasure she had had for four months.

"Why don't you kill yourself, Ma?" she continued. "You're only in the way here and you know it. It's just because you're a mean old woman and want to make trouble for us that you hang on."

Grandma Twilly shot a dirty look at her daughter-in-law. She had always hated her. Stringy hair, Mabel had. Dank, stringy hair. Grandma Twilly thought how it would look hanging at an Indian's belt. But all that

134

she did was to place her tongue against her two front teeth and make a noise like the bath-room faucet.

Wilbur Twilly was reading the paper by the oil lamp. Wilbur had watery blue eyes and cigar ashes all over his knees. The third and fourth buttons of his vest were undone. It was too hideous.

He was conscious of his family seated in chairs about him. His mother, chewing crumbs. His wife Mabel, with her stringy hair, reading. His sister Bernice, with project-ing front teeth, who sat thinking of the man who came every day to take away the waste paper. Bernice was wondering how long it would be before her family would discover that she had been married to this man for three years.

How Wilbur hated them all. It didn't seem as if he could stand it any longer. He wanted to scream and stick pins into every one of them and then rush out and see the girl who worked in his office snapping rubber-bands all day. He hated her too, but she wore side-combs.

PART 2

The street was covered with slimy mud. It oozed out from under Bernice's rubbers in unpleasant bubbles until it seemed to her as if she must kill herself. Hot air coming out from a steam laundry. Hot, stifling air. Ber-nice didn't work in the laundry but she wished that she did so that the hot air would kill her. She wanted to be stifled. She needed torture to be happy. She also needed a good swift clout on the side of the face.

A drunken man lurched out from a door-way and flung his arms about her. It was only her husband. She loved her husband. She loved him so much that, as she pushed him away and into the gutter, she stuck her little finger into his eye. She also untied his neck-tie. It was a bow neck-tie, with white, dirty spots on it and it was wet with gin. It didn't seem as if Bernice could stand it any longer. All the repressions of nineteen sordid years behind protruding teeth surged through her untidy soul. She wanted love. But it was not her husband that she loved so fiercely. It was old Grandfather Twilly. And he was too dead.

PART 3

In the dining-room of the Twillys' house everything was very quiet. Even the vinegar-cruet which was covered with fly-specks. Grandma Twilly lay with her head in the baked potatoes, poisoned by Mabel, who, in her turn had been poisoned by her husband and sprawled in an odd posture over the china-closet. Wilbur and his sister Bernice had just finished choking each other to death and between them completely covered the carpet in that corner of the room where the worn spot showed the bare boards beneath, like ribs on a chicken carcass.

Only the baby survived. She had a mean face and had great spillings of Imperial Granum down her bib. As she looked about her at her family, a great hate surged through her tiny body and her eyes snapped viciously. She wanted to get down from her high-chair and show them all how much she hated them.

Bernice's husband, the man who came after the waste paper, staggered into the room. The tips were off both his shoe-lacings. The baby experienced a voluptuous sense of futility at the sight of the tipless-lacings and leered suggestively at her uncle-in-law.

"We must get the roof fixed," said the man, very quietly. "It lets the sun in."

LEONARD Q. ROSS

Mr. K*a*p*l*a*n and Shakespeare

It was Miss Higby's idea in the first place. She had suggested to Mr. Parkhill that the students came to her class unaware of the *finer* side of English, of its beauty and, as she put it, "the glorious heritage of our literature." She suggested that perhaps poetry might be worked into the exercises of Mr. Parkhill's class. The beginners' grade had, after all, been subjected to almost a year of English and might be presumed to have achieved some linguistic sophistication. Poetry would make the students conscious of precise enunciation; it would make them read with greater care and an ear for sounds. Miss Higby, who had once begun a master's thesis on Coventry Patmore, *loved* poetry. And, it should be said in all justice, she argued her cause with considerable logic. Poetry *would* be excellent for the enunciation of the students, thought Mr. Parkhill.

So it was that when he faced the class the following

Tuesday night, Mr. Parkhill had a volume of Shakespeare on his desk, and an eager, almost an expectant, look in his eye. The love that Miss Higby bore for poetry in general was as nothing compared to the love that Mr. Parkhill bore for Shakespeare in particular. To Mr. Parkhill, poetry meant Shakespeare. Many years ago he had played Polonius in his senior class play.

"Tonight, class," said Mr. Parkhill, "I am going to try an experiment."

The class looked up dutifully. They had come to regard Mr. Parkhill's pedagogical innovations as part of the natural order.

"I am going to introduce you to poetry—great poetry. You see—" Mr. Parkhill delivered a modest lecture on the beauty of poetry, its expression of the loftier thoughts of men, its economy of statement. He hoped it would be a relief from spelling and composition exercises to use poetry as the subject matter of the regular Recitation and Speech period. "I shall write a passage on the board and read it for you. Then, for Recitation and Speech, you will give short addresses, using the passage as the general topic, telling us what it has brought to your minds, what thoughts and ideas."

The class seemed quite pleased by the announcement. Miss Mitnick blushed happily. (This blush was different from most of Miss Mitnick's blushes; there was aspiration and idealism in it.) Mr. Norman Bloom sighed with a business-like air: you could tell that for him poetry was merely another assignment, like a speech on "What I Like to Eat Best" or a composition on "A Day at a

Picnic." Mrs. Moskowitz, to whom any public performance was unpleasant, tried to look enthusiastic, without
much success. And Mr. Hyman Kaplan, the heroic smile
on his face as indelibly as ever, looked at Mr. Parkhill
with admiration and whispered to himself: "Poyetry!
Now is poyetry! My! Mus' be progriss ve makink aw-
reddy!"

"The passage will be from Shakespeare," Mr. Parkhill
announced, opening the volume.

An excited buzz ran through the class as the magic
of that name fell upon them.

"Imachine!" murmured Mr. Kaplan. "Jakesbeer!"

"*Shake*speare, Mr. Kaplan!"

Mr. Parkhill took a piece of chalk and, with care and
evident love, wrote the following passage on the board
in large, clear letters:

> Tomorrow, and tomorrow, and tomorrow
> Creeps in this petty pace from day to day,
> To the last syllable of recorded time;
> And all our yesterdays have lighted fools
> The way to dusty death. Out, out, brief candle!
> Life's but a walking shadow, a poor player
> That struts and frets his hour upon the stage,
> And then is heard no more; it is a tale
> Told by an idiot, full of sound and fury,
> Signifying nothing.

A reverent hush filled the classroom, as eyes gazed
with wonder on this passage from the Bard. Mr. Parkhill was pleased at this.

"I shall read the passage first," he said. "Listen carefully to my enunciation—and—er—let Shakespeare's thoughts sink into your minds."

Mr. Parkhill read: "Tomorrow, and tomorrow, and tomorrow . . ." Mr. Parkhill read very well and this night, as if some special fire burned in him, he read with rare eloquence. "Out, out, brief candle!" In Miss Mitnick's eyes there was inspiration and wonder. "Life's but a walking shadow . . ." Mrs. Moskowitz sat with a heavy frown, indicating cerebration. "It is a tale told by an idiot . . ." Mr. Kaplan's smile had taken on something luminous; but his eyes were closed: it was not clear whether Mr. Kaplan had surrendered to the spell of the Immortal Bard or to that of Morpheus.

"I shall—er—read the passage again," said Mr. Parkhill, clearing his throat vociferously until he saw Mr. Kaplan's eyes open. "Tomorrow, and tomorrow, and tomorrow. . . ."

When Mr. Parkhill had read the passage for the second time, he said: "That should be quite clear now. Are there any questions?"

There were a few questions. Mr. Scymzak wanted to know whether "frets" was "a little kind excitement." Miss Schneiderman asked about "struts." Mr. Kaplan wasn't sure about "cripps." Mr. Parkhill explained the words carefully, with several illustrative uses of each word. "No more questions? Well, I shall allow a few minutes for you all to—er—think over the meaning of the passage. Then we shall begin Recitation and Speech."

Mr. Kaplan promptly closed his eyes again, his smile

beatific. The students sank into that revery miscalled thought, searching their souls for the symbols evoked by Shakespeare's immortal words.

"Miss Caravello, will you begin?" asked Mr. Parkhill at last.

Miss Caravello went to the front of the room. "Da poem isa gooda," she said slowly. "Itsa have—"

"It *has.*"

"It hasa beautiful wordsa. Itsa lak Dante, Italian poet——"

"Ha!" cried Mr. Kaplan scornfully. "Shaksbeer you metchink mit Tante? *Shaksbeer?* Mein Gott!"

It was obvious that Mr. Kaplan had identified himself with Shakespeare and would tolerate no disparagement of his *alter ego.*

"Miss Caravello is merely expressing her own ideas," said Mr. Parkhill pacifically. (Actually, he felt completely sympathetic to Mr. Kaplan's point of view.)

"Hau Kay," agreed Mr. Kaplan, with a generous wave of the hand. "But to me is no comparink a high-cless man like Shaksbeer mit a Tante, dat's all."

Miss Caravello, her poise shattered, said a few more words and sat down.

Mrs. Yampolsky's contribution was brief. "This is full deep meanings," she said, her eyes on the floor. "Is hard for a person not so good in English to unnistand. But I like."

" '*Like!*' " cried Mr. Kaplan with a fine impatience. " '*Like?*' Batter *love*, Yampolsky. Mit Shaksbeer mus' be *love!*"

142

Mr. Parkhill had to suggest that Mr. Kaplan control his aesthetic passions. He did understand how Mr. Kaplan felt, however, and sensed a new bond between them. Mrs. Yampolsky staggered through several more nervous comments and retired.

Mr. Bloom was next. He gave a long declamation, ending: "So is passimistic ideas in the poem, and I am optimist. Life should be happy—so we should remember this is only a poem. Maybe is Shakespeare too passimistic."

"You wronk, Bloom!" cried Mr. Kaplan with prompt indignation. "Shaksbeer is passimist because is de *life* passimist also!"

Mr. Parkhill, impressed by this philosophical stroke, realized that Mr. Kaplan, afire with the glory of the Swan of Avon, could not be suppressed. Mr. Kaplan was the kind of man who brooked no criticism of his gods. The only solution was to call on Mr. Kaplan for his recitation at once. Mr. Parkhill was, indeed, curious about what fresh thoughts Mr. Kaplan would utter after his passionate defences of the Bard. When Mr. Parkhill had corrected certain parts of Mr. Bloom's speech, emphasizing Mr. Bloom's failure to use the indefinite article, he said: "Mr. Kaplan, will *you* speak next?"

Mr. Kaplan's face broke into a glow; his smile was like a rainbow. "Soitinly," he said, walking to the front of the room. Never had he seemed so dignified, so eager, so conscious of a great destiny.

"Er—Mr. Kaplan," added Mr. Parkhill, suddenly

aware of the possibilities which the situation (Kaplan on Shakespeare) involved: "Speak *carefully*."

"*Spacially* careful vill I be," Mr. Kaplan reassured him. He cleared his throat, adjusted his tie, and began: "Ladies an' gantleman, you hoid all kinds minninks abot dis piece poyetry, an'—"

"*Po*etry."

"—abot dis piece *po*etry. But to me is a difference minnink altogadder. Ve mus' tink abot Julius Scissor an' how *he* falt!"

Mr. Parkhill moved nervously, puzzled.

"In dese exact voids is Julius Scissor sayink—"

"Er—Mr. Kaplan," said Mr. Parkhill once he grasped the full import of Mr. Kaplan's error. "The passage is from 'Macbeth.'"

Mr. Kaplan looked at Mr. Parkhill with injured surprise. "*Not* fromm 'Julius Scissor'?" There was pain in his voice.

"No. And it's—er—'Julius *Cae*sar.'"

Mr. Kaplan waited until the last echo of the name had permeated his soul. "Podden me, Mr. Pockheel. Isn't '*see*zor' vat you cottink somting op mit?"

"That," said Mr. Parkhill quickly, "is 'Scissor.' You have used 'Caesar' for 'scissor' and 'scissor' for 'Caesar.'"

Mr. Kaplan nodded, marvelling at his own virtuosity.

"But go on with your speech, please." Mr. Parkhill, to tell the truth, felt a little guilty that he had not announced at the very beginning that the passage was from "Macbeth." "Tell us *why* you thought the lines were from 'Julius Caesar.'"

144

"Vell," said Mr. Kaplan to the class, his smile assuming its normal serenity. "I vas positif, becawss I can *see* de whole ting." He paused, debating how to explain this cryptic remark. Then his eyes filled with a strange enchantment. "I see de whole scinn. It's in a tant, on de night bafore dey makink Julius de Kink fromm Rome. So he is axcited an' ken't slip. He is layink in bad, tinking: 'Tomorrow an' tomorrow an' tomorrow. How slow dey movink! Almost cripps! Soch a pity de pace!'"

Before Mr. Parkhill could explain that "petty pace" did not mean "Soch a pity de pace!" Mr. Kaplan had soared on.

"De days go slow, fromm day to day, like leetle tsyllables on phonograph racords fromm time."

Anxiety and bewilderment invaded Mr. Parkhill's eyes.

"'An' vat abot yestidday?' tinks Julius Scissor. Ha! 'All our yestiddays are only makink a good light for fools to die in de dost!'"

"'Dusty death' doesn't mean—" There was no interrupting Mr. Kaplan.

"An' Julius Scissor is so tired, an' he vants to fallink aslip. So he hollers, mit fillink, 'Go ot! Go ot! Short candle!' So it goes ot."

Mr. Kaplan's voice dropped to a whisper. "But he ken't slip. Now is bodderink him de idea fromm life. 'Vat is de life altogadder?' tinks Julius Scissor. An' he gives enswer, de pot I like de bast. 'Life is like a bum actor, strottink an' hollerink arond de stage for only vun hour bafore he's kicked ot. Life is a tale told by idjots, dat's all, full of fonny sonds an' phooey!' "

Mr. Parkhill could be silent no longer. " 'Full of sound and fury!' " he cried desperately. But inspiration, like an irresistible force, swept Mr. Kaplan on.

" 'Life is monkey business! It don' minn a ting. It signifies nottink!' An' den Julius Scissor closes his ice fest—" Mr. Kaplan demonstrated the Consul's exact ocular process in closing his "ice"—"—an' falls dad!"

The class was hushed as Mr. Kaplan stopped. In the silence, a tribute to the fertility of Mr. Kaplan's imagination and the power of his oratory, Mr. Kaplan went to his seat. But just before he sat down, as if adding a postscript, he sighed: "Dat vas mine idea. But ufcawss is all wronk, becawss Mr. Pockheel said de voids ain't abot Julius Scissor altogadder. It's all abot an Irishman by de name Macbat."

Then Mr. Kaplan sat down.

It was some time before Mr. Parkhill could bring himself to criticize Mr. Kaplan's pronunciation, enunciation, diction, grammar, idiom, and sentence structure. For Mr. Parkhill discovered that he could not easily return to the world of reality. He was still trying to tear himself away from that tent outside Rome, where "Julius Scissor," cursed with insomnia, had thought of time and life—and philosophized himself to a strange and sudden death.

Mr. Parkhill was distinctly annoyed with Miss Higby.

SAKI

The Mouse

Theodoric Voler had been brought up, from infancy to the confines of middle age, by a fond mother whose chief solicitude had been to keep him screened from what she called the coarser realities of life. When she died she left Theodoric alone in a world that was as real as ever, and a good deal coarser than he considered it had any need to be. To a man of his temperament and upbringing even a simple railway journey was crammed with petty annoyances and minor discords, and as he settled himself down in a second-class compartment one September morning he was conscious of ruffled feelings and general mental discomposure. He had been staying at a country vicarage, the inmates of which had been certainly neither brutal nor bacchanalian, but their supervision of the domestic establishment had been of that lax order which invites disaster. The pony carriage that was to take him to the station had never been properly ordered, and when the moment for his departure drew near the handyman who should have produced the required article was nowhere to be found. In this emergency Theodoric, to his mute but very intense disgust, found himself obliged to collaborate with the vicar's daughter in the task of harnessing the pony, which necessitated groping about in an ill-lighted outhouse called a stable, and smelling very like one—except in patches where it smelt of mice. Without being actually afraid of mice, Theodoric classed them among the coarser incidents of life, and considered that Providence, with a little exercise of moral courage, might long ago have recognized that they were not indispensable, and have withdrawn them from circulation. As the train glided out of the station Theodoric's nervous imagination accused himself of exhaling a weak odour of stable-yard, and possibly of displaying a mouldy straw or two on his usually well-brushed garments. Fortunately the only other occupant of the compartment, a lady of about the same age as himself, seemed inclined for slumber rather than scrutiny; the train was not due to stop till the terminus was reached, in about an hour's time, and the carriage was of the old-fashioned sort, that held no communication with a corridor, therefore no further travelling companions were likely to intrude on Theodoric's semi-privacy. And yet the train had scarcely attained its normal speed before he became reluctantly but vividly aware that he was not alone with the slumbering lady; he was not even alone in his own clothes. A warm, creeping movement over his flesh betrayed the unwelcome and highly resented presence, unseen but poignant, of a strayed mouse, that had evidently dashed into its present retreat during the episode of the pony harnessing. Furtive stamps and shakes and wildly directed pinches failed to dislodge the intruder, whose motto, indeed, seemed to be Excelsior; and the lawful occupant of the clothes lay back against the cushions and endeavoured rapidly to evolve some means for putting an end to the dual ownership. It was unthinkable that he should continue for the space of a whole hour in the horrible position of a Rowton House for vagrant mice (already his imagination had at least doubled the numbers of the alien invasion). On the other hand, nothing less drastic than partial disrobing would ease him of his tormentor, and to undress in the presence of a lady, even for so laudable a purpose, was an idea that made his ear-tips tingle in a blush of abject shame. He had never been able to bring himself even to the mild exposure of open-work socks in the presence of the fair sex. And yet—the lady in this case was to all appearances soundly and securely asleep; the mouse, on the other hand, seemed to be trying to crowd a Wanderjahr into a few strenuous minutes. If there is any truth in the theory of transmigration, this particular mouse must certainly have been in a former state a member of the Alpine Club. Sometimes in its eagerness it lost its footing and slipped for half an inch or so; and then, in fright, or

more probably temper, it bit. Theodoric was goaded
into the most audacious undertaking of his life. Crim-
soning to the hue of a beetroot and keeping an agonized
watch on his slumbering fellow-traveller, he swiftly and
noiselessly secured the ends of his railway-rug to the
racks on either side of the carriage, so that a substantial
curtain hung athwart the compartment. In the narrow
dressing-room that he had thus improvised he proceeded with violent haste to extricate himself partially
and the mouse entirely from the surrounding casings of
tweed and half-wool. As the unravelled mouse gave a
wild leap to the floor, the rug, slipping its fastening at
either end, also came down with a heart-curdling flop,
and almost simultaneously the awakened sleeper opened
her eyes. With a movement almost quicker than the
mouse's, Theodoric pounced on the rug, and hauled its
ample folds chin-high over his dismantled person as he
collapsed into the further corner of the carriage. The
blood raced and beat in the veins of his neck and forehead, while he waited dumbly for the communication-
cord to be pulled. The lady, however, contented herself
with a silent stare at her strangely muffled companion.
How much had she seen, Theodoric queried to himself,
and in any case what on earth must she think of his
present posture?

"I think I have caught a chill," he ventured desperately.

"Really, I'm sorry," she replied. "I was just going to
ask you if you would open this window."

"I fancy it's malaria," he added, his teeth chattering

150

slightly, as much from fright as from a desire to support his theory.

"I've got some brandy in my hold-all, if you'll kindly reach it down for me," said his companion.

"Not for worlds—I mean, I never take anything for it," he assured her earnestly.

"I suppose you caught it in the Tropics?"

Theodoric, whose acquaintance with the Tropics was limited to an annual present of a chest of tea from an uncle in Ceylon, felt that even the malaria was slipping from him. Would it be possible, he wondered, to disclose the real state of affairs to her in small instalments?

"Are you afraid of mice?" he ventured, growing, if possible, more scarlet in the face.

"Not unless they came in quantities, like those that ate up Bishop Hatto. Why do you ask?"

"I had one crawling inside my clothes just now," said Theodoric in a voice that hardly seemed his own. "It was a most awkward situation."

"It must have been, if you wear your clothes at all tight," she observed; "but mice have strange ideas of comfort."

"I had to get rid of it while you were asleep," he continued; then, with a gulp, he added, "it was getting rid of it that brought me to—to this."

"Surely leaving off one small mouse wouldn't bring on a chill," she exclaimed, with a levity that Theodoric accounted abominable.

Evidently she had detected something of his predicament, and was enjoying his confusion. All the blood in his body seemed to have mobilized in one concentrated blush, and an agony of abasement, worse than a myriad mice, crept up and down over his soul. And then, as reflection began to assert itself, sheer terror took the place of humiliation. With every minute that passed the train was rushing nearer to the crowded and bustling terminus where dozens of prying eyes would be exchanged for the one paralyzing pair that watched him from the further corner of the carriage. There was one slender despairing chance, which the next few minutes must decide. His fellow-traveller might relapse into a blessed slumber. But as the minutes throbbed by that chance ebbed away. The furtive glance which Theodoric stole at her from time to time disclosed only an unwinking wakefulness.

"I think we must be getting near now," she presently observed.

Theodoric had already noted with growing terror the recurring stacks of small, ugly dwellings that heralded the journey's end. The words acted as a signal. Like a hunted beast breaking cover and dashing madly towards some other haven of momentary safety he threw aside his rug, and struggled frantically into his dishevelled garments. He was conscious of dull suburban stations racing past the window, of a choking, hammering sensation in his throat and heart, and of an icy silence in that corner towards which he dared not look. Then as he sank back in his seat, clothed and almost delirious, the train slowed down to a final crawl, and the woman spoke.

"Would you be so kind," she asked, "as to get me a porter to put me into a cab? It's a shame to trouble you when you're feeling unwell, but being blind makes one so helpless at a railway station."

SAKI

The Story-Teller

It was a hot afternoon, and the railway carriage was correspondingly sultry, and the next stop was at Temple-combe, nearly an hour ahead. The occupants of the carriage were a small girl, and a smaller girl, and a small boy. An aunt belonging to the children occupied one corner seat, and the further corner seat on the opposite side was occupied by a bachelor who was a stranger to their party, but the small girls and the small boy emphatically occupied the compartment. Both the aunt and the children were conversational in a limited, persistent way, reminding one of the attentions of a house-fly that refused to be discouraged. Most of the aunt's remarks seemed to begin with "Don't," and nearly all of the children's remarks began with "Why?" The bachelor said nothing out loud.

"Don't, Cyril, don't," exclaimed the aunt, as the small

boy began smacking the cushions of the seat, producing a cloud of dust at each blow.

"Come and look out of the window," she added.

The child moved reluctantly to the window. "Why are those sheep being driven out of that field?" he asked.

"I expect they are being driven to another field where there is more grass," said the aunt weakly.

"But there is lots of grass in that field," protested the boy; "there's nothing else but grass there. Aunt, there's lots of grass in that field."

"Perhaps the grass in the other field is better," suggested the aunt fatuously.

"Why is it better?" came the swift, inevitable question.

"Oh, look at those cows!" exclaimed the aunt. Nearly every field along the line had contained cows or bullocks, but she spoke as though she were drawing attention to a rarity.

"Why is the grass in the other field better?" persisted Cyril.

The frown on the bachelor's face was deepening to a scowl. He was a hard, unsympathetic man, the aunt decided in her mind. She was utterly unable to come to any satisfactory decision about the grass in the other field.

The smaller girl created a diversion by beginning to recite "On the Road to Mandalay." She only knew the first line, but she put her limited knowledge to the fullest possible use. She repeated the line over and over again in a dreamy but resolute and very audible voice; it seemed to the bachelor as though some one had had a bet with her that she could not repeat the line aloud two thousand times without stopping. Whoever it was who had made the wager was likely to lose his bet.

"Come over here and listen to a story," said the aunt, when the bachelor had looked twice at her and once at the communication cord.

The children moved listlessly towards the aunt's end of the carriage. Evidently her reputation as a story-teller did not rank high in their estimation.

In a low, confidential voice, interrupted at frequent intervals by loud, petulant questions from her listeners, she began an unenterprising and deplorably uninteresting story about a little girl who was good, and made friends with every one on account of her goodness, and was finally saved from a mad bull by a number of rescuers who admired her moral character.

"Wouldn't they have saved her if she hadn't been good?" demanded the bigger of the small girls. It was exactly the question that the bachelor had wanted to ask.

"Well, yes," admitted the aunt lamely, "but I don't think they would have run quite so fast to her help if they had not liked her so much."

"It's the stupidest story I've ever heard," said the bigger of the small girls, with immense conviction.

"I didn't listen after the first bit, it was so stupid," said Cyril.

The smaller girl made no actual comment on the story, but she had long ago recommenced a murmured repetition of her favourite line.

"You don't seem to be a success as a story-teller," said the bachelor suddenly from his corner.

The aunt bristled in instant defence at this unexpected attack.

"It's a very difficult thing to tell stories that children can both understand and appreciate," she said stiffly.

"I don't agree with you," said the bachelor.

"Perhaps *you* would like to tell them a story," was the aunt's retort.

"Tell us a story," demanded the bigger of the small girls.

"Once upon a time," began the bachelor, "there was a little girl called Bertha, who was extraordinarily good."

The children's momentarily-aroused interest began at once to flicker; all stories seemed dreadfully alike, no matter who told them.

"She did all that she was told, she was always truthful, she kept her clothes clean, ate milk puddings as though they were jam tarts, learned her lessons perfectly, and was polite in her manners."

"Was she pretty?" asked the bigger of the small girls.

"Not as pretty as any of you," said the bachelor, "but she was horribly good."

There was a wave of reaction in favour of the story; the word horrible in connection with goodness was a novelty that commended itself. It seemed to introduce a ring of truth that was absent from the aunt's tales of infant life.

"She was so good," continued the bachelor, "that she won several medals for goodness, which she always wore, pinned on to her dress. There was a medal for obedience, another medal for punctuality, and a third for good behaviour. They were large metal medals and they clicked against one another as she walked. No other child in the town where she lived had as many as three medals, so everybody knew that she must be an extra good child."

"Horribly good," quoted Cyril.

"Everybody talked about her goodness, and the Prince of the country got to hear about it, and he said that as she was so very good she might be allowed once a week to walk in his park, which was just outside the town. It was a beautiful park, and no children were ever allowed in it, so it was a great honour for Bertha to be allowed to go there."

"Were there any sheep in the park?" demanded Cyril.

"No," said the bachelor, "there were no sheep."

"Why weren't there any sheep?" came the inevitable question arising out of that answer.

The aunt permitted herself a smile, which might almost have been described as a grin.

"There were no sheep in the park," said the bachelor, "because the Prince's mother had once had a dream that her son would either be killed by a sheep or else by a clock falling on him. For that reason the Prince never kept a sheep in his park or a clock in his palace."

The aunt suppressed a gasp of admiration.

"Was the Prince killed by a sheep or by a clock?" asked Cyril.

"He is still alive, so we can't tell whether the dream

will come true," said the bachelor unconcernedly; "anyway, there were no sheep in the park, but there were lots of little pigs running all over the place."

"What colour were they?"

"Black with white faces, white with black spots, black all over, grey with white patches, and some were white all over."

The story-teller paused to let a full idea of the park's treasures sink into the children's imaginations; then he resumed:

"Bertha was rather sorry to find that there were no flowers in the park. She had promised her aunts, with tears in her eyes, that she would not pick any of the kind Prince's flowers, and she had meant to keep her promise, so of course it made her feel silly to find that there were no flowers to pick."

"Why weren't there any flowers?"

"Because the pigs had eaten them all," said the bachelor promptly. "The gardeners had told the Prince that you couldn't have pigs and flowers, so he decided to have pigs and no flowers."

There was a murmur of approval at the excellence of the Prince's decision; so many people would have decided the other way.

"There were lots of other delightful things in the park. There were ponds with gold and blue and green fish in them, and trees with beautiful parrots that said clever things at a moment's notice, and humming-birds that hummed all the popular tunes of the day. Bertha walked up and down and enjoyed herself immensely, and thought to herself: 'If I were not so extraordinarily good I should not have been allowed to come into this beautiful park and enjoy all that there is to be seen in it,' and her three medals clinked against one another as she walked and helped to remind her how very good she really was. Just then an enormous wolf came prowling into the park to see if it could catch a fat little pig for its supper."

"What colour was it?" asked the children, amid an immediate quickening of interest.

"Mud-colour all over, with a black tongue and pale grey eyes that gleamed with unspeakable ferocity. The first thing that it saw in the park was Bertha; her pinafore was so spotlessly white and clean that it could be seen from a great distance. Bertha saw the wolf and saw that it was stealing towards her, and she began to wish that she had never been allowed to come into the park. She ran as hard as she could, and the wolf came after her with huge leaps and bounds. She managed to reach a shrubbery of myrtle bushes and she hid herself in one of the thickest of the bushes. The wolf came sniffing among the branches, its black tongue lolling out of its mouth and its pale grey eyes glaring with rage. Bertha was terribly frightened, and thought to herself: 'If I had not been so extraordinarily good I should have been safe in the town at this moment.' However, the scent of the myrtle was so strong that the wolf could not sniff out where Bertha was hiding, and the bushes were so thick that he might have hunted about in them for a long time without catching sight of her, so he thought he might as well go off and catch a little pig instead. Bertha was trembling very much at having the wolf prowling and sniffing so near her, and as she trembled the medal for obedience clinked against the medals for good conduct and punctuality. The wolf was just moving away when he heard the sound of the medals clinking and stopped to listen; they clinked again in a bush quite near him. He dashed into the bush, his pale grey eyes gleaming with ferocity and triumph, and dragged Bertha out and devoured her to the last morsel. All that was left of her were her shoes, bits of clothing and the three medals for goodness."

"Were any of the little pigs killed?"

"No, they all escaped."

"The story began badly," said the smaller of the small girls, "but it had a beautiful ending."

"It is the most beautiful story that I ever heard," said the bigger of the small girls, with immense decision.

"It is the *only* beautiful story I have ever heard," said Cyril.

A dissentient opinion came from the aunt.

"A most improper story to tell to young children! You have undermined the effect of years of careful teaching."

"At any rate," said the bachelor, collecting his belongings preparatory to leaving the carriage, "I kept them quiet for ten minutes, which was more than you were able to do."

"Unhappy woman!" he observed to himself as he walked down the platform of Templecombe station; "for the next six months or so those children will assail her in public with demands for an improper story!"

H. F. ELLIS

Statement of Arthur James Wentworth, Bachelor of Arts

My name is Arthur James Wentworth, I am unmarried and I am by profession an assistant master at Burgrove Preparatory School, Wilminster. The Headmaster is the Reverend Gregory Saunders, M.A. He is known to the boys as the Squid—not necessarily, I think, a term of opprobrium. He is a classical scholar of moderate attainments, a generous employer and much given to the use of the expression "The School must come first, Wentworth." I attach no particular meaning to this remark.

At 11:15 on the morning of Saturday, 8th July, I entered Classroom 4 for the purpose of instructing Set IIIA in Algebra. There were present Anderson, Atkins, Clarke, Etheridge, Hillman, Hopgood II, Mason, Otterway, Sapoulos, Trench and Williamson. Heathcote, who has, I am told, a boil, was absent. It should be explained that though I have given these names in the

163

alphabetical order in which they appear in the school list, that is not the order in which the boys were sitting on this occasion. It is the custom at Burgrove for boys to sit according to their position in the previous week's mark-lists. Thus in the front row were seated Etheridge, a most promising mathematician, Hillman, Mason, Otterway and Clarke. Hopgood II, the boy whom I am now accused of assaulting, was in the middle of the second row. The third and last row was shared by Sapoulos, a Greek, and Atkins, a cretin. I do not think these facts have any bearing on anything that is to follow, but I give them for the sake of completeness.

"This morning," I remarked, taking up my Hall and Knight, "we will do problems," and I told them at once that if there was any more of that groaning they would do nothing but problems for the next month. It is my experience, as an assistant master of some years' standing, that if groaning is not checked immediately it may swell to enormous proportions. I make it my business to stamp on it.

Mason, a fair-haired boy with glasses, remarked when the groaning had died down that it would not be possible to do problems for the next month, and on being asked why not, replied that there were only three weeks more of term. This was true, and I decided to make no reply. He then asked if he could have a mark for that. I said, "No, Mason, you may not," and, taking up my book and a piece of chalk, read out, "I am just half as old as my father and in twenty years I shall be five years older than he was twenty years ago. How old am I?" Atkins promptly replied, "Forty-two." I inquired of him how, unless he was gifted with supernatural powers, he imagined he could produce the answer without troubling to do any working out. He said, "I saw it in the School's Year-book." This stupid reply caused a great deal of laughter, which I suppressed.

I should have spoken sharply to Atkins, but at this moment I noticed that his neighbour Sapoulos, the Greek boy, appeared to be eating toffee, a practice which is forbidden at Burgrove during school hours. I ordered him to stand up. "Sapoulos," I said, "you are not perhaps quite used yet to our English ways, and I shall not punish you this time for your disobedience; but please understand that I will not have eating in my class. You did not come here to eat but to learn. If you try hard and pay attention I do not altogether despair of teaching you something, but if you do not wish to learn I cannot help you. You might as well go back to your own country." Mason, without being given permission to speak, cried excitedly, "He can't, sir. Didn't you know? His father was chased out of Greece in a revolution or something. A big man with a black beard chased him for three miles and he had to escape in a small boat. It's true, sir. You ask him. Sapoulos got hit on the knee with a brick, didn't you, Sappy? And his grandmother— at least I think it was his grandmother——"

"That will do, Mason," I said. "Who threw that?"

I am not, I hope, a martinet, but I will not tolerate the throwing of paper darts or other missiles in my algebra set. Some of the boys make small pellets out of their blotting paper and flick them with their garters. This sort of thing has to be put down with a firm hand or work becomes impossible. I accordingly warned the boy responsible that another offence would mean an imposition. He had the impertinence to ask what sort of an imposition. I said that it would be a pretty stiff imposition, and if he wished to know more exact details he had only to throw another dart to find out. He thereupon threw another dart.

I confess that at this I lost patience and threatened to keep the whole set in during the afternoon if I had any more trouble. The lesson then proceeded.

It was not until I had completed my working out of the problem on the board that I realised I had worked on the assumption—of course ridiculous—that I was twice my father's age instead of half. This gave the false figure of minus ninety for my own age. Some boy said "Crikey!" I at once whipped round and demanded to know who had spoken. Otterway suggested that it might have been Hopgood II talking in his sleep. I was about to reprimand Otterway for impertinence when I realised that Hopgood actually was asleep and had in fact, according to Williamson, been asleep since the beginning of the period. Mason said, "He hasn't missed much anyway."

I then threw my Hall and Knight. It has been suggested that it was intended to hit Hopgood II. This is false. I never wake up sleeping boys by throwing books at them, as hundreds of old Burgrove boys will be able to testify.

I intended to hit Mason, and it was by a mischance which I shall always regret that Hopgood was struck. I have had, as I told my Headmaster, a great deal to put up with from Mason, and no one who knows the boy blames me for the attempt to do him some physical violence. It is indeed an accepted maxim in the Common Room that physical violence is the only method of dealing with Mason which produces any results; to this the Headmaster some time ago added a rider that the boy be instructed to remove his spectacles before being assaulted. That I forgot to do this must be put down to the natural agitation of a mathematics master caught out in an error. But I blame myself for it.

I do not blame myself for the unfortunate stunning of Hopgood II. It was an accident. I did all I could for the boy when it was discovered (I think by Etheridge) that he had been rendered unconscious. I immediately summoned the Headmaster and we talked the matter over. We agreed that concealment was impossible and that I must give a full account of the circumstances to the police. Meanwhile the work of the school was to go on as usual; Hopgood himself would have wished it. The Headmaster added that in any case the School must come first.

I have made this statement after being duly cautioned, of my own free will and in the presence of witnesses. I have read it through three times with considerable satisfaction, and am prepared to state on oath that it is a true and full account of the circumstances leading up to the accident to Hopgood II. I wish only to add that the boy is now none the worse for the blow, and has indeed shown increased zeal for his studies since the occurrence.

8th July, 1939   (Signed) A. J. WENTWORTH, B.A.

O. HENRY

The Third Ingredient

The (so-called) Vallambrosa Apartment-House is not an apartment-house. It is composed of two old-fashioned, brownstone-front residences welded into one. The parlor floor of one side is gay with the wraps and headgear of a modiste; the other is lugubrious with the sophistical promises and grisly display of a painless dentist. You may have a room there for two dollars a week or you may have one for twenty dollars. Among the Vallambrosa's roomers are stenographers, musicians, brokers, shop-girls, space-rate writers, art students, wire-tappers, and other people who lean far over the banister-rail when the door-bell rings.

This treatise shall have to do with but two of the Vallambrosians—though meaning no disrespect to the others.

At six o'clock one afternoon Hetty Pepper came back

to her third-floor rear $3.50 room in the Vallambrosa with her nose and chin more sharply pointed than usual. To be discharged from the department store where you have been working four years, and with only fifteen cents in your purse, does have a tendency to make your features appear more finely chiseled.

And now for Hetty's thumb-nail biography while she climbs the two flights of stairs.

She walked into the Biggest Store one morning four years before with seventy-five other girls, applying for a job behind the waist department counter. The phalanx of wage-earners formed a bewildering scene of beauty, carrying a total mass of blond hair sufficient to have justified the horseback gallops of a hundred Lady Godivas.

The capable, cool-eyed, impersonal, young, bald-headed man whose task it was to engage six of the contestants, was aware of a feeling of suffocation as if he were drowning in a sea of frangipanni, while white clouds, hand-embroidered, floated about him. And then a sail hove in sight. Hetty Pepper, homely of countenance, with small, contemptuous, green eyes and chocolate-colored hair, dressed in a suit of plain burlap and a common-sense hat, stood before him with every one of her twenty-nine years of life unmistakably in sight.

"You're on!" shouted the bald-headed young man, and was saved. And that is how Hetty came to be employed in the Biggest Store. The story of her rise to an eight-dollar-a-week salary is the combined stories of Hercules, Joan of Arc, Una, Job, and Little-Red-Riding-Hood. You shall not learn from me the salary that was paid her as a beginner. There is a sentiment growing about such things, and I want no millionaire store-proprietors climbing the fire-escape of my tenement-house to throw dynamite bombs into my skylight boudoir.

The story of Hetty's discharge from the Biggest Store is so nearly a repetition of her engagement as to be monotonous.

In each department of the store there is an omniscient, omnipresent, and omnivorous person carrying always a mileage book and a red necktie, and referred to as a "buyer." The destinies of the girls in his department who live on (see Bureau of Victual Statistics)—so much per week are in his hands.

This particular buyer was a capable, cool-eyed, impersonal, young, bald-headed man. As he walked along the aisles of his department he seemed to be sailing on a sea of frangipanni, while white clouds, machine-embroidered, floated around him. Too many sweets bring surfeit. He looked upon Hetty Pepper's homely countenance, emerald eyes, and chocolate-colored hair as a welcome oasis of green in a desert of cloying beauty. In a quiet angle of a counter he pinched her arm kindly, three inches above the elbow. She slapped him three feet away with one good blow of her muscular and not especially lily-white right. So, now you know why Hetty Pepper came to leave the Biggest Store at thirty minutes' notice, with one dime and a nickel in her purse.

This morning's quotations list the price of rib beef at six cents per (butcher's) pound. But on the day that

Hetty was "released" by the B. S. the price was seven and one-half cents. That fact is what makes this story possible. Otherwise, the extra four cents would have——

But the plot of nearly all the good stories in the world is concerned with shorts who were unable to cover; so you can find no fault with this one.

Hetty mounted with her rib beef to her $3.50 third-floor back. One hot, savory beef-stew for supper, a night's good sleep, and she would be fit in the morning to apply again for the tasks of Hercules, Joan of Arc, Una, Job, and Little-Red-Riding-Hood.

In her room she got the granite-ware stew-pan out of the 2 x 4-foot china—er—I mean earthenware closet, and began to dig down in a rat's-nest of paper bags for the potatoes and onions. She came out with her nose and chin just a little sharper pointed.

There was neither a potato nor an onion. Now, what kind of a beef-stew can you make out of simply beef? You can make oyster-soup without oysters, turtle-soup without turtles, coffee-cake without coffee, but you can't make beef-stew without potatoes and onions.

But rib beef alone, in an emergency, can make an ordinary pine door look like a wrought-iron gambling-house portal to the wolf. With salt and pepper and a tablespoonful of flour (first well stirred in a little cold water) 'twill serve—'tis not so deep as a lobster à la New-burg nor so wide as a church festival doughnut; but 'twill serve.

Hetty took her stew-pan to the rear of the third-floor hall. According to the advertisements of the Vallambrosa there was running water to be found there. Between you and me and the water-meter, it only ambled or walked through the faucets; but technicalities have no place here. There was also a sink where housekeeping roomers often met to dump their coffee grounds and glare at one another's kimonos.

At this sink Hetty found a girl with heavy, gold-brown, artistic hair and plaintive eyes, washing two large "Irish" potatoes. Hetty knew the Vallambrosa as well as any one not owning "double hextra-magnifying eyes" could compass its mysteries. The kimonos were her encyclopedia, her "Who's What?" her clearing-house of news, of goers and comers. From a rose-pink kimono edged with Nile green she had learned that the girl with the potatoes was a miniature-painter living in a kind of attic—or "studio," as they prefer to call it— on the top floor. Hetty was not certain in her mind what a miniature was; but it certainly wasn't a house; be-cause house-painters, although they wear splashy over-alls and poke ladders in your face on the street, are known to indulge in a riotous profusion of food at home.

The potato girl was quite slim and small, and handled her potatoes as an old bachelor uncle handles a baby who is cutting teeth. She had a dull shoemaker's knife in her right hand, and she had begun to peel one of the potatoes with it.

Hetty addressed her in the punctiliously formal tone of one who intends to be cheerfully familiar with you in the second round.

"Beg pardon," she said, "for butting into what's not

my business, but if you peel them potatoes you lose out. They're new Bermudas. You want to scrape 'em. Lemme show you."

She took a potato and the knife, and began to demonstrate.

"Oh, thank you," breathed the artist. "I didn't know. And I *did* hate to see the thick peeling go; it seemed such a waste. But I thought they always had to be peeled. When you've got only potatoes to eat, the peelings count, you know."

"Say, kid," said Hetty, staying her knife, "you ain't up against it, too, are you?"

The miniature artist smiled starvedly.

"I suppose I am. Art—or, at least, the way I interpret it—doesn't seem to be much in demand. I have only these potatoes for my dinner. But they aren't so bad boiled and hot, with a little butter and salt."

"Child," said Hetty, letting a brief smile soften her rigid features, "Fate has sent me and you together. I've had it handed to me in the neck, too; but I've got a chunk of meat in my room as big as a lap-dog. And I've done everything to get potatoes except pray for 'em. Let's me and you bunch our commissary departments and make a stew of 'em. We'll cook it in my room. If we only had an onion to go in it! Say, kid, you haven't got a couple of pennies that've slipped down into the lining of your last winter's sealskin, have you? I could step down to the corner and get one at old Giuseppe's stand. A stew without an onion is worse'n a matinée without candy."

174

"You may call me Cecilia," said the artist. "No; I spent my last penny three days ago."

"Then we'll have to cut the onion out instead of slicing it in," said Hetty. "I'd ask the janitress for one, but I don't want 'em hep just yet to the fact that I'm pounding the asphalt for another job. But I wish we did have an onion."

In the shop-girl's room the two began to prepare their supper. Cecilia's part was to sit on the couch helplessly and beg to be allowed to do something, in the voice of a cooing ring-dove. Hetty prepared the rib beef, putting it in cold salted water in the stew-pan and setting it on the one-burner gas-stove.

"I wish we had an onion," said Hetty, as she scraped the two potatoes.

On the wall opposite the couch was pinned a flaming, gorgeous advertising picture of one of the new ferry-boats of the P. U. F. F. Railroad that had been built to cut down the time between Los Angeles and New York City one-eighth of a minute.

Hetty, turning her head during her continuous monologue, saw tears running from her guest's eyes as she gazed on the idealized presentment of the speeding, foam-girdled transport.

"Why, say, Cecilia, kid," said Hetty, poising her knife, "is it as bad art as that? I ain't a critic; but I thought it kind of brightened up the room. Of course, a manicure-painter could tell it was a bum picture in a minute. I'll take it down if you say so. I wish to the holy Saint Pot-luck we had an onion."

175

But the miniature miniature-painter had tumbled down, sobbing, with her nose indenting the hard-woven drapery of the couch. Something was here deeper than the artistic temperament offended at crude lithography.

Hetty knew. She had accepted her rôle long ago. How scant the words with which we try to describe a single quality of a human being! When we reach the abstract we are lost. The nearer to Nature that the babbling of our lips comes, the better do we understand. Figuratively (let us say), some people are Bosoms, some are Hands, some are Heads, some are Muscles, some are Feet, some are Backs for burdens.

Hetty was a Shoulder. Hers was a sharp, sinewy shoulder; but all her life people had laid their heads upon it, metaphorically or actually, and had left there all or half their troubles. Looking at Life anatomically, which is as good a way as any, she was preordained to be a Shoulder. There were few truer collar-bones anywhere than hers.

Hetty was only thirty-three, and she had not yet outlived the little pang that visited her whenever the head of youth and beauty leaned upon her for consolation. But one glance in her mirror always served as an instantaneous pain-killer. So she gave one pale look into the crinkly old looking-glass on the wall above the gasstove, turned down the flame a little lower from the bubbling beef and potatoes, went over to the couch, and lifted Cecilia's head to its confessional.

"Go on and tell me, honey," she said. "I know now

that it ain't art that's worrying you. You met him on a ferry-boat, didn't you? Go on, Cecilia, kid, and tell your —your Aunt Hetty about it."

But youth and melancholy must first spend the surplus of sighs and tears that waft and float the barque of romance to its harbor in the delectable isles. Presently, through the stringy tendons that formed the bars of the confessional, the penitent—or was it the glorified communicant of the sacred flame?—told her story without art or illumination.

"It was only three days ago. I was coming back on the ferry from Jersey City. Old Mr. Schrum, an art dealer, told me of a rich man in Newark who wanted a miniature of his daughter painted. I went to see him and showed him some of my work. When I told him the price would be fifty dollars he laughed at me like a hyena. He said an enlarged crayon twenty times the size would cost him only eight dollars.

"I had just enough money to buy my ferry ticket back to New York. I felt as if I didn't want to live another day. I must have looked as I felt, for I saw *him* on the row of seats opposite me, looking at me as if he understood. He was nice-looking, but oh, above everything else, he looked kind. When one is tired or unhappy or hopeless, kindness counts more than anything else.

"When I got so miserable that I couldn't fight against it any longer, I got up and walked slowly out the rear door of the ferry-boat cabin. No one was there, and I slipped quickly over the rail and dropped into the water. Oh, friend Hetty, it was cold, cold!

"For just one moment I wished I was back in the old Vallambrosa, starving and hoping. And then I got numb, and didn't care. And then I felt that somebody else was in the water close by me, holding me up. *He* had followed me, and jumped in to save me.

"Somebody threw a thing like a big, white doughnut at us, and he made me put my arms through the hole. Then the ferry-boat backed, and they pulled us on board. Oh, Hetty, I was so ashamed of my wickedness in trying to drown myself; and, besides, my hair had all tumbled down and was sopping wet, and I was such a sight.

"And then some men in blue clothes came around; and *he* gave them his card, and I heard him tell them he had seen me drop my purse on the edge of the boat outside the rail, and in leaning over to get it I had fallen overboard. And then I remembered having read in the papers that people who try to kill themselves are locked up in cells with people who try to kill other people, and I was afraid.

"But some ladies on the boat took me downstairs to the furnace-room and got me nearly dry and did up my hair. When the boat landed, *he* came and put me in a cab. He was all dripping himself, but laughed as if he thought it was all a joke. He begged me, but I wouldn't tell him my name nor where I lived, I was so ashamed."

"You were a fool, child," said Hetty, kindly. "Wait till I turn the light up a bit. I wish to Heaven we had an onion."

"Then he raised his hat," went on Cecilia, "and said:

'Very well. But I'll find you, anyhow. I'm going to claim my rights of salvage.' Then he gave money to the cab-driver and told him to take me where I wanted to go, and walked away. What is 'salvage,' Hetty?"

"The edge of a piece of goods that ain't hemmed," said the shop-girl. "You must have looked pretty well frazzled out to the little hero boy."

"It's been three days," moaned the miniature-painter, "and he hasn't found me yet."

"Extend the time," said Hetty. "This is a big town. Think of how many girls he might have to see soaked in water with their hair down before he would recognize you. The stew's getting on fine—but oh, for an onion! I'd even use a piece of garlic if I had it."

The beef and potatoes bubbled merrily, exhaling a mouth-watering savor that yet lacked something, leaving a hunger on the palate, a haunting, wistful desire for some lost and needful ingredient.

"I came near drowning in that awful river," said Cecilia, shuddering.

"It ought to have more water in it," said Hetty; "the stew, I mean. I'll go get some at the sink."

"It smells good," said the artist.

"That nasty old North River?" objected Hetty. "It smells to me like soap factories and wet setter-dogs—oh, you mean the stew. Well, I wish we had an onion for it. Did he look like he had money?"

"First, he looked kind," said Cecilia. "I'm sure he was rich; but that matters so little. When he drew out his billfolder to pay the cabman you couldn't help seeing hundreds and thousands of dollars in it. And I looked over the cab doors and saw him leave the ferry station in a motor-car; and the chauffeur gave him his bearskin to put on, for he was sopping wet. And it was only three days ago."

"What a fool!" said Hetty, shortly.

"Oh, the chauffeur wasn't wet," breathed Cecilia. "And he drove the car away very nicely."

"I mean *you*," said Hetty. "For not giving him your address."

"I never give my address to chauffeurs," said Cecilia, haughtily.

"I wish we had one," said Hetty, disconsolately.

"What for?"

"For the stew, of course—oh, I mean an onion."

Hetty took a pitcher and started to the sink at the end of the hall.

A young man came down the stairs from above just as she was opposite the lower step. He was decently dressed, but pale and haggard. His eyes were dull with the stress of some burden of physical or mental woe. In his hand he bore an onion—a pink, smooth, solid, shining onion as large around as a ninety-eight-cent alarm-clock.

Hetty stopped. So did the young man. There was something Joan of Arc-ish, Herculean, and Una-ish in the look and pose of the shop-lady—she had cast off the rôles of Job and Little-Red-Riding-Hood. The young man stopped at the foot of the stairs and coughed distract-edly. He felt marooned, held up, attacked, assailed, levied upon, sacked, assessed, pan-handled, browbeaten, though he knew not why. It was the look in Hetty's eyes that did it. In them he saw the Jolly Roger fly to the masthead and an able seaman with a dirk between his teeth scurry up the ratlines and nail it there. But as yet he did not know that the cargo he carried was the thing that had caused him to be so nearly blown out of the water without even a parley.

"*Beg* your pardon," said Hetty, as sweetly as her dilute acetic acid tones permitted, "but did you find that onion on the stairs? There was a hole in the paper bag; and I've just come out to look for it."

The young man coughed for half a minute. The interval may have given him the courage to defend his own property. Also, he clutched his pungent prize greedily, and, with a show of spirit, faced his grim waylayer.

"No," he said huskily, "I didn't find it on the stairs. It was given to me by Jack Bevens, on the top floor. If you don't believe it, ask him. I'll wait until you do."

"I know about Bevens," said Hetty, sourly. "He writes books and things up there for the paper-and-rags man. We can hear the postman guy him all over the house when he brings them thick envelopes back. Say—do you live in the Vallambrosa?"

"I do not," said the young man. "I come to see Bevens sometimes. He's my friend. I live two blocks west."

"What are you going to do with the onion?—*begging* your pardon," said Hetty.

"I'm going to eat it."

"Raw?"

"Yes: as soon as I get home."

"Haven't you got anything else to eat with it?"

The young man considered briefly.

"No," he confessed; "there's not another scrap of anything in my diggings to eat. I think old Jack is pretty hard up for grub in his shack, too. He hated to give up the onion, but I worried him into parting with it."

"Man," said Hetty, fixing him with her world-sapient eyes, and laying a bony but impressive finger on his sleeve, "you've known trouble, too, haven't you?"

"Lots," said the onion owner, promptly. "But this onion is my own property, honestly come by. If you will excuse me, I must be going."

"Listen," said Hetty, paling a little with anxiety. "Raw onion is a mighty poor diet. And so is a beef-stew without one. Now, if you're Jack Bevens' friend, I guess you're nearly right. There's a little lady—a friend of mine—in my room there at the end of the hall. Both of us are out of luck; and we had just potatoes and meat between us. They're stewing now. But it ain't got any soul. There's something lacking to it. There's certain things in life that are naturally intended to fit and belong together. One is pink cheesecloth and green roses, and one is ham and eggs, and one is Irish and trouble. And the other one is beef and potatoes *with* onions. And still another one is people who are up against it and other people in the same fix."

The young man went into a protracted paroxysm of coughing. With one hand he hugged his onion to his bosom.

"No doubt; no doubt," said he, at length. "But, as I said, I must be going, because——"

Hetty clutched his sleeve firmly.

"Don't be a Dago, Little Brother. Don't eat raw onions. Chip it in toward the dinner and line yourself inside with the best stew you ever licked a spoon over. Must two ladies knock a young gentleman down and drag him inside for the honor of dining with 'em? No harm shall befall you, Little Brother. Loosen up and fall into line."

The young man's pale face relaxed into a grin.

"Believe I'll go you," he said, brightening. "If my onion is good as a credential, I'll accept the invitation gladly."

"It's good as that, but better as seasoning," said Hetty. "You come and stand outside the door till I ask my lady friend if she has any objections. And don't run away with that letter of recommendation before I come out."

Hetty went into her room and closed the door. The young man waited outside.

"Cecilia, kid," said the shop-girl, oiling the sharp saw of her voice as well as she could, "there's an onion outside. With a young man attached. I've asked him in to dinner. You ain't going to kick, are you?"

"Oh, dear!" said Cecilia, sitting up and patting her artistic hair. She cast a mournful glance at the ferry-boat poster on the wall.

"Nit," said Hetty. "It ain't him. You're up against real life now. I believe you said your hero friend had money and automobiles. This is a poor skeezicks that's got nothing to eat but an onion. But he's easy-spoken and not a freshy. I imagine he's been a gentleman, he's so low down now. And we need the onion. Shall I bring him in? I'll guarantee his behavior."

"Hetty, dear," sighed Cecilia, "I'm so hungry. What difference does it make whether he's a prince or a burglar? I don't care. Bring him in if he's got anything to eat with him."

Hetty went back into the hall. The onion man was gone. Her heart missed a beat, and a gray look settled over her face except on her nose and cheek-bones. And then the tides of life flowed in again, for she saw him leaning out of the front window at the other end of the hall. She hurried there. He was shouting to some one below. The noise of the street overpowered the sound of her footsteps. She looked down over his shoulder, saw whom he was speaking to, and heard his words. He pulled himself in from the window-sill and saw her standing over him.

Hetty's eyes bored into him like two steel gimlets.

"Don't lie to me," she said, calmly. "What were you going to do with that onion?"

The young man suppressed a cough and faced her resolutely. His manner was that of one who had been bearded sufficiently.

"I was going to eat it," said he, with emphatic slowness; "just as I told you before."

"And you have nothing else to eat at home?"

"Not a thing."

"What kind of work do you do?"

"I am not working at anything just now."

"Then why," said Hetty, with her voice set on its sharpest edge, "do you lean out of windows and give orders to chauffeurs in green automobiles in the street below?"

The young man flushed, and his dull eyes began to sparkle.

"Because, madam," said he, in *accelerando* tones, "I pay the chauffeur's wages and I own the automobile— and also this onion—this onion, madam."

He flourished the onion within an inch of Hetty's nose. The shop-lady did not retreat a hair's-breadth.

"Then why do you eat onions," she said, with biting contempt, "and nothing else?"

"I never said I did," retorted the young man, heatedly. "I said I had nothing else to eat where I live. I am not a delicatessen storekeeper."

"Then why," pursued Hetty, inflexibly, "were you going to eat a raw onion?"

"My mother," said the young man, "always made me eat one for a cold. Pardon my referring to a physical infirmity; but you may have noticed that I have a very, very severe cold. I was going to eat the onion and go to bed. I wonder why I am standing here and apologizing to you for it."

"How did you catch this cold?" went on Hetty, suspiciously.

The young man seemed to have arrived at some extreme height of feeling. There were two modes of descent open to him—a burst of rage or a surrender to the ridiculous. He chose wisely; and the empty hall echoed his hoarse laughter.

"You're a dandy," said he. "And I don't blame you for being careful. I don't mind telling you. I got wet. I was on a North River ferry a few days ago when a girl jumped overboard. Of course, I——"

Hetty extended her hand, interrupting his story.

"Give me the onion," she said.

The young man set his jaw a trifle harder.

"Give me the onion," she repeated.

He grinned, and laid it in her hand.

Then Hetty's infrequent, grim, melancholy smile showed itself. She took the young man's arm and pointed with her other hand to the door of her room.

"Little Brother," she said, "go in there. The little fool you fished out of the river is there waiting for you. Go on in. I'll give you three minutes before I come. Potatoes is in there, waiting. Go on in, Onions."

After he had tapped at the door and entered, Hetty began to peel and wash the onion at the sink. She gave a gray look at the gray roofs outside, and the smile on her face vanished by little jerks and twitches.

"But it's us," she said, grimly, to herself, "it's *us* that furnishes the beef."

SALLY BENSON

Junior Miss

The coat was advertised in Sunday's paper. There was a
picture of it which showed a lovely squirrel collar and a
belt that tied in a soft bow. Mrs. Graves saw it and
called to Judy, who was reading the funny paper. "Isn't
this nice-looking?" she asked.

Judy couldn't believe her eyes. At first she thought
that her mother must be thinking of getting the coat
for Lois, but reason told her that Lois had a winter coat,
new last year, and that her own coat was too tight across
the shoulders and too short in the sleeves. She drew in
her breath so sharply and with such rapture that she
hiccoughed. Mrs. Graves frowned. "Judy!" she said,
mechanically.

"Fur!" Judy gasped. "Oh, boy!"

She leaned over her mother's shoulder to read the ad-
vertisement. "Coat of feathery wool tweed, gossamer

soft, with lamb's-wool interlining, dashing squirrel collar which buttons snugly under the chin, and fitted waist to give you the new Continental look. Comes in colors as gay as the autumn woods. Brown, grape, leaf red, and henna. Sizes 7 to 14. Price—$29.50."

"Well, my dear, do you like it?" Mrs. Graves asked.

"Like it!" Judy repeated. "It's perfect. Oh, Mother!"

"Let's see it," Lois said. She folded her part of the funny paper and laid it neatly on the table. When she walked, she took short, prim steps and her skirt swung from side to side from her slender, childish hips. She looked at the coat critically.

"It's *awfully* nice," she agreed, "except that the belt is going to look peculiar, to say the least."

Her eyes travelled coldly to Judy's middle. "Judy shouldn't wear a belt, especially a belt with a *bow*. She'll be excruciating in it. It will make her look like a sack of meal."

"I suppose you're right," Mrs. Graves said.

"She's not!" Judy cried. "She's jealous, that's all. She doesn't want me to have a coat with a fur collar because *she* has a coat with a fur collar, and she wants to be the *only* one."

Lois laughed tolerantly. "Don't be absurd," she said. "*Get* the coat, by all means, if you don't mind looking like a sack of meal. Or worse."

"What do you mean *worse?*" Judy asked grimly.

"You know," Lois said meaningly. "What I told you."

Judy's face was white and her lips trembled. "I won't."

"Oh yes, you will. With that big bow."

"Will what?" Mrs. Graves asked. "What are you two talking about?"

"She's mean," Judy said. "She wants to spoil everything, and I won't let her."

"Will what?" Mrs. Graves repeated.

"Look pregnant." Judy blurted it out.

Mrs. Graves put the paper down in her lap. "I have never," she told them sternly, "heard such dreadful talk. You ought to be ashamed of yourselves."

"Lois was the one. She's always saying it."

"Go to your room, Lois, and stay there until I say you may come out," Mrs. Graves said. Her eyes followed Lois's slim figure as she left, and she sighed. "Well, we'll see."

"Please," Judy begged. She stood in front of her mother, her dark-brown eyebrows meeting in a line as she frowned anxiously.

Mrs. Graves leaned forward and pulled at her daughter's skirt. "I don't know why your skirts always hike up that way. It must be the way you sit on them."

Judy smoothed her dress over her round, firm little stomach. "Please," she said.

"I'll see."

"Can we go tomorrow?" she asked.

"If we go at all, we'll go next Saturday morning," Mrs. Graves answered. "And I don't want to hear another word about it."

"But it might be gone by next Saturday." Judy had a sharp vision of dozens of little girls snatching at the

coats and wearing them out of the store, looking triumphantly Continental.

"Don't be silly," Mrs. Graves said. "They have hundreds of them."

Judy walked slowly back to her chair and picked up
the funny paper, but it had lost its flavor. She went
quietly to her mother's room and stood in front of the
long mirror that was set in the door of the closet. She was
tall for her twelve years and heavily built. From her
shoulders to her knees she was entirely shapeless, which
gave her a square, broad look in spite of her height.
Her summer tan had faded and her face had a rather
ghastly yellow tinge. Below her skirt, which was too
short for her, her legs were hard, muscular, and covered
with scratches. Her dress, a soft-blue one, smocked at
the sleeves, was supposed to hang gracefully from the
shoulders in straight folds, but instead it pulled as
though she had been stuffed into it. She wore two rings
on her fingers—an aquamarine and a turquoise in gold
settings. She had outgrown them and they drew her
fingers in at their bases and made them look like sau-
sages. She wore two charm bracelets of a brassy color
and a locket and chain that fastened so tightly around
her neck it seemed it might throttle her. In the locket was
a rather dim snapshot of a kitten and a clear picture of
Tyrone Power, clipped from a movie magazine. Her
dark-brown hair hung straight below her ears and was
held in place by numerous bobbie pins and two ready-
made bows. Her toenails, under her wool socks, and

scuffed brown oxfords, were painted with a decadent pink mother-of-pearl polish.

She sucked in her stomach, held her breath, and pulled her dress in at the waist. And, while the change in her silhouette reflected in the mirror was almost imperceptible, her eyes shone with a terrible optimism.

She lived through the week that followed slightly breathless from holding her stomach in and quite faint from going without her lunch. She wore her old coat tolerantly to school each day and treated it with disrespect, throwing it on the floor of the coatroom and kicking it into the closet of her room at night. And at recess, in the warm security of friendship, she boasted a little. "Oh, bilge!" she exclaimed. "I just now remembered that I've got to go *shopping* Saturday. Have to get a new coat and stuff."

Her best friend murmured, "How too filthy," with understanding.

"Oh, foul," Judy said complacently. "Of course, *this* poor old thing's a wreck. I always loathed it, anyway. I wouldn't have picked it out in the first place if it hadn't been for snotty old Lois. *She's* always right, of course."

"Oh, needless to say."

"But," Judy went on, "as long as what will be will be, I might as well get something stunning while I'm about it. Something with a fur collar and fitted."

"If charming Lois doesn't butt in."

"Oh, I guess charming Lois won't butt in *this* time. I think fur softens the face, don't you?"

"Definitely."

When she awoke Saturday morning, she had the half-sick feeling of anticipation of Christmas Eve. She bathed and dressed carefully, rubbing a little talcum powder on her nose and looking at her face closely to make sure it didn't show. She was on time for breakfast.

"Good morning, Judy," her mother said. "You have a little talcum powder on your nose, dear. Rub it off."

Across the table, Lois smiled and her eyes closed like a cat's.

"Well, Judy," her father said, "I hear you're going shopping today."

She sighed. "I suppose so."

"You *suppose* so," Lois jeered. "She hasn't been able to eat for a week."

"Mother," Judy pleaded, "does *she* have to come with us?"

"She does," Mrs. Graves answered. "Now, not so early in the morning, girls, please!"

As Judy helped herself to two tablespoons of sugar, Lois shook her head meaningly. "Better watch yourself," she said. "Not that it isn't too late, P. K."

P. K. meant Powerful Katrinka.

"You're getting too old to tease your sister every minute, Lois," Mrs. Graves said.

"Fifteen isn't so old," Judy scoffed. "She tells everyone she's sixteen. Fifteen is just a baby age, really."

"If I'm a baby, what does that make you?" Lois asked.

"Quiet! Or you both stay home," Mrs. Graves said.

It was after ten when they left the house. The day was

sharp and bright, and the wind blew the dried brown leaves along the brick sidewalk next to the Park. Judy noticed that Lois and her mother had that expression on their faces. It was a look they put on every time they went out. An aloof, indifferent look. When they wore it, they never glanced directly at anyone or anything, as though there was something indecent about a direct gaze. Lois wore her coat with the beaver collar and a tiny hat tilted forward on her head. Her kid gloves were immaculate, and she seemed like a delicate miniature of her mother. As they waited for a bus she stood quietly, and when the bus came she helped her mother on. "As though she were a lousy cripple," Judy thought. She resentfully pinched Lois.

"Would you like to sit next to the window, Judy?" Mrs. Graves asked.

"Heavens, no!" Judy exclaimed, her voice polite and amused.

"I'd feel better if you did." Her mother stood holding on to the back of the seat until Judy slid past her. "If you begin to feel funny, let me know and I'll open the window wider."

Mrs. Graves took three dimes from her bag and handed them to Judy. "Here," she said. "You may put them in."

Judy took the money in her slippery fabric glove and one dime dropped to the floor. "How can you be so clumsy?" Mrs. Graves said. She moved her feet to one side. "Do you see it?"

Judy leaned over and her coat pulled at the seams.

The conductor passed down the aisle, clicking his machine and calling, "Fares, please!"

Lois turned around in her seat. "Never a dull moment," she said.

It was some time before Judy found the dime, and her gloves were dusty from the floor. She paid the fares and sat back in her seat, looking out the window, her cheeks crimson.

They got off the bus at Thirty-eighth Street. As they entered the store, Judy took off her coat and carried it. It would not do, she thought, for the saleswoman to see her wearing anything so decidedly un-Continental.

The carpets were soft in the coat department and the place looked sleekly elegant. The girl who came to wait on them was slim and smart in a black silk dress with a lace jabot. Her face lit up when she saw Lois. "Something for this young lady?" she asked.

"Not today," Mrs. Graves answered. "I would like to see the coat you advertised in last Sunday's *Tribune* for this little girl." She rested her hand on Judy's shoulder.

"Oh, yes," the salesgirl said vaguely. She looked at Judy speculatively. "Well, we'll see. Were you interested in any particular color?"

"Leaf red," Judy said.

The girl went away, and after a time reappeared with a coat hanging over her arm. As she approached, Judy could see the soft gray of a squirrel collar. The girl held up the coat before Judy's dazzled eyes. "This is the one that was advertised, size fourteen."

It was a soft, bright red and the fur collar was even

bigger than it had looked in the picture. The back was fitted and the belt that tied in a bow hung below the hem.

"That's it!" Judy cried. "That's the one!"

"Goodness! Not so loud," Mrs. Graves reproved her.

Judy took off her gloves and laid them on the chair. She turned her back to the salesgirl and held her arms stiffly and slipped them into the sleeves. They went in easily at first, but the coat caught above the elbows.

"I was afraid of that," the salesgirl said. "I'm afraid she's a little large for a fourteen."

"Oh," Mrs. Graves said. "Does it come any larger?"

"No," the girl answered. "Size fourteen is the largest we carry on this floor. You'd better try the Junior Misses."

Judy stood with her arms in the coat. She pulled it up and could feel the fur collar around her neck. "Have they one exactly like this?" she asked.

"I really couldn't say," the girl answered.

"Come, Judy," her mother said briskly. "Take it off and we'll look some place else."

Judy pulled at the sleeves and the coat slipped to the floor. The sight of it lying there was more than she could bear, and she stooped quickly and caught it in her arms. "I don't want another coat," she said. "If I can't have this one, I'd rather wear my old coat forever."

She held it close and buried her chin in the fur. Her hard, plump little body was tense.

The salesgirl smiled tolerantly. "It's too bad," she said. "Now, if it were for this young lady . . ." She nodded at Lois.

Lois drew herself up and looked at the girl coldly. "Really, it's not my coat at all. I should think anyone could see that."

She stepped forward and pulled the coat from Judy's arms. "For heaven's sake, turn around and get into this," she said.

Something in her voice lifted the bleakness from Judy's heart. She put her arms back in the sleeves and Lois tugged. The coat went on. It was too tight across the shoulders and it didn't meet by two inches in the front, but it went on.

"Lois," Mrs. Graves said. "It won't do. Have you lost your mind?"

"Anybody would think," Lois told her, pulling the coat into place and tying the belt in a big bow, "that nobody had ever heard of alterations in this family. Besides, it's perfectly silly to think that Judy could wear a junior-miss coat. It would be too old for her. You don't want her to look like her own grandmother, do you?"

"But——" the salesgirl said.

"It would be too old," Lois repeated firmly.

"Well," Mrs. Graves said doubtfully.

Lois walked backward and looked at Judy. Her wrists hung awkwardly from the sleeves, the bow caught her in the pit of the stomach, but the fur collar buttoned snugly about her chin and her eyes were shining.

"*I* think it's perfectly charming," Lois said. "Of course, no matter what you put on Judy, she looks as though she were going to you know what."

SALLY BENSON

Primrose Path

Judy Graves opened the pale-blue envelope addressed to her in Mary Caswell's handwriting. She was prepared for the invitation it contained, but she was not prepared for the formal and elegant wording. To the left of the page, on the upper corner, was a butterfly printed in a darker shade of blue, and underneath it was Mary's name, also printed. The invitation, which was written in longhand, read:

Miss Mary Caswell
Requests the pleasure of
Miss Judy Graves' company
At a dance to be given at her home,
Twenty East Seventy-eighth Street,
New York City,
on

Friday, February Twenty-first,
Nineteen Hundred and Forty-One.

R.S.V.P.

Judy stared at it, impressed. "Well," she said. "What
do you know about that!"

Her sister, Lois, who was rubbing vaseline into her
eyebrows in front of the dressing-table mirror, turned
around. "What is it?" she asked.

"It's the invite to Mary's dance," Judy said. "And it's
formal."

Lois took the sheet of paper. "How too silly! If she was
trying to be ritzy, why didn't she have them engraved?
And a dance for a lot of kids. You'll trample one another to death. Thank heavens, I don't have to go."

"You're too old," Judy said. "I wonder if Mrs. Caswell
will stay in her room the whole time the way Mrs. Adams
did when Fuffy had her party."

"Well, if she does, there won't be much dancing," Lois
said. "The boys will go into a huddle and the whole
thing will end in a brawl. Besides, what are you going to
dance *to?* Victrola records or the radio or something?"

"To records," Judy told her. "Mary wanted a band,
but there wasn't room. Mr. Caswell is going to change
the records. They're going to move the victrola out into
the hall so he won't be in the way."

She took the invitation from Lois and read it again. "I
don't get it," she said. "Mrs. Caswell wrote one out for
a sample and Mary brought it to school. It wasn't like this
one at all. It just said that Mary was going to have a

party. Jean Drummond told Mary it was too babyish, and she loaned Mary an etiquette book. I guess Mary copied this one out of the book."

"I wouldn't know."

"Well," Judy said, "I better get going. I have to be at Fuffy's this morning to meet a friend of her brother's. If it's all right, he's going to take me to the dance."

"If what's all right?" Lois asked.

"Oh, you know." Judy's eyelids fluttered nervously. "If it's O.K. If he says he won't, Mrs. Adams told Barlow he'd have to take both Fuffy and me."

Lois's laugh was scornful. "Before I'd go and be looked over like a prize horse or something!"

"I don't mind," Judy said mildly. She went to her closet and took out her coat and hat. "Barlow says he doesn't like girls."

"Who?"

"This boy. His name is Haskell Cummings. He's going to Exeter next year." Judy smoothed her hair carefully before she put on her hat. "Barlow says he really doesn't mind girls so much if they're good sports. Well, I'll be seeing you."

"Mmm," Lois murmured. She turned back to the mirror and again massaged her eyebrows gently.

When Judy rang the bell at the Adamses' apartment, Fuffy opened the door. "They're in Barlow's room," she whispered. "They're throwing darts."

"Oh," Judy said. She followed Fuffy into the living room and took off her coat and hat and laid them across the arm of the couch. "How tall is he?" she asked.

199

"As tall as you are. Maybe a little bit taller," Fuffy said. "If they don't come out pretty soon, I'll call them."

"You'd better not," Judy said. "They'll have to come out sometime."

Fuffy sat down on the couch. "Maybe you're right," she said. "Mom asked them if they didn't want to stay for lunch with us, but they said they'd rather eat at the Automat."

"The Automat *is* nice."

The two girls were silent. They could hear the sound of the darts as they hit the target, which was nailed to the door of Barlow's room, and they could hear Barlow's voice as he called "Bull's-eye!"

"Let's play cards or something," Judy said. "It will look funny if they find us just sitting here waiting."

"O.K.," Fuffy said. She went to the hall closet and got out the card table. "Beat you at double Canfield!" Her voice was loud and enthusiastic. She set the table up and, taking two packs of cards from the desk drawer, held them out to Judy. "Which'll you have? The reds or the greens?"

"The reds." Judy drew a straight chair up to the table and began to shuffle. "Have you answered your invitation yet?"

"What did you think of it?" Fuffy asked. "Did you ever?"

"Well," Judy said, "I suppose she wanted it formal."

"Formal!" Fuffy laughed. "I thought it looked lousy."

"It did look funny," Judy agreed. "But that's on account of Mary's handwriting. I think it was all right, though. I mean the way it was put."

"It slayed Daddy. And Mom says she doesn't think Mrs. Caswell *knew*. She thinks Mary did it on her own."

"Oh, I don't doubt *that*," Judy said. "I don't doubt that at all." She put a two and a three of hearts on Fuffy's ace.

The door of Barlow's room opened, and at the sound the two girls began to laugh shrilly. "Oh!" Fuffy screamed. "You rat! That was my ace!"

They started to play furiously, slapping the cards down on the table and knocking them to the floor in their excitement. They appeared to be too engrossed in their game to look up as the boys entered the room.

"And a nine, and a ten, and a jack!" Judy cried. "I can't move until you get something. Get a hump on! You're too slow!"

Fuffy went through the remaining cards in her hand once more. "I'm bust, too," she said. She glanced at the boys carelessly. "Hello. Oh, that's right, Haskell. You don't know Judy Graves, do you? Judy, this is Haskell Cummings."

Judy stopped sorting the cards long enough to look up and smile. "Hello," she said. "Hello, Barlow."

The two boys moved nearer the table, and Fuffy counted the score. "Thirty-nine for you, Judy. And only *twenty* for me!"

Judy threw herself back heavily in the chair. "Wow! I'm bushed!" she said. "Well, I'm nineteen ahead anyway. Of course, it doesn't matter as long as we're not playing for money."

Haskell Cummings took a dime from his pocket, tossed it into the air, and caught it expertly. "I took this away from Adams," he said.

The girls looked at him in admiration. He was a slender boy with straight, light hair that fell over his forehead. He wore a belted tweed jacket and long, pale-gray trousers. His nose was slightly hooked and his chin receded only slightly, thanks to the family dentist, who had been working on it for five years.

"I wish," Fuffy said, "that Mary would have games. Not silly games, you know, but real ones with cards."

"Me too," Judy said. "I've known how to play poker for years."

"Even if she doesn't," Fuffy went on, "there's no good reason why we four can't play something if we want to. After all, what's the good of *dancing* all evening?"

"Well, I said I'd go, but I didn't say I'd dance." Barlow kicked at the leg of the bridge table.

"I tell you what we could do," Judy said. "We could do exactly what we *want*. I mean what's the sense of sitting around like sticks? As long as we *have* to go, we might as well have some fun. We had loads of fun at your party, Fuffy."

"What happened?" Haskell Cummings asked.

"Oh, that's right, you weren't there," Judy said. "It was last year and I guess you didn't know Barlow then. Well, for one thing, we threw water out the window."

"Judy hit a man on the street." Fuffy laughed and shook her head at the happy memory. "For a while we thought he was going to come up and complain or something. But he didn't. Not that we'd of cared."

"If he had come," Judy said, "I'd of told him to go sell his papers."

"Judy's *crazy*," Fuffy said loyally. "She'll do anything."

Haskell Cummings looked at Judy speculatively, and she stared back at him unflinching. "I'll do anything when I happen to feel like it," she said.

"She's the best basketball player at school," Fuffy said.

"Oh, for heaven's sake!" Judy protested modestly.

"Where do you go in the summer?" Haskell Cummings asked her.

"South Dorset, Vermont," Judy said. "We've been going there for years. Where do you go?"

"Madison, Connecticut," he answered.

"I've been there. I visited my Aunt Julia there one summer."

"Do you know Jane Garside?" Haskell Cummings asked.

Judy held her breath and took the plunge. "That drip," she said.

Haskell's face lighted up. "Drip is right!" he said. "Where did you swim? At the Yacht Club or at the Country Club?"

"At the Country Club," Judy answered. She waited for Haskell Cummings' decision.

"That's where I swim," he said.

"Well, isn't that the funniest thing!" Judy said, and began to laugh. There was relief and excitement in her laughter.

"Hey, look out!" Fuffy warned her. "You'll get the hiccoughs!"

"Oh, don't!" Judy gasped. "Every time you say that, I *do* get them. And"—she drew in her breath—"I *have* got them!"

"Grab her arms! Grab her arms, and hold them over her head, and I'll get the vinegar!" Fuffy cried, and ran to the kitchen.

Haskell Cummings sprang into action and, taking Judy's arms, he yanked them in the air. "Somebody scare her!" he called. He let her arms go and, grabbing the back of her chair, tipped it over until it almost reached the floor. She shrieked wildly as he tilted the chair down and brought it swiftly up again. Her hair fell over her face and she giggled weakly.

"Well," Fuffy asked, as she came back into the room carrying the vinegar bottle, "how are they?"

Judy waited, scarcely breathing. "They're gone," she said. "Haskell cured them."

"That's the first time I've ever known Judy to have the hiccoughs and get over them like that," Fuffy said.

"When they get hiccoughs, the best thing to do is to scare them," Haskell said.

"It certainly worked, all right," Judy said. "Thanks a lot."

"Well," Barlow said, "we'd better get going."

"Thanks an *awful* lot," Judy said.

Haskell pulled down his tweed jacket and straightened his tie. "I can almost always cure hiccoughs," he said.

The two boys went out in the hall to get their hats and coats, and Fuffy followed them. Judy could hear them as they whispered together. Fuffy came back into the room as the front door closed.

"It's all right," she said. "He's going to take you. He says you are a darned good sport and not a *bit* affected."

They looked at one another and smiled. "I think he's nice," Judy said. "And we can have some fun now. I mean, we can stir up something and not poke around dancing."

"Oh, dancing!" Fuffy said. "Phooey to that stuff."

In the week that followed, Judy called Fuffy up every night to talk about the party, and by the time Friday arrived she was weak with excitement. She bathed before dinner, which was served at half past six on her account. And when she had finished her dessert, Mrs. Graves offered to help her get into her dress.

"No, thanks just the same," Judy said. "Just keep Lois out of the way. She makes me nervous picking on me."

"Well, don't yank at your dress too hard when you pull it down or the net will tear," her mother said.

Judy laughed. "It'll probably be a *wreck* before the night's over! Fuffy and Haskell and Barlow and I aren't going to bother much about *dancing*. *We're* going to play games and stuff."

"Don't be too rough," Mrs. Graves said.

The lamp on the bureau was lighted when Judy went into the room she shared with Lois. She closed the door

205

and took off her flannel bathrobe, standing in front of her mirror in a white slip that reached to the floor. Earlier in the day she had rolled up the ends of her hair in curlers, and now she began to unfasten them slowly. Her dark-brown hair, which usually fell straight to her shoulders, lay in soft curls around her head. She fluffed it out and, going to the closet, took out her new white net dress. Although she had bought it early in January with the money her Aunt Julia had sent her for Christmas, there had been no occasion to wear it before. It had a long, full skirt, caught up in places by tiny blue bows, and there was another, larger bow on the right shoulder. She slipped it over her head. As she walked back to the mirror, the skirts swirled and rustled about her feet.

Leaning closer to the mirror, she rested her elbows on the top of the bureau, her chin in the palms of her hands. The light from the lamp cast oblique shadows across her face. Her eyes looked bright and dark, and her hair was a dusky contrast against the whiteness of her throat. She tilted her head up, lowered her eyes, and studied herself through her lashes. The round fullness of her face seemed to fade, and she could see the outlines of her cheekbones. She looked older and slimmer. "I look as pretty as Lois," she thought.

For a long while she stood there, her eyes half closed. Then she turned and, walking briskly across the room, opened the top bureau drawer of Lois's bureau. She found a small bottle of pale-pink nail polish and, sitting on the edge of the bed, she carefully applied it to her nails. When the polish was dry, she put the bottle back in the drawer and rummaged around until she found a small white enamel compact and a rose-colored Roger & Gallet lipstick. She brushed the powder on her face and neck and applied the lipstick. In her own hand-kerchief case she found a large white chiffon handker-chief embroidered with pink roses, and she carefully wrapped the compact and lipstick in it.

Once more she leaned close to the mirror, and fell in love with what she saw reflected there. Her blue satin slippers were soft on her feet, and her dress, billowing out below the waist, gave her a sense of lightness and well-being. She heard the doorbell ring and knew that Haskell Cummings had arrived to take her to the dance.

There was a rap on the door, and her mother's voice called "Judy!"

"In a minute," she answered.

She picked up the handkerchief, opened the door, and walked across the hall to the living room. Haskell Cum-mings was talking to her mother and father and Lois. He stood with his back to Judy as she entered the room. He wore a dark-blue suit and his hair was brushed slickly back.

Mr. Graves looked up at Judy. "Well," he said. "Well."

Haskell Cummings turned around. He started to say "Hiyah there, Judy," but the words died in his throat.

"Good evening," Judy said, and held out her hand. "Aren't you nice to be so prompt!"

Something about the tone of her voice made him feel that he had been more than prompt, that he had been too early.

"We don't have to go yet if you don't want to," he said. "We can wait a while."

"Oh, goodness, it doesn't matter. As long as you're here we might as well go," Judy said.

Mr. Graves got up from his chair. "I'll get your cape," he said. He went to the hall closet and brought Judy's cape to her.

"Here, Haskell," she said, handing him the compact and lipstick wrapped in her chiffon handkerchief. "Keep these in your pocket for me. I'm simply terrible. I lose everything."

He tucked them into the pocket of his coat and stared at Judy, not saying a word. She turned to her father and, raising her face, kissed him tenderly on the cheek.

"Well, good night, Daddy," she said. She walked across the room, her skirts swaying and her soft hair moving gently across the collar of her cape. Bending down, she kissed her mother lightly. "Good night," she said again.

"Have a nice time, darling."

Judy shrugged her shoulders and smiled. Her eyes drooped wearily. "Well, you know parties," she said. She nodded brightly to Lois and swept from the room, followed by Haskell Cummings, who had managed to mutter something that sounded like "Good night."

Judy stood to one side, waiting for Haskell to open the front door for her. "I do love to dance, though," she said. "Don't you?" she went out and Haskell followed her, closing the door behind him.

Mr. and Mrs. Graves looked at one another. "She had

lipstick on," Lois said. "And powder. And nail polish. And that Haskell Cummings acted like a dope."

Mr. Graves jingled the coins in his pocket. "Can you beat it!" he said. "She sold him down the river. Sold him down the river, by God!" His voice was rich with pride and satisfaction. "By God, if she didn't!"

NATHANIEL HAWTHORNE

Mr. Higginbotham's Catastrophe

A young fellow, a tobacco pedler by trade, was on his way from Morristown, where he had dealt largely with the Deacon of the Shaker settlement, to the village of Parker's Falls, on Salmon River. He had a neat little cart, painted green, with a box of cigars depicted on each side-panel, and an Indian chief, holding a pipe and a golden tobacco-stalk, on the rear. The pedler drove a small little mare, and was a young man of excellent character, keen at a bargain, but none the worse liked by the Yankees; who, as I have heard them say, would rather be shaved with a sharp razor than a dull one. Especially was he beloved by the pretty girls along the Connecticut, whose favor he used to court by presents of the best smoking tobacco in his stock, knowing well that the country lasses of New England are generally great performers on pipes. Moreover, as will be seen in the course of my story, the pedler was inquisitive, and something of a tatler, always itching to hear the news, and anxious to tell it again.

After an early breakfast at Morristown, the tobacco pedler, whose name was Dominicus Pike, had traveled seven miles through a solitary piece of woods, without speaking a word to anybody but himself and his little gray mare. It being nearly seven o'clock, he was as eager to hold a morning gossip as a city shopkeeper to read the morning paper. An opportunity seemed at hand, when, after lighting a cigar with a sun-glass, he looked up, and perceived a man coming over the brow of the hill, at the foot of which the pedler had stopped his green cart. Dominicus watched him as he descended, and noticed that he carried a bundle over his shoulder on the end of a stick, and traveled with a weary, yet determined pace. He did not look as if he had started in the freshness of the morning, but had footed it all night, and meant to do the same all day.

"Good morning, mister," said Dominicus, when within speaking distance. "You go a pretty good jog. What's the latest news at Parker's Falls?"

The man pulled the broad brim of a gray hat over his eyes, and answered, rather sullenly, that he did not come from Parker's Falls, which, as being the limit of his own day's journey, the pedler had naturally mentioned in his inquiry.

"Well, then," rejoined Dominicus Pike, "let's have the latest news where you did come from. I'm not particular about Parker's Falls. Any place will answer."

Being thus importuned, the traveler—who was as ill-looking a fellow as one would desire to meet in a solitary piece of woods—appeared to hesitate a little, as if he was either searching his memory for news, or weighing the expediency of telling it. At last, mounting on the step of the cart, he whispered in the ear of Dominicus, though he might have shouted aloud, and no other mortal would have heard him.

"I do remember one little trifle of news," said he. "Old Mr. Higginbotham, of Kimballton, was murdered in his orchard, at eight o'clock last night, by an Irishman and a nigger. They strung him up to the branch of a St. Michael's pear-tree, where nobody would find him till the morning."

As soon as this horrible intelligence was communicated, the stranger betook himself to his journey again, with more speed than ever, not even turning his head when Dominicus invited him to smoke a Spanish cigar and relate all the particulars. The pedler whistled to his mare and went up the hill, pondering on the doleful fate of Mr. Higginbotham, whom he had known in the way of trade, having sold him many a bunch of long nines, and a great deal of pig-tail, lady's twist, and fig tobacco. He was rather astonished at the rapidity with which the news had spread. Kimballton was nearly sixty miles distant in a straight line; the murder had been perpetrated only at eight o'clock the preceding night; yet Dominicus had heard of it at seven in the morning, when, in all probability, poor Mr. Higginbotham's own family had but just discovered his corpse, hanging on the St. Michael's pear-tree. The stranger on foot must have worn seven-league boots to travel at such a rate.

"Ill news flies fast, they say," thought Dominicus Pike; "but this beats railroads. The fellow ought to be hired to go express with the President's message."

The difficulty was solved by supposing that the narrator had made a mistake of one day in the date of occurrence; so that our friend did not hesitate to introduce the story at every tavern and country store along the road, expending a whole bunch of Spanish wrappers among at least twenty horrified audiences. He found himself invariably the first bearer of the intelligence, and was so pestered with questions that he could not avoid filling up the outline, till it became quite a respectable narrative. He met with one piece of corroborative evidence. Mr. Higginbotham was a trader; and a former clerk of his, to whom Dominicus related the facts, testified that the old gentleman was accustomed to return home through the orchard about nightfall with the money and valuable papers of the store in his pocket. The clerk manifested but little grief at Mr. Higginbotham's catastrophe, hinting, what the pedler had discovered in his own dealings with him, that he was a crusty old fellow, as close as a vise. His property would descend to a pretty niece who was now keeping school at Kimballton.

What with telling the news for the public good, and driving bargains for his own, Dominicus was so much delayed on the road, that he chose to put up at a tavern, about five miles short of Parker's Falls. After supper, lighting one of his prime cigars, he seated himself in the barroom, and went through the story of the murder, which had grown so fast that it took him half an hour to tell. There were as many as twenty people in the room, nineteen of whom received it all for gospel. But the twentieth was an elderly farmer, who had arrived on horseback a short time before, and was now seated in a corner, smoking his pipe. When the story was concluded, he rose up very deliberately, brought his chair right in front of Dominicus, and stared him full in the face, puffing out the vilest tobacco-smoke the pedler had ever smelt.

"Will you make affidavit," demanded he, in the tone of a country justice taking an examination, "that old Squire Higginbotham, of Kimballton, was murdered in his orchard the night before last, and found hanging on his great pear-tree yesterday morning?"

"I tell the story as I heard it, mister," answered Dominicus, dropping his half-burnt cigar; "I don't say that I saw the thing done. So I can't take my oath that he was murdered exactly in that way."

"But I can take mine," said the farmer, "that if Squire Higginbotham was murdered night before last, I drank a glass of bitters with his ghost this morning. Being a neighbor of mine, he called me into his store as I was riding by and treated me, and then asked me to do a little business for him on the road. He didn't seem to know any more about his own murder than I did."

"Why, then it can't be a fact!" exclaimed Dominicus Pike.

"I guess he'd have mentioned if it was," said the old farmer; and he removed his chair back to the corner, leaving Dominicus quite down in the mouth.

Here was a sad resurrection of old Mr. Higginbotham! The pedler had no heart to mingle in the conversation any more, but comforted himself with a glass of gin and water, and went to bed, where, all night long, he dreamt of hanging on the St. Michael's pear-tree. To avoid the old farmer (whom he so detested that his suspension would have pleased him better than Mr. Higginbotham's), Dominicus rose in the gray of the morning, put the little mare into the green cart, and trotted swiftly away towards Parker's Falls. The fresh breeze, the dewy road, and the pleasant summer dawn revived his spirits, and might have encouraged him to repeat the old story had there been anybody awake to hear it. But he met neither ox-team light wagon, chaise, horseman, nor foot-traveler, till just as he crossed Salmon River a man came trudging down to the bridge with a bundle over his shoulder on the end of a stick.

"Good morning, mister," said the pedler, reining in his mare. "If you come from Kimballton or that neighborhood, may be you can tell me the real fact about this affair of old Mr. Higginbotham. Was the old fellow actually murdered two or three nights ago by an Irishman and a nigger?"

Dominicus had spoken in too great a hurry to observe

at first that the stranger himself had a deep tinge of Negro blood. On hearing this sudden question the Ethiopian appeared to change his skin, its yellow hue becoming a ghastly white, while, shaking and stammering, he thus replied—

"No! No! There was no colored man! It was an Irishman that hanged him last night, at eight o'clock. I came away at seven! His folks can't have looked for him in the orchard yet."

Scarcely had the yellow man spoken, when he interrupted himself, and though he seemed weary enough before, continued his journey at a pace which would have kept the pedler's mare on a smart trot. Dominicus stared after him in great perplexity. If the murder had not been committed till Tuesday night, who was the prophet that had foretold it, in all its circumstances, on Tuesday morning? If Mr. Higginbotham's corpse were not yet discovered by his own family, how came the mulatto, at above thirty miles distance, to know that he was hanging in the orchard, especially as he had left Kimballton before the unfortunate man was hanged at all? These ambiguous circumstances, with the stranger's surprise and terror, made Dominicus think of raising a hue and cry after him, as an accomplice in the murder; since a murder, it seemed, had really been perpetrated.

"But let the poor devil go," thought the pedler. "I don't want his black blood on my head; and hanging the nigger wouldn't unhang Mr. Higginbotham. Unhang the old gentleman! It's a sin, I know; but I should hate to have him come to life a second time and give me the lie!"

With these meditations, Dominicus Pike drove into the street of Parker's Falls, which, as everybody knows, is as thriving a village as three cotton factories and a slitting mill can make it. The machinery was not in motion, and but a few of the shop doors unbarred, when he alighted in the stable yard of the tavern, and made it his first business to order the mare four quarts of oats. His second duty, of course, was to impart Mr. Higginbotham's catastrophe to the hostler. He deemed it advisable, however, not to be too positive as to the date of the direful fact, and also to be uncertain whether it were perpetrated by an Irishman and a mulatto, or by the son of Erin alone. Neither did he profess to relate it on his own authority, or that of any one person, but mentioned it as a report generally diffused.

The story ran through the town like fire among girdled trees, and became so much the universal talk that nobody could tell whence it had originated. Mr. Higginbotham was as well known at Parker's Falls as any citizen of the place, being part owner of the slitting mill, and a considerable stockholder in the cotton factories. The inhabitants felt their own prosperity interested in his fate. Such was the excitement that the *Parker's Falls Gazette* anticipated its regular day of publication, and came out with half a form of blank paper and a column of double pica, emphasized with capitals, and headed HORRID MURDER OF MR. HIGGINBOTHAM! Among other dreadful details, the printed account described the mark of the cord round the dead man's neck, and stated the number of thousand dollars of which he

had been robbed; there was much pathos also about
the affliction of his niece, who had gone from one fainting fit to another ever since her uncle was found hanging
on the St. Michael's pear-tree with his pockets inside
out. The village poet likewise commemorated the young
lady's grief in seventeen stanzas of a ballad. The selectmen held a meeting, and in consideration of Mr. Higginbotham's claims on the town, determined to issue
handbills offering a reward of five hundred dollars for
the apprehension of his murderers, and the recovery of
the stolen property.

Meanwhile, the whole population of Parker's Falls, consisting of shopkeepers, mistresses of boarding-houses,
factory girls, millmen, and schoolboys, rushed into the
street and kept up such a terrible loquacity as more than
compensated for the silence of the cotton machines,
which refrained from their usual din, out of respect to
the deceased. Had Mr. Higginbotham cared about post-
humous renown, his untimely ghost would have ex-
ulted in this tumult. Our friend Dominicus, in his vanity of heart, forgot his intended precautions, and mounting on the town pump, announced himself as the bearer
of the authentic intelligence which had caused so wonderful a sensation. He immediately became the great man
of the moment, and had just begun a new edition of the
narrative, with a voice like a field preacher, when the
mail-stage drove into the village street. It had traveled
all night, and must have shifted horses at Kimballton at
three in the morning.

"Now we shall hear all the particulars," shouted the crowd.

The coach rumbled up to the piazza of the tavern, followed by a thousand people; for if any man had been minding his own business till then, he now left it at sixes and sevens to hear the news. The pedler, foremost in the race, discovered two passengers, both of whom had been startled from a comfortable nap to find themselves in the center of a mob. Every man assailing them with separate questions, all propounded at once, the couple were struck speechless, though one was a lawyer and the other a young lady.

"Mr. Higginbotham! Mr. Higginbotham! Tell us the particulars about old Mr. Higginbotham!" bawled the mob. "What is the coroner's verdict? Are the murderers apprehended? Is Mr. Higginbotham's niece come out of her fainting fits? Mr. Higginbotham! Mr. Higginbotham! !"

The coachman said not a word, except to swear awfully at the hostler for not bringing him a fresh team of horses. The lawyer inside had generally his wits about him, even when asleep; the first thing he did, after learning the cause of the excitement, was to produce a large red pocket-book. Meantime Dominicus Pike, being an extremely polite young man, and also suspecting that a female tongue would tell the story as glibly as a lawyer's, had handed the lady out of the coach. She was a fine smart girl, now wide awake and bright as a button, and had such a sweet pretty mouth that Dominicus would almost as lief have heard a love tale from it as a tale of murder.

"Gentlemen and ladies," said the lawyer to the shop-keepers, the millmen, and the factory girls, "I can assure you that some unaccountable mistake, or more probably a wilful falsehood maliciously contrived to injure Mr. Higginbotham's credit, has excited this singular uproar. We passed through Kimballton at three o'clock this morning, and most certainly should have been informed of the murder had any been perpetrated. But I have proof nearly as strong as Mr. Higginbotham's own oral testimony in the negative. Here is a note, relating to a suit of his in the Connecticut Courts, which was deliv-ered me from that gentleman himself. I find it dated at ten o'clock last evening."

So saying, the lawyer exhibited the date and signa-ture of the note, which irrefragably proved, either that this perverse Mr. Higginbotham was alive when he wrote it, or—as some deemed the more probable case of two doubtful ones—that he was so absorbed in worldly business as to continue to transact it even after his death. But unexpected evidence was forthcoming. The young lady, after listening to the pedler's expla-nation, merely seized a moment to smooth her gown and put her curls in order, and then appeared at the tavern door, making a modest signal to be heard.

"Good people," said she, "I am Mr. Higginbotham's niece."

A wondering murmur passed through the crowd on beholding her so rosy and bright, that same unhappy niece whom they had supposed, on the authority of the *Parker's Falls Gazette,* to be lying at death's door in a fainting fit. But some shrewd fellows had doubted all along whether a young lady would be quite so desperate at the hanging of a rich old uncle.

"You see," continued Miss Higginbotham, with a smile, "that this strange story is quite unfounded as to myself; and I believe I may affirm it to be equally so in regard to my dear uncle Higginbotham. He has the kindness to give me a home in his house, though I contribute to my own support by teaching a school. I left Kimballton this morning, to spend the vacation of commencement week with a friend about five miles from Parker's Falls. My generous uncle, when he heard me on the stairs, called me to his bedside, and gave me two dollars and fifty cents to pay my stage-fare, and another dollar for my extra expenses. He then laid his pocket-book under his pillow, shook hands with me, and advised me to take some biscuit in my bag, instead of breakfasting on the road. I feel confident, therefore, that I left my beloved relative alive, and trust that I shall find him so on my return."

The young lady curtsied at the close of her speech, which was so sensible and well worded, and delivered with such grace and propriety, that everybody thought her fit to be preceptress of the best academy in the state. But a stranger would have supposed that Mr. Higginbotham was an object of abhorrence at Parker's Falls, and that a thanksgiving had been proclaimed for his murder, so excessive was the wrath of the inhabitants on learning their mistake. The millmen resolved to bestow public honors on Dominicus Pike, only hesitating whether to tar and feather him, ride him on a rail, or refresh him with an ablution at the town pump, on the top of which he had declared himself the bearer of the news. The selectmen, by advice of the lawyer, spoke of prosecuting him for a misdemeanor, in circulating unfounded reports, to the great disturbance of the peace of the commonwealth. Nothing saved Dominicus either from mob law or a court of justice but an eloquent appeal made by the young lady in his behalf. Addressing a few words of heartfelt gratitude to his benefactress, he mounted the green cart and rode out of town, under a discharge of artillery from the schoolboys, who found plenty of ammunition in the neighboring clay-pits and mud-holes. As he turned his head to exchange a farewell glance with Mr. Higginbotham's niece, a ball, of the consistency of hasty-pudding, hit him slap in the mouth, giving him a most grim aspect. His whole person was so bespattered with the like filthy missiles that he had almost a mind to ride back and supplicate for the threatened ablution at the town pump, for, though not meant in kindness, it would have been a deed of charity.

However, the sun shone bright on poor Dominicus, and the mud, an emblem of all stains of undeserved opprobrium, was easily brushed off when dry. Being a funny rogue, his heart soon cheered up; nor could he refrain from a hearty laugh at the uproar which his story had excited. The handbills of the selectmen would cause the commitment of all the vagabonds in the state;

the paragraph in the *Parker's Falls Gazette* would be re-printed from Maine to Florida, and perhaps from an item in the London newspapers; and many a miser would tremble for his money-bags and life on learning the catastrophe of Mr. Higginbotham. The pedler meditated with much fervor on the charms of the young schoolmistress, and swore that Daniel Webster never spoke nor looked so like an angel as Miss Higginbotham while defending him from the wrathful populace at Parker's Falls.

Dominicus was now on the Kimballton turnpike, having all along determined to visit that place, though business had drawn him out of the most direct road from Morristown. As he approached the scene of the supposed murder he continued to revolve the circumstances in his mind, and was astonished at the aspect which the whole case assumed. Had nothing occurred to corroborate the story of the first traveler, it might now have been considered as a hoax; but the yellow man was evidently acquainted either with the report or the fact, and there was a mystery in his dismayed and guilty look on being abruptly questioned. When to this singular combination of incidents it was added that the rumor tallied exactly with Mr. Higginbotham's character and habits of life, and that he had an orchard, and a St. Michael's pear-tree near which he always passed at nightfall, the circumstantial evidence appeared so strong that Dominicus doubted whether the autograph produced by the lawyer or even the niece's direct testimony ought to be equivalent. Making cautious inquiries along the road, the pedler further learned that Mr. Higginbotham had in his service an Irishman of doubtful character, whom he had hired without a recommendation, on the score of economy.

"May I be hanged myself," exclaimed Dominicus Pike aloud, on reaching the top of a lonely hill, "if I'll believe old Higginbotham is unhanged till I see him with my own eyes, and hear it from his own mouth! And as he's a real shaver, I'll have the minister or some other responsible man for an indorser."

It was growing dusk when he reached the toll-house on Kimballton turnpike, about a quarter of a mile from the village of this name. His little mare was fast bringing him up with a man on horseback, who trotted through the gate a few rods in advance of him, nodded to the toll-gatherer, and kept on towards the village. Dominicus was acquainted with the toll-man, and while making change, the usual remarks on the weather passed between them.

"I suppose," said the pedler, throwing back his whip-lash, to bring it down like a feather on the mare's flank, "you have not seen anything of old Mr. Higginbotham within a day or two?"

"Yes," answered the toll-gatherer. "He passed the gate just before you drove up, and yonder he rides now, if you can see him through the dusk. He's been to Woodfield this afternoon, attending a sheriff's sale there. The old man generally shakes hands and has a little chat with me; but tonight he nodded—as if to say, 'charge my toll'—and jogged on; for wherever he goes, he must always be at home by eight o'clock."

"So they tell me," said Dominicus.

"I never saw a man look so yellow and thin as the squire does," continued the toll-gatherer. "Says I to myself, tonight, he's more like a ghost or an old mummy than good flesh and blood."

The pedler strained his eyes through the twilight, and could just discern the horseman now far ahead on the village road. He seemed to recognize the rear of Mr. Higginbotham; but through the evening shadows, and amid the dust from the horse's feet, the figure appeared dim and unsubstantial, as if the shape of the mysterious old man were faintly molded of darkness and gray light. Dominicus shivered.

"Mr. Higginbotham has come back from the other world, by way of the Kimballton turnpike," thought he.

He shook the reins and rode forward, keeping about the same distance in the rear of the gray old shadow, till the latter was concealed by a bend of the road. On reaching this point, the pedler no longer saw the man on horseback, but found himself at the head of the village street, not far from a number of stores and two taverns clustered round the meeting-house steeple. On his left was a stone wall and a gate, the boundary of a wood-lot, beyond which lay an orchard, farther still a mowing field, and last of all a house. These were the premises of Mr. Higginbotham, whose dwelling stood beside the old highway, but had been left in the background by the Kimballton turnpike. Dominicus knew the place; and the little mare stopped short by instinct, for he was not conscious of tightening the reins.

"For the soul of me I cannot get by this gate!" said he, trembling. "I shall never be my own man again till I see whether Mr. Higginbotham is hanging on the St. Michael's pear-tree!"

He leaped from the cart, gave the rein a turn round the gatepost, and ran along the green path of the wood-lot, as if Old Nick were chasing behind. Just then the village clock tolled eight, and as each deep stroke fell, Dominicus gave a fresh bound and flew faster than before, till, dim in the solitary center of the orchard, he saw the fated pear-tree. One great branch stretched from the old contorted trunk across the path, and threw the darkest shadow on that one spot. But something seemed to struggle beneath the branch!

The pedler had never pretended to more courage than befits a man of peaceable occupation, nor could he account for his valor on this awful emergency. Certain it is, however, that he rushed forward, prostrated a sturdy Irishman with the butt-end of his whip, and found—not indeed hanging on the St. Michael's pear-tree, but trembling beneath it, with a halter round his neck—the old, identical Mr. Higginbotham!

"Mr. Higginbotham," said Dominicus tremulously, "you're an honest man, and I'll take your word for it. Have you been hanged, or not?"

If the riddle be not already guessed, a few words will explain the simple machinery by which this "coming event" was made to "cast its shadow before." Three men had plotted the robbery and murder of Mr. Higginbotham; two of them successively lost courage and fled, each delaying the crime one night by their disappearance; the third was in the act of perpetration when a champion, blindly obeying the call of fate like the heroes of old romance, appeared in the person of Dominicus Pike.

It only remains to say that Mr. Higginbotham took the pedler into high favor, sanctioned his addresses to the pretty schoolmistress, and settled his whole property on their children, allowing themselves the interest. In due time, the old gentleman capped the climax of his favors by dying a Christian death in bed, since which melancholy event Dominicus Pike has removed from Kimballton, and established a large tobacco manufactory in my native village.

RING LARDNER

I Can't Breathe

I am staying here at the Inn for two weeks with my Uncle Nat and Aunt Jule and I think I will keep a kind of a diary while I am here to help pass the time and so I can have a record of things that happen though goodness knows there isn't likely to anything happen, that is, anything exciting with Uncle Nat and Aunt Jule making the plans as they are both at least 35 years old and maybe older.

Dad and mother are abroad to be gone a month and me coming here is supposed to be a recompense from them not taking me with them. A fine recompense to be left with old people that come to a place like this to rest. Still it would be a heavenly place under different conditions, for instance, if Walter were here, too. It would be heavenly if he were here, the very thought of it makes my heart stop.

I can't stand it. I won't think about it.

This is our first separation since we have been engaged, nearly 17 days. It will be 17 days tomorrow. And the hotel orchestra at dinner this evening played that old thing "Oh how I miss you tonight" and it seemed as if they must be playing it for my benefit though, of course, the person in that song is talking about how they miss their mother though, of course, I miss mother, too, but a person gets used to missing their mother and it isn't like Walter or the person you are engaged to.

But there won't be any more separations much longer, we are going to be married in December even if mother does laugh when I talk to her about it because she says I am crazy to even think of getting married at 18.

She got married herself when she was 18, but of course that was "different," she wasn't crazy like I am, she knew whom she was marrying. As if Walter were a policeman or a foreigner or something. And she says she was only engaged once while I have been engaged at least five times a year since I was 14, of course, it really isn't as bad as that and I have really only been really what I call engaged six times altogether, but is getting engaged my fault when they keep insisting and hammering at you and if you didn't say yes they would never go home.

But it is different with Walter. I honestly believe if he had not asked me I would have asked him. Of course I wouldn't have, but I would have died. And this is the first time I have even been engaged to be really married. The other times when they talked about when should we get married I just laughed at them, but I hadn't been engaged to Walter ten minutes when he brought up the subject of marriage and I didn't laugh. I wouldn't be engaged to him unless it was to be married. I couldn't stand it.

Anyway mother may as well get used to the idea because it is "No Foolin'" this time and we have got our plans all made and I am going to be married at home and go out to California and Hollywood on our honeymoon. December, five months away. I can't stand it. I can't wait.

There were a couple of awfully nice looking boys sitting together alone in the dining room tonight. One of them wasn't so much, but the other was cute. And he——

There's the dance orchestra playing "Always," what they played at the Biltmore the day I met Walter. "Not for just an hour not for just a day." I can't live. I can't breathe.

July 13

This has been a much more exciting day than I expected under the circumstances. In the first place I got two long night letters, one from Walter and one from Gordon Flint. I don't see how Walter ever had the nerve to send his, there was everything in it and it must have been horribly embarrassing for him while the telegraph operator was reading it over and counting the words to say nothing of embarrassing for the operator.

But the one from Gordon was a kind of a shock. He just got back from a trip around the world, left last December to go on it and got back yesterday and called up our house and Helga gave him my address, and his telegram, well it was nearly as bad as Walter's. The trouble is that Gordon and I were engaged when he went away, or at least he thought so and he wrote to me right along all the time he was away and sent cables and things and for a while I answered his letters, but then I lost track of his itinery and couldn't write to him any more and when I got really engaged to Walter I couldn't let Gordon know because I had no idea where he was besides not wanting to spoil his trip.

And now he still thinks we are engaged and he is going to call me up tomorrow from Chicago and how in the world can I explain things and get him to understand because he is really serious and I like him ever and ever so much and in lots of ways he is nicer than Walter, not really nicer but better looking and there is no comparison between their dancing. Walter simply can't learn to dance, that is really dance. He says it is because he is flat footed, he says that as a joke, but it is true and I wish to heavens it wasn't.

All afternoon I thought and thought and thought about what to say to Gordon when he calls up and finally I couldn't stand thinking about it any more and just made up my mind I wouldn't think about it any more. But I will tell the truth though it will kill me to hurt him.

I went down to lunch with Uncle Nat and Aunt Jule and they were going out to play golf this afternoon and were insisting that I go with them, but I told them I had

a headache and then I had a terrible time getting them
to go without me. I didn't have a headache at all and
just wanted to be alone to think about Walter and besides when you play with Uncle Nat he is always correct-
ing your stance or your swing or something and always
puts his hands on my arms and shoulders to show me
the right way and I can't stand it to have old men touch
me, even if they are your uncle.

I finally got rid of them and I was sitting watching
the tennis when that boy that I saw last night, the cute
one, came and sat right next to me and of course I didn't
look at him. So we got to talking and he is even cuter
than he looks, the most original and wittiest person I
believe I ever met and I haven't laughed so much in I
don't know how long.

For one thing he asked me if I had heard Rockefeller's
song and I said no and he began singing "Oil alone."
Then he asked me if I knew the orange juice song and I
told him no again and he said it was "Orange juice sorry
you made me cry." I was in hysterics before we had been
together ten minutes.

His name is Frank Caswell and he has been out of Dart-
mouth a year and is 24 years old. That isn't so terribly
old, only two years older than Walter and three years
older than Gordon. I hate the name Frank, but Caswell
is all right and he is so cute.

He was out in California last winter and visited Hollywood and met everybody in the world and it is fascinating to listen to him. He met Norma Shearer and he
said he thought she was the prettiest thing he had ever

seen. What he said was "I did think she was the prettiest girl in the world, till today." I was going to pretend I didn't get it, but I finally told him to be sensible or I would never be able to believe anything he said.

Well, he wanted me to dance with him tonight after dinner and the next question was how to explain how we had met each other to Uncle Nat and Aunt Jule. Frank said he would fix that all right and sure enough he got himself introduced to Uncle Nat when Uncle Nat came in from golf and after dinner Uncle Nat introduced him to me and Aunt Jule and we danced together all evening, that is not Aunt Jule. They went to bed, thank heavens.

He is a heavenly dancer, as good as Gordon. One dance we were dancing and for one of the encores the orchestra played "In a cottage small by a waterfall" and I simply couldn't dance to it. I just stopped still and said "Listen, I can't bear it, I can't breathe" and poor Frank thought I was sick or something and I had to explain that that was the tune the orchestra played the night I sat at the next table to Jack Barrymore at Barney Gallant's.

I made him sit out that encore and wouldn't let him talk till they got through playing it. Then they played something else and I was all right again and Frank told me about meeting Jack Barrymore. Imagine meeting him. I couldn't live.

I promised Aunt Jule I would go to bed at eleven and it is way past that now, but I am all ready for bed and have just been writing this. Tomorrow Gordon is going to call up and what will I say to him? I just won't think about it.

July 14

Gordon called up this morning from Chicago and it was wonderful to hear his voice again though the connection was terrible. He asked me if I still loved him and I tried to tell him no, but I knew that would mean an explanation and the connection was so bad that I never could make him understand so I said yes, but I almost whispered it purposely, thinking he wouldn't hear me, but he heard me all right and he said that made everything all right with the world. He said he thought I had stopped loving him because I had stopped writing.

I wish the connection had been decent and I could have told him how things were, but now it is terrible because he is planning to get to New York the day I get there and heaven knows what I will do because Walter will be there, too. I just won't think about it.

Aunt Jule came in my room just after I was through talking to Gordon, thank heavens. The room was full of flowers. Walter had sent me some and so had Frank. I got another long night letter from Walter, just as silly as the first one. I wish he would say those things in letters instead of night letters so everybody in the world wouldn't see them. Aunt Jule wanted me to read it aloud to her. I would have died.

While she was still in the room, Frank called up and asked me to play golf with him and I said all right and Aunt Jule said she was glad my headache was gone. She was trying to be funny.

I played golf with Frank this afternoon. He is a beautiful golfer and it is thrilling to watch him drive, his
swing is so much more graceful than Walter's. I asked
him to watch me swing and tell me what was the matter
with me, but he said he couldn't look at anything but
my face and there wasn't anything the matter with that.

He told me the boy who was here with him had been
called home and he was glad of it because I might have
liked him, the other boy, better than himself. I told him
that couldn't be possible and he asked me if I really
meant that and I said of course, but I smiled when I said
it so he wouldn't take it too seriously.

We danced again tonight and Uncle Nat and Aunt
Jule sat with us a while and danced a couple of dances
themselves, but they were really there to get better acquainted with Frank and see if he was all right for me
to be with. I know they certainly couldn't have enjoyed
their own dancing, no old people really can enjoy it because they can't really *do* anything.

They were favorably impressed with Frank I think,
at least Aunt Jule didn't say I must be in bed at eleven,
but just not to stay up too late. I guess it is a big surprise
to a girl's parents and aunts and uncles to find out that
the boys you go around with are all right, they always
seem to think that if I seem to like somebody and the
person pays a little attention to me, why he must be a
convict or a policeman or a drunkard or something
queer.

Frank had some more songs for me tonight. He asked
me if I knew the asthma song and I said I didn't and he

said "Oh, you must know that. It goes, Yes, sir, asthma baby." Then he told me about the underwear song, "I underwear my baby is tonight." He keeps you in hysterics and yet he has his serious side, in fact he was awfully serious when he said good night to me and his eyes simply shone. I wish Walter were more like him in some ways, but I mustn't think about that.

July 15

I simply can't live and I know I'll never sleep tonight. I am in a terrible predicament or rather I won't know whether I really am or not till tomorrow and that is what makes it so terrible.

After we had danced two or three dances, Frank asked me to go for a ride with him and we went for a ride in his car and finally he told me he loved me and I said not to be silly, but he said he was perfectly serious and he certainly acted that way. He asked me if I loved anybody else and I said yes and he asked if I didn't love him more than anybody else and I said yes, but only because I thought he wouldn't remember it anyway and the best thing to do was humor him under the circumstances.

Then all of a sudden he asked me when I could marry him and I said, just as a joke, that I couldn't possibly marry him before December. He said that was a long time to wait, but I was certainly worth waiting for and he said a lot of other things and maybe I humored him a little too much, but that is just the trouble, I don't know.

I was absolutely sure he would forget the whole thing.

If he doesn't remember anything about it, of course I am all right. But if he does remember and if he took me seriously, I will simply have to tell him about Walter and maybe about Gordon, too. And it isn't going to be easy. The suspense is what is maddening and I know I'll never live through this night.

July 16

I can't stand it, I can't breathe, life is impossible. Frank remembered everything about last night and firmly believes we are engaged and going to be married in December. His people live in New York and he says he is going back when I do and have them meet me.

Of course it can't go on and tomorrow I will tell him about Walter or Gordon or both of them. I know it is going to hurt him terribly, perhaps spoil his life and I would give anything in the world not to have had it happen. I hate so to hurt him because he is so nice besides being so cute and attractive.

He sent me the loveliest flowers this morning and called up at ten and wanted to know how soon he could see me and I hope the girl wasn't listening in because the things he said were, well, like Walter's night letters.

And that is another terrible thing, today I didn't get a night letter from Walter, but there was a regular letter instead and I carried it around in my purse all this afternoon and evening and never remembered to read it till ten minutes ago when I came up in the room. Walter is worried because I have only sent him two telegrams and written him one letter since I have been here. He

237

would be a lot more worried if he knew what has happened now, though of course it can't make any difference because he is the one I am really engaged to be married to and the one I told mother I was going to marry in December and I wouldn't dare tell her it was somebody else.

I met Frank for lunch and we went for a ride this afternoon and he was so much in love and so lovely to me that I simply did not have the heart to tell him the truth, I am surely going to tell him tomorrow and telling him today would have just meant one more day of unhappiness for both of us.

He said his people had plenty of money and his father had offered to take him into partnership and he might accept, but he thinks his true vocation is journalism with a view to eventually writing novels and if I was willing to undergo a few hardships just at first we would probably both be happier later on if he was doing something he really liked. I didn't know what to say, but finally I said I wanted him to suit himself and money wasn't everything.

He asked me where I would like to go on my honeymoon and I suppose I ought to have told him my honeymoon was all planned, that I was going to California, with Walter, but all I said was that I had always wanted to go to California and he was enthusiastic and said that is where we would surely go and he would take me to Hollywood and introduce me to all those wonderful people he met there last winter. It nearly takes my breath away to think of it, going there with someone who really knows people and has the entrée.

We danced again tonight, just two or three dances, and then went out and sat in the tennis court, but I came upstairs early because Aunt Jule had acted kind of funny at dinner. And I wanted to be alone, too, and think, but the more I think the worse it gets.

Sometimes I wish I were dead, maybe that is the only solution and it would be best for everyone concerned. I *will* die if things keep on the way they have been. But of course tomorrow it will be all over, with Frank I mean, for I must tell him the truth no matter how much it hurts us both. Though I don't care how much it hurts me. The thought of hurting him is what is driving me mad. I can't bear it.

July 18

I have skipped a day. I was busy every minute of yesterday and so exhausted when I came upstairs that I was tempted to fall into bed with all my clothes on. First Gordon called me up from Chicago to remind me that he would be in New York the day I got there and that when he comes he wants me all to himself all the time and we can make plans for our wedding. The connection was bad again and I just couldn't explain to him about Walter.

I had an engagement with Frank for lunch and just as we were going in another long·distance call came, from Walter this time. He wanted to know why I haven't written more letters and sent him more telegrams and asked me if I still loved him and of course I told him yes because I really do. Then he asked me if I had met any men here and I told him I had met one, a friend of Uncle Nat's. After all it was Uncle Nat who introduced me to Frank. He reminded me that he would be in New York on the 25th which is the day I expect to get home, and said he would have theater tickets for that night and we would go somewhere afterwards and dance.

Frank insisted on knowing who had kept me talking so long and I told him it was a boy I had known a long while, a very dear friend of mine and a friend of my family's. Frank was jealous and kept asking questions till I thought I would go mad. He was so serious and kind of cross and gruff that I gave up the plan of telling him the truth till some time when he is in better spirits.

I played golf with Frank in the afternoon and we took a ride last night and I wanted to get in early because I had promised both Walter and Gordon that I would write them long letters, but Frank wouldn't bring me back to the Inn till I had named a definite date in December. I finally told him the 10th, and he said all right if I was sure that wasn't a Sunday. I said I would have to look it up, but as a matter of fact I know the 10th falls on a Friday because the date Walter and I have agreed on for our wedding is Saturday the 11th.

Today has just been the same thing over again, two more night letters, a long distance call from Chicago, golf and a ride with Frank, and the room full of flowers. But tomorrow I am going to tell Frank, and I am going to write Gordon a long letter and tell him, too, because this simply can't go on any longer. I can't breathe. I can't live.

July 21

I wrote to Gordon yesterday, but I didn't say anything about Walter because I don't think it is a thing a person ought to do by letter. I can tell him when he gets to New York and then I will be sure that he doesn't take it too hard and I can promise him that I will be friends with him always and make him promise not to do anything silly, while if I told it to him in a letter there is no telling what he would do, there all alone.

And I haven't told Frank because he hasn't been feeling well, he is terribly sunburned and it hurts him terribly so he can hardly play golf or dance, and I want him to be feeling his best when I do tell him, but whether he is all right or not I simply must tell him tomorrow because he is actually planning to leave here on the same train with us Saturday night and I can't let him do that.

Life is so hopeless and it could be so wonderful.

It is only half past ten, the earliest I have gone to bed in weeks, but I am worn out and Frank went to bed early so he could put cold cream on his sunburn.

Listen, diary, the orchestra is playing "Limehouse Blues," the first tune I danced to with Merle Oliver, two years ago. I can't stand it. And how funny that they should play that old tune tonight of all nights, when I have been thinking of Merle off and on all day, and I hadn't thought of him before in weeks and weeks. I won-

241

der where he is, I wonder if it is just an accident or if it means I am going to see him again. I simply mustn't think about it or I'll die.

July 22

I knew it wasn't an accident. I knew it must mean something, and it did.

Merle is coming here today, here to this Inn, and just to see me. And there can only be one reason. And only one answer, I knew that when I heard his voice calling from Boston. How could I ever have thought I loved anyone else? How could he ever have thought I meant it when I told him I was engaged to George Morse?

A whole year and he still cares and I still care. That shows we were always intended for each other and for no one else. I won't make *him* wait till December. I doubt if we even wait till dad and mother get home. And as for a honeymoon I will go with him to Long Beach or the Bronx Zoo, wherever he wants to take me.

After all, this is the best way out of it, the only way. I won't have to say anything to Frank, he will guess when he sees me with Merle. And when I get home Sunday and Walter and Gordon call me up, I will invite them both to dinner and Merle can tell them himself. With two of them there it will only hurt each one half as much as if they were alone.

The train is due at 2:40, almost three hours from now. I can't wait. And what if it should be late? I can't stand it.

H. C. BUNNER

A Sisterly Scheme

Away up in the very heart of Maine there is a mighty lake among the mountains. It is reached after a journey of many hours from the place where you "go in." That is the phrase of the country, and when you have once "gone in," you know why it is not correct to say that you have gone *through* the woods, or, simply, *to* your destination. You find that you have plunged into a new world —a world that has nothing in common with the world that you live in; a world of wild, solemn, desolate grandeur, a world of space and silence; a world that oppresses your soul—and charms you irresistibly. And after you have once "come out" of that world, there will be times, to the day of your death, when you will be homesick for it, and will long with a childlike longing to go back to it.

Up in this wild region you will find a fashionable

Summer hotel, with electric bells and seven-course dinners, and "guests" who dress three times a day. It is perched on a little flat point, shut off from the rest of the mainland by a huge rocky cliff. It is an impertinence in that majestic wilderness, and Leather-Stocking would doubtless have had a hankering to burn such an affront to Nature; but it is a good hotel, and people go to it and breathe the generous air of the great woods.

On the beach near this hotel, where the canoes were drawn up in line, there stood one Summer morning a curly-haired, fair young man—not so very young, either —whose cheeks were uncomfortably red as he looked first at his own canoe, high and dry, loaded with rods and landing-net and luncheon-basket, and then at another canoe, fast disappearing down the lake, wherein sat a young man and a young woman.

"Dropped again, Mr. Morpeth?"

The young man looked up and saw a saucy face laughing at him. A girl was sitting on the string-piece of the dock. It was the face of a girl between childhood and womanhood. By the face and the figure, it was a woman grown. By the dress, you would have judged it a girl.

And you would have been confirmed in the latter opinion by the fact that the young person was doing something unpardonable for a young lady, but not inexcusable in the case of a youthful tomboy. She had taken off her canvas shoe, and was shaking some small stones out of it. There was a tiny hole in her black stocking, and a glimpse of her pink toe was visible. The girl was sunburnt, but the toe was prettily pink.

"Your sister," replied the young man with dignity, "was to have gone fishing with me; but she remembered at the last moment that she had a prior engagement with Mr. Brown."

"She hadn't," said the girl. "I heard them make it up last evening, after you went upstairs."

The young man clean forgot himself.

"She's the most heartless coquette in the world!" he cried, and clinched his hands.

"She is all that," said the young person on the string-piece of the dock, "and more, too. And yet, I suppose, you want her all the same?"

"I'm afraid I do," said the young man, miserably.

"Well," said the girl, putting her shoe on again, and beginning to tie it up, "I'll tell you what it is, Mr. Morpeth. You've been hanging around Pauline for a year, and you are the only one of the men she keeps on a string who hasn't snubbed me. Now, if you want me to, I'll give you a lift."

"A—a—*what?*"

"A lift. You're wasting your time. Pauline has no use for devotion. It's a drug in the market with her—has been for five seasons. There's only one way to get her worked up. Two fellows tried it, and they nearly got there; but they weren't game enough to stay to the bitter end. I think you're game, and I'll tell you. You've got to make her jealous."

"Make her jealous of me?"

"No!" said his friend, with infinite scorn; "make her jealous of the other girl. *Oh!* but you men are stupid!"

245

The young man pondered a moment.

"Well, Flossy," he began, and then he became conscious of a sudden change in the atmosphere, and perceived that the young lady was regarding him with a look that might have chilled his soul.

"Miss Flossy—Miss Belton—" he hastily corrected himself. Winter promptly changed to Summer in Miss Flossy Belton's expressive face.

"Your scheme," he went on, "is a good one. Only—it involves the discovery of another girl."

"Yes," assented Miss Flossy, cheerfully.

"Well," said the young man, "doesn't it strike you that if I were to develop a sudden admiration for any one of these other young ladies whose charms I have hitherto neglected, it would come tardy off—lack artistic verisimilitude, so to speak?"

"Rather," was Miss Flossy's prompt and frank response; "especially as there isn't one of them fit to flirt with."

"Well, then, where am I to discover the girl?"

Miss Flossy untied and retied her shoe. Then she said, calmly:

"What's the matter with—" a hardly perceptible hesitation—"*me?*"

"With *you?*" Mr. Morpeth was startled out of his manners.

"Yes."

Mr. Morpeth simply stared.

"Perhaps," suggested Miss Flossy, "I'm not good-looking enough?"

"You are good-looking enough," replied Mr. Morpeth, recovering himself, "for *anything*—" and he threw a convincing emphasis into the last word as he took what was probably his first real inspection of his adored one's junior—"but—aren't you a trifle—young?"

"How old do you suppose I am?"

"I know. Your sister told me. You are sixteen."

"Sixteen!" repeated Miss Flossy, with an infinite and uncontrollable scorn, "yes, and I'm the kind of sixteen that stays sixteen till your elder sister's married. I was eighteen years old on the third of last December—unless they began to double on me before I was old enough to know the difference—it would be just like Mama to play it on me in some such way," she concluded, reflectively.

"Eighteen years old!" said the young man. "The deuce!" Do not think that he was an ill-bred young man. He was merely astonished, and he had much more astonishment ahead of him. He mused for a moment.

"Well," he said, "what's your plan of campaign? I am to—to discover you."

"Yes," said Miss Flossy, calmly, "and to flirt with me like fun."

"And may I ask what attitude you are to take when you are—discovered?"

"Certainly," replied the imperturbable Flossy. "I am going to dangle you."

"To—to dangle me?"

"As a conquest, don't you know. Let you hang around and laugh at you."

"Oh, indeed!"

"There, don't be wounded in your masculine pride. You might as well face the situation. You don't think that Pauline's in love with you, do you?"

"No!" groaned the young man.

"But you've got lots of money. Mr. Brown has got lots more. You're eager. Brown is coy. That's the reason that Brown is in the boat and you are on the cold, cold shore, talking to Little Sister. Now if Little Sister jumps at you, why, she's simply taking Big Sister's leavings; it's all in the family, any way, and there's no jealousy, and Pauline can devote her whole mind to Brown. There, *don't* look so limp. You men are simply childish. Now, after you've asked me to marry you—"

"Oh, I'm to ask you to marry me?"

"Certainly. You needn't look frightened, now. I won't accept you. But then you are to go around like a wet cat, and mope, and hang on worse than ever. Then Big Sister will see that she can't afford to take that sort of thing from Little Sister, and then—there's your chance."

"Oh, there's my chance, is it?" said Mr. Morpeth. He seemed to have fallen into the habit of repetition.

"There's your *only* chance," said Miss Flossy, with decision.

Mr. Morpeth meditated. He looked at the lake, where there was no longer sign or sound of the canoe, and he looked at Miss Flossy, who sat calm, self-confident and careless, on the string-piece of the dock.

"I don't know how feasible—" he began.

"It's feasible," said Miss Flossy, with decision. "Of course, Pauline will write to Mama, and of course

248

Mama will write and scold me. But she's got to stay in New York, and nurse Papa's gout; and the Miss Redingtons are all the chaperons we've got up here, and they don't amount to anything—so I don't care."

"But why," inquired the young man; and his tone suggested a complete abandonment to Miss Flossy's idea; "why should you take so much trouble for *me?*"

"Mr. Morpeth," said Miss Flossy, solemnly, "I'm two years behind the time-table, and I've got to make a strike for liberty, or die. And besides," she added, "if you are *nice,* it needn't be such an *awful* trouble."

Mr. Morpeth laughed.

"I'll try to make it as little of a bore as possible," he said, extending his hand. The girl did not take it.

"Don't make any mistake," she cautioned him, searching his face with her eyes; "this isn't to be any little-girl affair. Little Sister doesn't want any kind, elegant, supercilious encouragement from Big Sister's young man. It's got to be a *real* flirtation—devotion no end, and ten times as much as ever Pauline could get out of you—and you've got to keep your end 'way—'way—'way up!"

The young man smiled.

"I'll keep my end up," he said; "but are you certain that you can keep yours up?"

"Well, I think so," replied Miss Flossy. "Pauline will raise an awful row; but if she goes too far, I'll tell my age, *and hers, too.*"

Mr. Morpeth looked in Miss Flossy's calm face. Then he extended his hand once more.

"It's a bargain, so far as I'm concerned," he said.

This time a soft and small hand met his with a firm, friendly, honest pressure.

"And I'll refuse you," said Miss Flossy.

Within two weeks, Mr. Morpeth found himself entangled in a flirtation such as he had never dreamed of. Miss Flossy's scheme had succeeded only too brilliantly. The whole hotel was talking about the outrageous behavior of "that little Belton girl" and Mr. Morpeth, who certainly ought to know better.

Mr. Morpeth had carried out his instructions. Before the week was out, he found himself giving the most lifelike imitation of an infatuated lover that ever delighted the old gossips of a Summer resort. And yet he had only done what Flossy told him to do.

He got his first lesson just about the time that Flossy, in the privacy of their apartments, informed her elder sister that if she, Flossy, found Mr. Morpeth's society agreeable, it was nobody's concern but her own, and that she was prepared to make some interesting additions to the census statistics if any one thought differently.

The lesson opened his eyes.

"Do you know," she said, "that it wouldn't be a bit of a bad idea to telegraph to New York for some real nice candy and humbly present it for my acceptance? I *might* take it—if the bonbonnière was pretty enough."

He telegraphed to New York and received, in the course of four or five days, certain marvels of sweets in a miracle of an upholstered box. The next day he found her on the verandah, flinging the bonbons on the lawn for the children to scramble for.

"Awfully nice of you to send me these things," she said languidly, but loud enough for the men around her to hear—she had men around her already: she had been discovered—"but I never eat sweets, you know. Here, you little mite in the blue sash, don't you want this pretty box to put your doll's clothes in?"

And Maillard's finest bonbonnière went to a yellow-haired brat of three.

But this was the slightest and lightest of her caprices. She made him send for his dog-cart and his horses, all the way from New York, only that he might drive her over the ridiculous little mile-and-a-half of road that bounded the tiny peninsula. And she christened him "Muffets," a nickname presumably suggested by "Morpeth"; and she called him "Muffets" in the hearing of all the hotel people.

And did such conduct pass unchallenged? No. Pauline scolded, raged, raved. She wrote to Mama. Mama wrote back and reproved Flossy. But Mama could not leave Papa. His gout was worse. The Miss Redingtons must act. The Miss Redingtons merely wept, and nothing more. Pauline scolded; the flirtation went on; and the people at the big hotel enjoyed it immensely.

And there was more to come. Four weeks had passed. Mr. Morpeth was hardly on speaking terms with the elder Miss Belton; and with the younger Miss Belton he was on terms which the hotel gossips characterized as "simply scandalous." Brown glared at him when they met, and he glared at Brown. Brown was having a hard time. Miss Belton the elder was not pleasant of temper in those trying days.

"And now," said Miss Flossy to Mr. Morpeth, "it's time you proposed to me, Muffets."

They were sitting on the hotel verandah, in the evening darkness. No one was near them, except an old lady in a Shaker chair.

"There's Mrs. Melby. She's pretending to be asleep, but she isn't. She's just waiting for us. Now walk me up and down and ask me to marry you so that she can hear it. It'll be all over the hotel inside of half an hour. Pauline will just *rage*."

With this pleasant prospect before him, Mr. Morpeth marched Miss Flossy Belton up and down the long verandah. He had passed Mrs. Melby three times before he was able to say, in a choking, husky, uncertain voice:

"Flossy—I—I—I *love* you!"

Flossy's voice was not choking nor uncertain. It rang out clear and silvery in a peal of laughter.

"Why, of course you do, Muffets, and I wish you didn't. That's what makes you so stupid half the time."

"But—" said Mr. Morpeth, vaguely; "but I—"

"But you're a silly boy," returned Miss Flossy; and she added in a swift aside: "*You haven't asked me to marry you!*"

"W-W-W-Will you be my wife?" stammered Mr. Morpeth.

"No!" said Miss Flossy, emphatically, "I will not. You

are too utterly ridiculous. The idea of it! No, Muffets, you are charming in your present capacity; but you aren't to be considered seriously."

They strolled on into the gloom at the end of the great verandah.

"That's the first time," he said, with a feeling of having only the ghost of a breath left in his lungs, "that I ever asked a woman to marry me."

"I should think so," said Miss Flossy, "from the way you did it. And you were beautifully rejected, weren't you? Now—look at Mrs. Melby, will you? She's scudding off to spread the news."

And before Mr. Morpeth went to bed, he was aware of the fact that every man and woman in the hotel knew that he had "proposed" to Flossy Belton, and had been "beautifully rejected."

Two sulky men, one sulky woman, and one girl radiant with triumphant happiness started out in two canoes, reached certain fishing-grounds known only to the elect, and began to cast for trout. They had indifferent luck. Miss Belton and Mr. Brown caught a dozen trout; Miss Flossy Belton and Mr. Morpeth caught eighteen or nineteen, and the day was wearing to a close. Miss Flossy made the last cast of the day, just as her escort had taken the paddle. A big trout rose—just touched the fly—and disappeared.

"It's this wretched rod!" cried Miss Flossy; and she rapped it on the gunwale of the canoe so sharply that the beautiful split-bamboo broke sharp off in the middle of the second joint. Then she tumbled it overboard, reel and all.

"I was tired of that rod, anyway, Muffets," she said; "row me home, now; I've got to dress for dinner."

Miss Flossy's elder sister, in the other boat, saw and hear this exhibition of tyranny; and she was so much moved that she stamped her small foot, and endangered the bottom of the canoe. She resolved that Mama should come back, whether Papa had the gout or not.

Mr. Morpeth, wearing a grave expression, was paddling Miss Flossy toward the hotel. He had said nothing whatever, and it was a noticeable silence that Miss Flossy finally broke.

"You've done pretty much everything that I wanted you to do, Muffets," she said; "but you haven't saved my life yet, and I'm going to give you a chance."

It is not difficult to overturn a canoe. One twist of Flossy's supple body did it, and before he knew just what had happened, Morpeth was swimming toward the shore, holding up Flossy Belton with one arm, and fighting for life in the icy water of a Maine lake.

The people were running down, bearing blankets and brandy, as he touched bottom in his last desperate struggle to keep the two of them above water. One yard further, and there would have been no strength left in him.

He struggled up on shore with her, and when he got breath enough, he burst out:

"Why did you do it? It was wicked! It was cruel!"

"There!" she said, as she reclined composedly in his arms, "that will do, Muffets. I don't want to be scolded."

A delegation came along, bringing blankets and brandy, and took her from him.

At five o'clock of that afternoon, Mr. Morpeth presented himself at the door of the parlor attached to the apartments of the Belton sisters. Miss Belton, senior, was just coming out of the room. She received his inquiry after her sister's health with a white face and a quivering lip.

"I should think, Mr. Morpeth," she began, "that you had gone far enough in playing with the feelings of a m-m-mere child, and that—oh! I have no words to express my *contempt* for you!"

And in a most unladylike rage Miss Pauline Belton swept down the hotel corridor.

She had left the door open behind her. Morpeth heard a voice, weak, but cheery, addressing him from the far end of the parlor.

"You've got her!" it said. "She's crazy mad. She'll make up to you to-night—see if she don't."

Mr. Morpeth looked up and down the long corridor. It was empty. He pushed the door open, and entered. Flossy was lying on the sofa, pale, but bright-eyed.

"You can get her," she whispered, as he knelt down beside her.

"Flossy," he said, "don't you know that that is all ended? Don't you know that I love you and you only?

255

Don't you know that I haven't thought about any one else since—since—oh, Flossy, don't you—is it possible that you don't understand?"

Flossy stretched out two weak arms, and put them around Mr. Morpeth's neck.

"Why have I had you in training all Summer?" said she. "Did you think it was for Pauline?"

FABLE

JAMES THURBER

The Foolhardy Mouse
and the Cautious Cat

Such sport there had been that day, in the kitchen and
the pantry, for the cat was away and the mice were playing all manner of games: mousy-wants-a-corner, hide-
and-squeak, one-old-cat, mouse-in-boots, and so on.
Then the cat came home.

"Cat's back!" whispered Father Mouse.

"Into the wainscoting, all of you!" said Mother Mouse,
and all of the mice except one hastily hid in the woodwork.

The exception was an eccentric mouse named Mervyn,
who had once boldly nipped a bulldog in the ear and
got away with it. Mervyn did not know at the time, and
never found out, that the bulldog was a stuffed bulldog,
and so he lived in a fool's paradise.

The day the cat, whose name was Pouncetta, came
back from wherever she had been, she was astonished

to encounter Mervyn in the butler's pantry, nonchalantly nibbling crumbs. She crept toward him in her stocking feet and was astounded when he turned, spit a crumb in her eye, and began insulting her with a series of insults.

"How did you get out of the bag?" Mervyn inquired calmly. "Put on your pajamas and take a cat nap." He went back to his nibbling, as blasé as you please.

"Steady, Pouncetta," said Pouncetta to herself. "There is more here than meets the eye. This mouse is probably a martyr mouse. He has swallowed poison in the hope that I will eat him and die, so that he can be a hero to a hundred generations of his descendants."

Mervyn looked over his shoulder at the startled and suspicious cat and began to mock her in a mousetto voice. "Doodness dwacious," said Mervyn, "it's a posse cat, in full pursuit of little me." He gestured impudently with one foot. "I went that-a-way," he told Pouncetta. Then he did some other imitations, including a pretty good one of W. C. Fieldmouse.

"Easy, girl," said Pouncetta to herself. "This is a mechanical mouse, a trick mouse with a built-in voice. If I jump on it, it will explode and blow me into a hundred pieces. Damned clever, these mice, but not clever enough for me."

"You'd make wonderful violin strings, if you had any guts," Mervyn said insolently. But Pouncetta did not pounce, in spite of the insult unforgivable. Instead, she turned and stalked out of the butler's pantry and into the sitting room and lay down on her pillow near the fireplace and went to sleep.

When Mervyn got back to his home in the woodwork, his father and mother and brothers and sisters and cousins and uncles and aunts were surprised to see him alive and well. There was great jollity, and the finest cheese was served at a family banquet. "She never laid a paw on me," Mervyn boasted. "I haven't got a scratch. I could take on all the cats in the Catskills." He finished his cheese and went to bed and fell asleep, and dreamed of taking a catamount in one minute and twenty-eight seconds of the first round.

MORAL: *Fools rush in where angels fear to tread, and the angels are all in Heaven, but few of the fools are dead.*

ROBERT BENCHLEY

Happy Childhood Tales

We have had so many stories lately dealing with the sordid facts of life, about kitchen sinks and lynchings and young girls thrown out into the streets by mean old farmers who live in horsehair trunks, to say nothing of incidental subjects, such as gin and cold oatmeal and unfortunate people who have only one glove apiece, that a reaction is taking place in the mind of the reading public and a demand is going up for some of the fanciful happy tales of our youth.

"Enough of these stories of crime and unhappiness!" the people are crying. "Tell us again some of the ancient myths of an older day, the gay little legends on which we were brought up before the world grew grim and sordid."

And so, my little readers, I am going to try to recall to you some of the charming fairy tales, or, at any rate, to make up some like them, and I hope that after this little trip back into the Never-Never Land of our youth, those little cheeks of yours will be blooming again and that you will shut your traps. For, after all, there must be *some* good in the world, else why were erasers put on the ends of lead pencils?

ENDREMIA AND LIASO
(*From the Greek Mythology*)

Endremia was the daughter of Polygaminous, the God of Ensilage, and Reba, the Goddess of Licorice. She was the child of a most unhappy union, it later turned out, for when she was a tiny child her father struck her mother with an anvil and turned himself into a lily pad to avoid the vengeance of Jove. But Jove was too sly for Polygaminous and struck him with a bolt of lightning the size of the Merchants Bank Building which threw him completely off his balance so that he toppled over into a chasm and was dashed to death.

In the meantime, Little Endremia found herself alone in the world with nobody but Endrocine, the Goddess of Lettuce, and her son Bilax, the God of Gum Arabic, to look after her. But, as Polygaminous (her father; have you forgotten so soon, you dope?) had turned Endremia into a mushroom before he turned himself into a lily pad, neither of her guardians knew who she was, so their protection did her no good.

But Jove had not so soon forgotten the daughter of his favorite (Reba), and appeared to her one night in the

263

shape of a mushroom gatherer. He asked her how she would like to get off that tree (she was one of those mushrooms which grow on trees) and get into his basket. Endremia, not knowing that it was Jove who was asking her, said not much. Whereupon Jove unloosed his mighty wrath and struck down the whole tree with a bolt of lightning which he had brought with him in case Endremia wouldn't listen to reason.

This is why it is never safe to eat the mushrooms which grow on trees, or to refuse to get into Jove's basket.

MILGRIG AND THE TREE WILFS
(*Something like Hans Christian Andersen*)

Once upon a time there was a little girl named Milgrig, believe it or not. She lived in the middle of a deep dark forest with her three ugly sisters and their husbands, who were charcoal burners. Every night the three ugly sisters used to take little Milgrig and pull out a strand of her golden hair, so that by the time she was thirteen years old she looked something awful. And after the three sisters had pulled out her hair, their three husbands (I forgot to tell you that the three husbands were even uglier than the three sisters and much nastier) would stick pins into little Milgrig until she looked like a war map.

One night, when little Milgrig was so full of pins that she couldn't see straight, a fairy prince came riding up to the door of the charcoal burners' hut and asked if he had lost his way.

"How should I know?" replied the oldest sister, who was uglier than all the rest. "What was your way?"

"My way was to the king's castle," replied the prince, "and I must get there before midnight, for my father is torturing my mother with red-hot irons."

"Your father sounds like a good egg," replied the oldest husband, who was uglier than all the rest. "We must ask him down some night."

The prince, however, did not think that this was very funny and asked if little Milgrig might not be allowed to show him the way to the castle.

The ugly husbands and sisters, thinking that Milgrig would not know the way and would get the prince lost in the forest, agreed heartily to this suggestion, and the pins were pulled out of Milgrig to make it possible for her to walk.

"Good luck and a happy landing!" they all called out after the two young people as they set forth on their perilous journey.

But the prince was no fool, and knew his way through the forest as well as you or I do (better, I'll wager), and he took little Milgrig to the palace just as fast as his palfrey would carry him.

She wasn't particularly crazy about going, but a prince is a prince, and she knew enough to keep her mouth shut.

When they reached the palace and the prince found that his father had already killed his mother, he turned to little Milgrig and said:

"Now you are the queen."

At this, little Milgrig was very pleased and immediately dispatched messengers to the charcoal burners' hut, where the three ugly sisters and three still uglier brothers-in-law were burned alive in a slow fire. Little Milgrig and the prince, happy in this termination to their little affair, lived happily ever after.

And so now, my readers, you must toddle off to bed, for we have had an evening with the happy, happy storytellers of an earlier day and have had a vacation, for one night at least, from the drab, unpleasant sordidness of present-day writing.

AESOP

The Ox and the Frog

For the weak to try to imitate the strong is courting destruction.

Once upon a time a frog saw an ox in a meadow and was envious of its huge bulk. So she swelled out her body till all the wrinkles disappeared and then asked her children if she was now fatter than the ox. "No," they said. With a still greater effort she stretched her skin tight, and asked which was the bigger now. "The ox," they answered. At last she got cross, and making frantic efforts to blow herself out still more, she burst herself and died.

O. HENRY

The Princess and the Puma

There had to be a king and queen, of course. The king was a terrible old man who wore sixshooters and spurs, and shouted in such a tremendous voice that the rattlers on the prairie would run into their holes under the prickly pear. Before there was a royal family they called the man "Whispering Ben." When he came to own 50,000 acres of land and more cattle than he could count, they called him O'Donnell "the Cattle King."

The queen had been a Mexican girl from Laredo. She made a good, mild, Coloradoclaro wife, and even succeeded in teaching Ben to modify his voice sufficiently while in the house to keep the dishes from being broken. When Ben got to be king she would sit on the gallery of Espinosa Ranch and weave rush mats. When wealth became so irresistible and oppressive that upholstered chairs and a centre table were brought down from San

Antone in the wagons, she bowed her smooth, dark head, and shared the fate of the Danaë.

To avoid *lèse-majesté* you have been presented first to the king and queen. They do not enter the story, which might be called "The Chronicle of the Princess, the Happy Thought, and the Lion that Bungled his Job."

Josefa O'Donnell was the surviving daughter, the princess. From her mother she inherited warmth of nature and a dusky, semi-tropic beauty. From Ben O'Donnell the royal she acquired a store of intrepidity, common sense, and the faculty of ruling. The combination was worth going miles to see. Josefa while riding her pony at a gallop could put five out of six bullets through a tomato-can swinging at the end of a string. She could play for hours with a white kitten she owned, dressing it in all manner of absurd clothes. Scorning a pencil, she could tell you out of her head what 1545 two-year-olds would bring on the hoof, at $8.50 per head. Roughly speaking, the Espinosa Ranch is forty miles long and thirty broad—but mostly leased land. Josefa, on her pony, had prospected over every mile of it. Every cowpuncher on the range knew her by sight and was a loyal vassal. Ripley Givens, foreman of one of the Espinosa outfits, saw her one day, and made up his mind to form a royal matrimonial alliance. Presumptuous? No. In those days in the Nueces country a man was a man. And, after all, the title of cattle king does not presuppose blood royal. Often it only signifies that its owner wears the crown in token of his magnificent qualities in the art of cattle stealing.

One day Ripley Givens rode over to the Double Elm Ranch to inquire about a bunch of strayed yearlings. He was late in setting out on his return trip, and it was sundown when he struck the White Horse Crossing of the Nueces. From there to his own camp it was sixteen miles. To the Espinosa ranch-house it was twelve. Givens was tired. He decided to pass the night at the Crossing.

There was a fine water hole in the river-bed. The banks were thickly covered with great trees, undergrown with brush. Back from the water hole fifty yards was a stretch of curly mesquite grass—supper for his horse and bed for himself. Givens staked his horse, and spread out his saddle blankets to dry. He sat down with his back against a tree and rolled a cigarette. From somewhere in the dense timber along the river came a sudden, rageful, shivering wail. The pony danced at the end of his rope and blew a whistling snort of comprehending fear. Givens puffed at his cigarette, but he reached leisurely for his pistol-belt, which lay on the grass, and twirled the cylinder of his weapon tentatively. A great gar plunged with a loud splash into the water hole. A little brown rabbit skipped around a bunch of catclaw and sat twitching his whiskers and looking humorously at Givens. The pony went on eating grass.

It is well to be reasonably watchful when a Mexican lion sings soprano along the arroyos at sundown. The burden of his song may be that young calves and fat lambs are scarce, and that he has a carnivorous desire for your acquaintance.

In the grass lay an empty fruit can, cast there by some

former sojourner. Givens caught sight of it with a grunt of satisfaction. In his coat pocket tied behind his saddle was a handful or two of ground coffee. Black coffee and cigarettes! What ranchero could desire more?

In two minutes he had a little fire going clearly. He started, with his can, for the water hole. When within fifteen yards of its edge he saw, between the bushes, a side-saddle pony with down-dropped reins cropping grass a little distance to his left. Just rising from her hands and knees on the brink of the water hole was Josefa O'Donnell. She had been drinking water, and she brushed the sand from the palms of her hands. Ten yards away, to her right, half concealed by a clump of sacuista, Givens saw the crouching form of the Mexican lion. His amber eyeballs glared hungrily; six feet from them was the tip of the tail stretched straight, like a pointer's. His hind-quarters rocked with the motion of the cat tribe preliminary to leaping.

Givens did what he could. His sixshooter was thirty-five yards away lying on the grass. He gave a loud yell, and dashed between the lion and the princess.

The "rucus," as Givens called it afterward, was brief and somewhat confused. When he arrived on the line of attack he saw a dim streak in the air, and heard a couple of faint cracks. Then a hundred pounds of Mexican lion plumped down upon his head and flattened him, with a heavy jar, to the ground. He remembered calling out: "Let up, now—no fair gouging!" and then he crawled from under the lion like a worm, with his mouth full of grass and dirt, and a big lump on the back of his head where it had struck the root of a water-elm. The lion lay motionless. Givens, feeling aggrieved, and suspicious of fouls, shook his fist at the lion, and shouted: "I'll rastle you again for twenty——" and then he got back to himself.

Josefa was standing in her tracks, quietly reloading her silver-mounted .38. It had not been a difficult shot. The lion's head made an easier mark than a tomato-can swinging at the end of a string. There was a provoking, teasing, maddening smile upon her mouth and in her dark eyes. The would-be-rescuing knight felt the fire of his fiasco burn down to his soul. Here had been his chance, the chance that he had dreamed of; and Momus, and not Cupid, had presided over it. The satyrs in the wood were, no doubt, holding their sides in hilarious, silent laughter. There had been something like vaudeville—say Signor Givens and his funny knockabout act with the stuffed lion.

"Is that you, Mr. Givens?" said Josefa, in her deliberate, saccharine contralto. "You nearly spoiled my shot when you yelled. Did you hurt your head when you fell?"

"Oh, no," said Givens, quietly; "that didn't hurt." He stooped ignominiously and dragged his best Stetson hat from under the beast. It was crushed and wrinkled to a fine comedy effect. Then he knelt down and softly stroked the fierce, open-jawed head of the dead lion.

"Poor old Bill!" he exclaimed, mournfully.

"What's that?" asked Josefa, sharply.

"Of course you didn't know, Miss Josefa," said Givens,

with an air of one allowing magnanimity to triumph over grief. "Nobody can blame you. I tried to save him, but I couldn't let you know in time."

"Save who?"

"Why, Bill. I've been looking for him all day. You see, he's been our camp pet for two years. Poor old fellow, he wouldn't have hurt a cottontail rabbit. It'll break the boys all up when they hear about it. But you couldn't tell, of course, that Bill was just trying to play with you."

Josefa's black eyes burned steadily upon him. Ripley Givens met the test successfully. He stood rumpling the yellow-brown curls on his head pensively. In his eyes was regret, not unmingled with a gentle reproach. His smooth features were set to a pattern of indisputable sorrow. Josefa wavered.

"What was your pet doing here?" she asked, making a last stand. "There's no camp near the White Horse Crossing."

"The old rascal ran away from camp yesterday," answered Givens, readily. "It's a wonder the coyotes didn't scare him to death. You see, Jim Webster, our horse wrangler, brought a little terrier pup into camp last week. The pup made life miserable for Bill—he used to chase him around and chew his hind legs for hours at a time. Every night when bedtime came Bill would sneak under one of the boy's blankets and sleep to keep the pup from finding him. I reckon he must have been worried pretty desperate or he wouldn't have run away. He was always afraid to get out of sight of camp."

Josefa looked at the body of the fierce animal. Givens gently patted one of the formidable paws that could have killed a yearling calf with one blow. Slowly a red flush widened upon the dark olive face of the girl. Was it the signal of shame of the true sportsmen who has brought down ignoble quarry? Her eyes grew softer, and the lowered lids drove away all their bright mockery.

"I'm very sorry," she said, humbly; "but he looked so big, and jumped so high that——"

"Poor old Bill was hungry," interrupted Givens, in quick defence of the deceased. "We always made him jump for his supper in camp. He would lie down and roll over for a piece of meat. When he saw you he thought he was going to get something to eat from you."

Suddenly Josefa's eyes opened wide.

"I might have shot you!" she exclaimed. "You ran right in between. You risked your life to save your pet! That was fine, Mr. Givens. I like a man who is kind to animals."

Yes; there was even admiration in her gaze now. After all, there was a hero rising out of the ruins of the anti-climax. The look on Givens's face would have secured him a high position in the S. P. C. A.

"I always loved 'em," said he; "horses, dogs, Mexican lions, cows, alligators——"

"I hate alligators," instantly demurred Josefa; "crawly, muddy things!"

"Did I say alligators?" said Givens. "I meant antelopes, of course."

Josefa's conscience drove her to make further amends.

She held out her hand penitently. There was a bright, unshed drop in each of her eyes.

"Please forgive me, Mr. Givens, won't you? I'm only a girl, you know, and I was frightened at first. I'm very, very sorry I shot Bill. You don't know how ashamed I feel. I wouldn't have done it for anything."

Givens took the proffered hand. He held it for a time while he allowed the generosity of his nature to overcome his grief at the loss of Bill. At last it was clear that he had forgiven her.

"Please don't speak of it any more, Miss Josefa. 'Twas enough to frighten any young lady the way Bill looked. I'll explain it all right to the boys."

"Are you really sure you don't hate me?" Josefa came closer to him impulsively. Her eyes were sweet—oh, sweet and pleading with gracious penitence. "I would hate any one who would kill my kitten. And how daring and kind of you to risk being shot when you tried to save him! How very few men would have done that!" Victory wrested from defeat! Vaudeville turned into drama! Bravo, Ripley Givens!

It was now twilight. Of course Miss Josefa could not be allowed to ride on to the ranch-house alone. Givens resaddled his pony in spite of that animal's reproachful glances, and rode with her. Side by side they galloped across the smooth grass, the princess and the man who was kind to animals. The prairie odors of fruitful earth and delicate bloom were thick and sweet around them. Coyotes yelping over there on the hill! No fear. And yet——

Josefa rode closer. A little hand seemed to grope. Givens found it with his own. The ponies kept an even gait. The hands lingered together, and the owner of one explained.

"I never was frightened before, but just think! How terrible it would be to meet a really wild lion! Poor Bill! I'm so glad you came with me!"

O'Donnell was sitting on the ranch gallery.

"Hello, Rip!" he shouted—"that you?"

"He rode in with me," said Josefa. "I lost my way and was late."

"Much obliged," called the cattle king. "Stop over, Rip, and ride to camp in the morning."

But Givens would not. He would push on to camp. There was a bunch of steers to start off on the trail at daybreak. He said goodnight, and trotted away.

An hour later, when the lights were out, Josefa, in her night-robe, came to her door and called to the king in his own room across the brick-paved hallway:

"Say, pop, you know that old Mexican lion they call the 'Gotch-eared Devil'—the one that killed Gonzales, Mr. Martin's sheep herder, and about fifty calves on the Salada range? Well, I settled his hash this afternoon over at the White Horse Crossing. Put two balls in his head with my .38 while he was on the jump. I knew him by the slice gone from his left ear that old Gonzales cut off with his machete. You couldn't have made a better shot yourself, daddy."

"Bully for you!" thundered Whispering Ben from the darkness of the royal chamber.

SYLVIA TOWNSEND WARNER

The Phœnix

Lord Strawberry, a nobleman, collected birds. He had the finest aviary in Europe, so large that eagles did not find it uncomfortable, so well laid out that both humming-birds and snow-buntings had a climate that suited them perfectly. But for many years the finest set of apartments remained empty, with just a label saying: "PHŒNIX. *Habitat: Arabia.*"

Many authorities on bird life had assured Lord Strawberry that the phœnix is a fabulous bird, or that the breed was long extinct. Lord Strawberry was unconvinced: his family had always believed in phœnixes. At intervals he received from his agents (together with statements of their expenses) birds which they declared were the phœnix but which turned out to be orioles, macaws, turkey buzzards dyed orange, etc., or stuffed cross-breeds, ingeniously assembled from various plumages. Finally

Lord Strawberry went himself to Arabia, where, after some months, he found a phœnix, won its confidence, caught it, and brought it home in perfect condition.

It was a remarkably fine phœnix, with a charming character—affable to the other birds in the aviary and much attached to Lord Strawberry. On its arrival in England it made a great stir among ornithologists, journalists, poets, and milliners, and was constantly visited. But it was not puffed by these attentions, and when it was no longer in the news, and the visits fell off, it showed no pique or rancour. It ate well, and seemed perfectly contented.

It costs a great deal of money to keep up an aviary. When Lord Strawberry died he died penniless. The aviary came on the market. In normal times the rarer birds, and certainly the phœnix, would have been bid for by the trustees of Europe's great zoological societies, or by private persons in the U.S.A.; but as it happened Lord Strawberry died just after a world war, when both money and bird-seed were hard to come by (indeed the cost of bird-seed was one of the things which had ruined Lord Strawberry). The London *Times* urged in a leader that the phœnix be bought for the London Zoo, saying that a nation of bird-lovers had a moral right to own such a rarity; and a fund, called the Strawberry Phœnix Fund, was opened. Students, naturalists, and school-children contributed according to their means; but their means were small, and there were no large donations. So Lord Strawberry's executors (who had the death

duties to consider) closed with the higher offer of Mr.
Tancred Poldero, owner and proprietor of Poldero's
Wizard Wonderworld.

For quite a while Mr. Poldero considered his phœnix a
bargain. It was a civil and obliging bird, and adapted itself readily to its new surroundings. It did not cost much
to feed, it did not mind children; and though it had no
tricks, Mr. Poldero supposed it would soon pick up some.
The publicity of the Strawberry Phœnix Fund was now
most helpful. Almost every contributor now saved up
another half-crown in order to see the phœnix. Others,
who had not contributed to the fund, even paid double
to look at it on the five-shilling days.

But then business slackened. The phœnix was as handsome as ever, and as amiable; but, as Mr. Poldero said, it
hadn't got Udge. Even at popular prices the phœnix was
not really popular. It was too quiet, too classical. So people went instead to watch the antics of the baboons, or
to admire the crocodile who had eaten the woman.

One day Mr. Poldero said to his manager, Mr. Ramkin:

"How long since any fool paid to look at the phœnix?"

"Matter of three weeks," replied Mr. Ramkin.

"Eating his head off," said Mr. Poldero. "Let alone the
insurance. Seven shillings a week it costs me to insure that
bird, and I might as well insure the Archbishop of Can-
terbury."

"The public don't like him. He's too quiet for
them, that's the trouble. Won't mate nor nothing. And

I've tried him with no end of pretty pollies, ospreys, and Cochin-Chinas, and the Lord knows what. But he won't look at them."

"Wonder if we could swap him for a livelier one," said Mr. Poldero.

"Impossible. There's only one of him at a time."

"Go on!"

"I mean it. Haven't you ever read what it says on the label?"

They went to the phœnix's cage. It flapped its wings politely, but they paid no attention. They read:

"PANSY. *Phœnix phœnixissima formoisissima arabiana.* This rare and fabulous bird is UNIQUE. The World's Old Bachelor. Has no mate and doesn't want one. When old, sets fire to itself and emerges miraculously reborn. Specially imported from the East."

"I've got an idea," said Mr. Poldero. "How old do you suppose that bird is?"

"Looks in its prime to me," said Mr. Ramkin.

"Suppose," continued Mr. Poldero, "we could somehow get him alight? We'd advertise it beforehand, of course, work up interest. Then we'd have a new bird, and a bird with some romance about it, a bird with a life-story. We could sell a bird like that."

Mr. Ramkin nodded.

"I've read about it in a book," he said. "You've got to give them scented woods and what not, and they build a nest and sit down on it and catch fire spontaneous. But they won't do it till they're old. That's the snag."

THE PHŒNIX

"Leave that to me," said Mr. Poldero. "You get those scented woods, and I'll do the ageing."

It was not easy to age the phœnix. Its allowance of food was halved, and halved again, but though it grew thinner its eyes were undimmed and its plumage glossy as ever. The heating was turned off; but it puffed out its feathers against the cold, and seemed none the worse. Other birds were put into its cage, birds of a peevish and quarrelsome nature. They pecked and chivied it; but the phœnix was so civil and amiable that after a day or two they lost their animosity. Then Mr. Poldero tried alley cats. These could not be won by good manners, but the phœnix darted above their heads and flapped its golden wings in their faces, and daunted them.

Mr. Poldero turned to a book on Arabia, and read that the climate was dry. "Aha!" said he. The phœnix was moved to a small cage that had a sprinkler in the ceiling. Every night the sprinkler was turned on. The phœnix began to cough. Mr. Poldero had another good idea. Daily he stationed himself in front of the cage to jeer at the bird and abuse it.

When spring was come, Mr. Poldero felt justified in beginning a publicity campaign about the ageing phœnix. The old public favourite, he said, was nearing its end. Meanwhile he tested the bird's reactions every few days by putting a few tufts of foul-smelling straw and some strands of rusty barbed wire into the cage, to see if it were interested in nesting yet. One day the phœnix began turning over the straw. Mr. Poldero signed a contract for the film rights. At last the hour seemed ripe. It was a fine Saturday evening in May. For some weeks the public interest in the ageing phœnix had been working up, and the admission charge had risen to five shillings. The enclosure was thronged. The lights and the cameras were trained on the cage, and a loud-speaker proclaimed to the audience the rarity of what was about to take place.

"The phœnix," said the loud-speaker, "is the aristocrat of bird-life. Only the rarest and most expensive specimens of oriental wood, drenched in exotic perfumes, will tempt him to construct his strange love-nest."

Now a neat assortment of twigs and shavings, strongly scented, was shoved into the cage.

"The phœnix," the loud-speaker continued, "is as capricious as Cleopatra, as luxurious as la du Barry, as heady as a strain of wild gypsy music. All the fantastic pomp and passion of the ancient East, its languorous magic, its subtle cruelties . . ."

"Lawks!" cried a woman in the crowd. "He's at it!"

A quiver stirred the dulled plumage. The phœnix turned its head from side to side. It descended, staggering, from its perch. Then wearily it began to pull about the twigs and shavings.

The cameras clicked, the lights blazed full on the cage. Rushing to the loud-speaker Mr. Poldero exclaimed:

"Ladies and gentlemen, this is the thrilling moment the world has breathlessly awaited. The legend of centuries is materializing before our modern eyes. The phœnix . . ."

The phœnix settled on its pyre and appeared to fall asleep.

The film director said:

"Well, if it doesn't evaluate more than this, mark it instructional."

At that moment the phœnix and the pyre burst into flames. The flames streamed upwards, leaped out on every side. In a minute or two everything was burned to ashes, and some thousand people, including Mr. Poldero, perished in the blaze.

WILLIAM MARCH

Aesop's Last Fable

Aesop, the messenger of King Croesus, finished his business with the Delphians, and went back to the tavern where he had taken lodgings. Later, he came into the taproom where a group of Delphians were drinking. When they realized who he was, they crowded about him. "Tell us," they began, "is Croesus as rich as people say?"

Aesop, since the habit of speaking in fables was so strongly fixed in him, said, "I can best answer your question with a parable, and it is this: The animals gathered together to crown their richest member king. Each animal in turn stated what he possessed, and it was soon apparent that the lion had the largest hunting preserves, the bee the most honey, the squirrel the largest supply of acorns, and so on; but when the voting began, the difficulty of arriving at a decision was plain to all, for to the bee, the nuts that represented the wealth of the squirrel were of no consequence; to the lion, the hay that the zebra and the buffalo owned was worthless; and the panther and the tiger set no value at all on the river that the crane and crocodile prized so highly."

Then Aesop called for his drink, looking into the faces of the Delphians with good-natured amusement. He said, "The moral of the fable is this: Wealth is an intangible thing, and its meaning is not the same to all men alike." The stolid Delphians looked at one another, and when the silence was becoming noticeable, one of them tried again: "How was the weather in Lydia when you left home?"

"I can best answer that question with another fable," said Aesop, "and it is this: During a rain storm, when the ditches were flooded and the ponds had overflowed their banks, a cat and a duck met on the road, and, wanting to make conversation, they spoke at the same instant. 'What a beautiful day this is,' said the delighted duck. 'What a terrible weather we're having,' said the disgusted cat."

Again the Delphians looked at one another, and again there was silence. "The moral of that tale," said Aesop, "is this: What pleases a duck, distresses a cat." He poured wine into his glass and leaned against the wall, well satisfied with the start he had made in instructing the barbarous Delphians. The Delphians moved uneasily in their seats, and after a long time, one of them said, "How long are you going to be here?"

"That," said Aesop, "can best be answered in the Fable

of the Tortoise, the Pelican, and the Wolf. You see, the pelican went to visit his friend the tortoise, and promised to remain as long as the latter was building his new house. Then one day as they were working together, with the tortoise burrowing and the pelican carrying away the dirt in his pouch, the wolf came on them unexpectedly, and——"

But Aesop got no farther, for the Delphians had surrounded him and were, an instant later, carrying him toward the edge of the cliff on which the tavern was built. When they reached it, they swung him outward and turned him loose, and Aesop was hurled to the rocks below, where he died. "The moral of what we have done," they explained later, "is so obvious that it needs no elaboration!"

ROBERT BENCHLEY

Animal Stories

HOW GEORGIE DOG GETS THE RUBBERS ON THE GUEST ROOM BED

Old Mother Nature gathered all her little pupils about her for the daily lesson in "How the Animals Do the Things They Do." Every day Waldo Lizard, Edna Elephant, and Lawrence Walrus came to Mother Nature's school, and there learned all about the useless feats performed by their brother and sister animals.

"Today," said Mother Nature, "we shall find out how it is that Georgie Dog manages to get the muddy rubbers from the hall closet, up the stairs, and onto the nice white bedspread in the guest room. You must be sure to listen carefully and pay strict attention to what Georgie Dog says. Only, don't take too much of it seriously, for Georgie is an awful liar."

And, sure enough, in came Georgie Dog, wagging his

entire torso in a paroxysm of camaraderie, although everyone knew that he had no use for Waldo Lizard.

"Tell us, Georgie," said Mother Nature, "how do you do your clever work of rubber-dragging? We would like so much to know. Wouldn't we, children?"

"No, Mother Nature!" came the instant response from the children.

So Georgie Dog began.

"Well, I'll tell you; it's this way," he said, snapping at a fly. "You have to be very niftig about it. First of all, I lie by the door of the hall closet until I see a nice pair of muddy rubbers kicked into it."

"How muddy ought they to be?" asked Edna Elephant, although little enough use she would have for the information.

"I am glad that you asked that question," replied Georgie. "Personally, I like to have mud on them about the consistency of gurry—that is, not too wet—because then it will all drip off on the way upstairs, and not so dry that it scrapes off on the carpet. For we must save it all for the bedspread, you know.

"As soon as the rubbers are safely in the hall closet, I make a great deal of todo about going into the other room, in order to give the impression that there is nothing interesting enough in the hall to keep me there. A good, loud yawn helps to disarm any suspicion of undue excitement. I sometimes even chew a bit of fringe on the sofa and take a scolding for it—anything to draw attention from the rubbers. Then, when everyone is at dinner, I sneak out and drag them forth."

"And how do you manage to take them both at once?" piped up Lawrence Walrus.

"I am glad that you asked that question," said Georgie, "because I was trying to avoid it. You can never guess what the answer is. It is very difficult to take two at a time, and so we usually have to take one and then go back and get the other. I had a cousin once who knew a grip which could be worked on the backs of overshoes, by means of which he could drag two at a time, but he was an exceptionally fine dragger. He once took a pair of rubber boots from the barn into the front room, where a wedding was taking place, and put them on the bride's train. Of course, not one dog in a million could hope to do that.

"Once upstairs, it is quite easy getting them into the guest room, unless the door happens to be shut. Then what do you think I do? I go around through the bathroom window onto the roof, and walk around to the sleeping porch, and climb down into the guest room that way. It is a lot of trouble, but I think that you will agree with me that the results are worth it.

"Climbing up on the bed with the rubbers in my mouth is difficult, but it doesn't make any difference if some of the mud comes off on the side of the bedspread. In fact, it all helps in the final effect. I usually try to smear them around when I get them at last on the spread, and if I can leave one of them on the pillow, I feel that it's a pretty fine little old world, after all. This done, and I am off."

And Georgie Dog suddenly disappeared in official

pursuit of an automobile going eighty-five miles an hour.

"So now," said Mother Nature to her little pupils, "we have heard all about Georgie Dog's work. To-morrow we may listen to Lillian Mosquito tell how she makes her voice carry across a room."

HOW LILLIAN MOSQUITO PROJECTS HER VOICE

All the children came crowding around Mother Nature one cold, raw afternoon in summer, crying in unison:

"Oh, Mother Nature, you promised us that you would tell us how Lillian Mosquito projects her voice! You promised that you would tell us how Lillian Mosquito projects her voice!"

"So I did! So I did!" said Mother Nature, laying down an oak, the leaves of which she was tipping with scarlet for the fall trade. "And so I will! So I will!"

At which Waldo Lizard, Edna Elephant and Lawrence Walrus jumped with imitation joy, for they had hoped to have an afternoon off.

Mother Nature led them across the fields to the piazza of a clubhouse on which there was an exposed ankle belonging to one of the members. There, as she had expected, they found Lillian Mosquito having tea.

"Lillian," called Mother Nature, "come off a minute. I have some little friends here who would like to know how it is that you manage to hum in such a manner as to give the impression of being just outside the ear of a person in bed, when actually you are across the room."

"Will you kindly repeat the question?" said Lillian, flying over to the railing.

"We want to know," said Mother Nature, "how it is that very often, when you have been fairly caught, it turns out that you have escaped without injury."

"I would prefer to answer the question as it was first put," said Lillian.

So Waldo Lizard, Edna Elephant and Lawrence Walrus, seeing that there was no way out, cried:

"Yes, yes, Lillian, do tell us."

"First of all, you must know," began Lillian Mosquito, "that my chief duty is to annoy. Whatever else I do, however many bites I total in the course of the evening, I do not consider that I have 'made good' unless I have caused a great deal of annoyance while doing it. A bite, quietly executed and not discovered by the victim until morning, does me no good. It is my duty, and my pleasure, to play with him before biting, as you have often heard a cat plays with a mouse, tormenting him with apprehension and making him struggle to defend himself. . . . If I am using too long words for you, please stop me."

"Stop!" cried Waldo Lizard, reaching for his hat, with the idea of possibly getting to the ball park by the fifth inning.

But he was prevented from leaving by kindly old Mother Nature, who stepped on him with her kindly old heel, and Lillian Mosquito continued:

"I must therefore, you see, be able to use my little

voice with great skill. Of course, the first thing to do is to make my victim think that I am nearer to him than I really am. To do this, I sit quite still, let us say, on the footboard of the bed, and, beginning to hum in a very, very low tone of voice, increase the volume and raise the pitch gradually, thereby giving the effect of approaching the pillow.

"The man in bed thinks that he hears me coming toward his head, and I can often see him, waiting with clenched teeth until he thinks that I am near enough to swat. Sometimes I strike a quick little grace-note, as if I were right above him and about to make a landing. It is great fun at such times to see him suddenly strike himself over the ear (they always think that I am right at their ear), and then feel carefully between his finger tips to see if he has caught me. Then, too, there is always the pleasure of thinking that perhaps he has hurt himself quite badly by the blow. I have often known victims of mine to deafen themselves permanently by jarring their eardrums in their wild attempts to catch me."

"What fun! What fun!" cried Edna Elephant. "I must try it myself just as soon as ever I get home."

"It is often a good plan to make believe that you have been caught after one of the swats," continued Lillian Mosquito, "and to keep quiet for a while. It makes him cocky. He thinks that he has demonstrated the superiority of man over the rest of the animals. Then he rolls over and starts to sleep. This is the time to begin work on him again. After he has slapped himself all over the face and head, and after he has put on the light and made a search of the room and then gone back to bed to think up some new words, that is the time when I usually bring the climax about.

"Gradually approaching him from the right, I hum loudly at his ear. Then, suddenly becoming quiet, I fly silently and quickly around to his neck. Just as he hits himself on the ear, I bite his neck and fly away. And, *voilà*, there you are!"

"How true that is!" said Mother Nature. "*Voilà*, there we are! . . . Come, children, let us go now, for we must be up bright and early to-morrow to learn how Lois Hen scratches up the beets and Swiss chard in the gentlemen's gardens."

RING LARDNER

Cinderella

Once upon a time they was a prominent clubman that killed his wife after a party where she doubled a bid of four diamonds and the other side made four odd, giving them game and a $26.00 rubber. Well, she left him a daughter who was beginning to run absolutely hog wild and he couldn't do nothing with her, so he married again, this time drawing a widow with two gals of her own, Patricia and Micaela.

These two gals was terrible. Pat had a wen, besides which they couldn't nobody tell where her chin started and her neck left off. The other one, Mike, got into a brawl the night she come out and several of her teeth had came out with her. These two gals was impossible.

Well, the guy's own daughter was a pip, so both her

294

stepmother and the two stepsisters hated her and made her sleep in the ashcan. Her name was Zelda, but they called her Cinderella on account of how the ashes and clinkers clang to her when she got up noons.

Well, they was a young fella in the town that to see him throw his money around, you would of thought he was the Red Sox infield trying to make a double play. So everybody called him a Prince. Finally he sent out invitations to a dance for just people that had dress suits. Pat and Mike was invited, but not Cinderella, as her best clothes looked like they worked in a garage. The other two gals made her help them doll up and they kidded her about not going, but she got partly even by garnisheeing their hair with eau de garlic.

Well, Pat and Mike started for Webster Hall in a bonded taxi and they hadn't much sooner than went when a little bit of an old dame stepped out of the kitchen sink and stood in front of Cinderella and says she was her fairy godmother.

"Listen," says Cinderella: "don't mention mother to me! I've tried two different kinds and they've both been a flop!"

"Yes, but listen yourself," says the godmother: "wouldn't you like to go to this here dance?"

"Who and the h--l wouldn't!" says Cinderella.

"Well, then," says the godmother, "go out in the garden and pick me a pumpkin."

"You're pie-eyed," was Cinderella's criticism, but anyway she went out and got a pumpkin and give it to the old dame and the last named touched it with her wand and it turned into a big, black touring car like murderers rides in.

Then the old lady made Cinderella go to the mouse-trap and fetch her six mice and she prodded them with her wand and they each became a cylinder. Next she had her bring a rat from the rat trap and she turned him into a big city chauffeur, which wasn't hardly any trouble.

"Now," says the godmother, "fetch me a couple lizards."

So Cinderella says, "What do you think this is, the zoo?" But she went in the living-room and choose a couple lizards off the lounge and the old lady turned them into footmen.

The next thing the old godmother done was tag Cinderella herself with the wand and all of a sudden the gal's rags had become a silk evening gown and her feet was wrapped up in a pair of plate-glass slippers.

"How do you like them slippers?" asked the old dame.

"Great!" says Cinderella. "I wished you had of made the rest of my garments of the same material."

"Now, listen," says the godmother: "don't stay no later than midnight because just as soon as the clock strikes twelve, your dress will fall off and your chauffeur and so forth will change back into vermin."

Well, Cinderella clumb in the car and they was about to start when the chauffeur got out and went around back of the tonneau.

"What's the matter?" says Cinderella.

"I want to be sure my tail-light was on," says the rat.

Finally they come to Webster Hall and when Cinderella entered the ballroom everybody stopped dancing and looked at her pop-eyed. The Prince went nuts and wouldn't dance with nobody else and when it come time for supper he got her two helpings of stewed rhubarb and liver and he also had her laughing herself sick at the different wows he pulled. Like for instance they was one occasion when he looked at her feet and asked her what was her shoes made of.

"Plate glass," says Cinderella.

"Don't you feel no pane?" asked the Prince.

Other guests heard this one and the laughter was general.

But finally it got to be pretty near twelve o'clock and Cinderella went home in her car and pretty soon Pat and Mike blowed in and found her in the ashcan and told her about the ball and how the strange gal had come and stole the show. "We may see her again tomorrow night," says Pat.

"Oh," says Cinderella, "is they going to be another ball?"

"Why, no, you poor sap!" says Mike. "It's a Marathon."

"I wished I could go," says Cinderella. "I could if you would leave me take your yellow dress."

The two stepsisters both razzed her, little wreaking that it was all as she could do to help from laughing outright.

297

Anyway they both went back to the dance the next night and Cinderella followed them again, but this time the gin made her drowsy and before she realized it, the clock was striking twelve. So in her hurry to get out she threw a shoe and everybody scrambled for it, but the Prince got it. Meanwhile on account of it being after midnight, the touring car had disappeared and Cindy had to walk home and her former chauffeur kept nibbling at her exposed foot and annoying her in many other ways.

Well, the Prince run a display ad the next morning that he would marry the gal who could wear the shoe and he sent a trumpeter and a shoe clerk to make a house to house canvass of Greater New York and try the shoe on all the dames they could find and finally they come to the clubman's house and the trumpeter woke up the two stepsisters for a fitting. Well, Pat took one look at the shoe and seen they was no use. Mike was game and tried her best to squeeze into it, but flopped, as her dogs was also mastiffs. She got sore and asked the trumpeter why hadn't he broughten a shoe horn instead of that bugle. He just laughed.

All of a sudden him and the shoe clerk catched a glimpse of Cinderella and seen that she had small feet and sure enough, the slipper fitted her and they run back to the Prince's apartment to tell him the news.

"Listen, Scott," they says, for that was the Prince's name: "we have found the gal!"

So Cinderella and the Prince got married and Cinderella forgive her two stepsisters for how they had treated her and she paid a high-price dentist to fix Mike up with a removable bridge and staked Pat to a surgeon that advertised a new, safe method of exterminating wens.

That is all of the story, but it strikes me like the plot—with the poor, ragged little gal finally getting all the best of it—could be changed around and fixed up so as it would make a good idear for a play.

FOOLING

H. L. CHACE

Ladle Rat Rotten Hut

(Heresy ladle furry starry toiling udder warts-warts welches attar girdle deferent firmes once inner regional verging) Wants pawn term dare worsted ladle gull hoe lift wetter murder inner ladle cordage honor itch offer lodge, dock, florist. Disk ladle gull orphan worry putty ladle rat cluck wetter ladle rat hut, an fur disk raisin pimple colder Ladle Rat Rotten Hut.

Wan moaning Ladle Rat Rotten Hut's murder colder inset, "Ladle Rat Rotten Hut, heresy ladle basking winsome burden barter an shirker cockles. Tick disk ladle basking tutor cordage offer groin-murder hoe lifts honor udder site offer florist. Shaker lake! Dun stopper laundry wrote! Dun stopper peck floors! Dun daily-doily inner florist, an yonder nor sorghum stenches, dun stopper torque wet strainers!"

"Hoe-cake, murder," resplendent Ladle Rat Rotten Hut, an tickle ladle basking an stuttered oft.

Honor wrote tutor cordage offer groin-murder, Ladle Rat Rotten Hut mitten anomalous woof.

"Wail, wail, wail!" set disk wicket woof, "Evanescent Ladle Rat Rotten Hut! Wares are putty ladle gull goring wizard ladle basking?"

"Armor goring tumor groin-murder's," reprisal ladle gull. "Grammar's seeking bet. Armor ticking arson burden barter an shirker cockles."

"O hoe! Heifer gnats woke," setter wicket woof, butter taught tomb shelf, "Oil tickle shirt court tutor cordage offer groin-murder. Oil ketchup wetter letter, an den —O bore!"

Soda wicket woof tucker shirt court, an whinny retched a cordage offer groin-murder, picked inner windrow, an sore debtor pore oil worming worse lion inner bet. Inner flesh, disk abdominal woof lipped honor bet, paunched honor pore oil worming, an garbled erupt. Den disk ratchet ammonol pot honor groin-murder's nut cup an gnat-gun, any curdled ope inner bet.

Inner ladle wile, Ladle Rat Rotten Hut a raft attar cordage, an ranker dough ball. "Comb ink, sweat hard," setter wicket woof, disgracing is verse.

Ladle Rat Rotten Hut entity bet rum, an stud buyer groin-murder's bet.

"O Grammar!" crater ladle gull historically, "Water bag icer gut! A nervous sausage bag ice!"

"Battered lucky chew whiff, sweat hard," setter bloat-Thursday woof, wetter wicket small honors phase.

"O, Grammar, water bag noise! A nervous sore suture anomalous prognosis!"

"Battered small your whiff, doling," whiskered dole woof, ants mouse worse waddling.

"O Grammar, water bag mouser gut! A nervous sore suture bag mouse!"

Daze worry on-forger-nut ladle gull's lest warts. Oil offer sodden, caking offer carvers an sprinkling otter bet, disk hoard-hoarded woof lipped own pore Ladle Rat Rotten Hut an garbled erupt.

MURAL: Yonder nor sorghum stenches shut ladle gulls stopper torque wet strainers.

JOSH BILLINGS

On Courting

Courting is a luxury, it is sallad, it is ise water, it is a beveridge, it is the pla spell ov the soul. The man who has never courted haz lived in vain; he haz bin a blind man amung landskapes and waterskapes; he has bin a deff man in the land ov hand orgins, and by the side ov murmuring canals. Courting iz like 2 little springs ov soft water that steal out from under a rock at the fut ov a mountain and run down the hill side by side singing and dansing and spatering each uther, eddying and frothing and kaskading, now hiding under bank, now full ov sun and now full ov shadder, till bimeby tha jine and then tha go slow. I am in faver ov long courting; it gives the parties a chance to find out each uther's trump kards, it is good exercise, and is jist as innersent as 2 merino lambs. Courting is like strawberries and cream, wants tew be did slow, then yu git the flaver. I hav saw folks

306

git ackquainted, fall in luv, git marrid, settel down and git tew wurk, in 3 weeks from date. This is just the wa sum folks larn a trade, and akounts for the grate number ov almitey mean mechanicks, we hav and the poor jobs tha turn out.

Perhaps it is best i shud state sum good advise tew yung men, who are about tew court with a final view to matrimony, az it waz. In the fust plase, yung man, yu want tew git yure systen awl rite, and then find a yung woman who iz willing tew be courted on the square. The nex thing is tew find out how old she is, which yu kan dew bi asking her and she will sa that she is 19 years old, and this yu will find won't be far from out ov the wa. The nex best thing iz tew begin moderate; say onse evry nite in the week for the fust six months, increasing the dose as the pasheint seems to require it. It is a fust rate wa tew court the girl's mother a leetle on the start, for there iz one thing a woman never despizes, and that iz, a leettle good courting, if it is dun strikly on the square. After the fust year yu will begin to be well ackquainted and will begin tew like the bizzness. Thare is one thing I alwus advise, and that iz not to swop fotograffs oftener than onse in 10 daze unless yu forgit how the gal looks.

Okasionally yu want tew look sorry and draw in yure wind az tho yu had pain, this will set the gal tew teazing yu tew find out what ails yu. Evening meetings are a good thing tu tend, it will keep yure religgion in tune; and then if the gal happens tew be thare, bi acksident, she kan ask yu tew go hum with her.

Az a ginral thing i wouldn't brag on uther gals mutch when i waz courting, it mite look az tho yu knu tew mutch. If yu will court 3 years in this wa, awl the time on the square, if yu don't sa it iz a leettle the slikest time in yure life, yu kan git measured for a hat at my expense, and pa for it. Don't court for munny, nor buty, nor relashuns, theze things are jist about az onsartin as the kerosene ile refining bissness, liabel tew git out ov repair and bust at enny minnit.

Court a gal for fun, for the luv yu bear her, for the vartue and bissness thare is in her; court her for a wife and for a mother, court her az yu wud court a farm—for the strength ov the sile and the parfeckshun ov the title; court her az tho she want a fule, and yu a nuther; court her in the kitchen, in the parlor, over the wash-tub, and at the pianner; court this wa, yung man, and if yu don't git a good wife and she don't git a good hustband, the falt won't be in the courting.

Yung man, yu kan rely upon Josh Billings, and if yu kant make these rules wurk jist send for him and he will sho yu how the thing is did, and it shant kost yu a cent.

JOSH BILLINGS

Kissing Considered

"Man was made tew mourn," so warbled Burns, "and woman was made tew kiss," so warbles Billings. One ov these centiments haz bin alreddy immortalised, and the other i intend shall be as soon as the Legislater meets. I am not yet lusid how i shall bring the matter befoar that honorabil boddy; but i dew kno how the honorabel boddy feals on the subject, and how tha will act if ever tha hav a good chanse. To give a fertile and golden opinyun, upon kissing in the lump, and kissing in the detale, requires a man ov truth, and sum experiense in tasteing.

IN THE LUMP

Kissing iz one ov those fu things that is easier dun than deskribed; in fack, about the onla way tew deskribe it

well is tew do it well. It iz, without doubt, a verry an-
shunt enterprise; and judgeing from what we kno ov human natur in this latitude, it must hav struk Adam as a
good investment when he fust diskovered hiz wife. If
Adam didn't kiss Eve at sight he aint the man i take him
tew be; and if Eve didn't relish it, it must hav bin be-
kause it want well did. Thare iz one thing about kissing
in the lump, diffrent from the rest ov the fine arts and
that iz, it don't require enny eddikashun tew dew it; i
hav even thort that the more unedikated it waz did
(provided it didn't miss the mark) the more touching it
was tew behold. But kissing is a good deal like eating;
thare is not much fun (when a person iz hungry) in
standing by, and see it did bi anuther fellow, if it iz did
ever so well. It is one ov the cheapess and healthyess
luxurys ov the season, and don't sho enny disposishun
tew go out ov fashion, and will keep sweet in enny climate. Upon the whole, if yu examine kissing in the lump,
clussly, yu will be led tew exclaim: Fustly, that it iz as
easy tew have it did, az it is handy tew dew it. Sekundly,
that it is like Cowpers tea, it cures a man without corning
him; and, Thirdly, it is a frugal, highly consentrated,
and reverend luxury.

IN DETALE

When we cum tew thro oph glittering generalitys and
approach our subjeck in single file, it is then that the
divinitee ov the art seems to be spotted; and reveals tew
us awl the shades ov pomp and sirkumstanze, from the

sublime and tender, clear down tew the redikilus and tuff. Mother's kiss and little baby's kiss are az pure az the utterance ov angells; so is the artless kiss ov sister Mary and—couzin Fanny; but thare is one cold, blu, lean kiss, that alwus makes me shiver tew see. Two persons (ov the femail perswashun) who have witnesst a grate menny younger and more pulpy daze meet in sum publik plase, and not having saw each uther for 24 hours tha kiss immegiately; then tha talk about the weather, and the young man who preached yesterday, and then tha kiss immegiately, and then tha blush and laff at what tha sa tew each other, and kiss agin immegiately. I would not objeckt tew awl this if it want sich a waste ov swetness on the dessart air. I am willing tew be sworn that this kind ov kissing alwus puts me in minde ov two olde flints trieing tew strike fire. How different this from the konnubial kiss i witnesst last nite. I knu he wast a husband jist got back from a bizzness tower, bi hiz haste. He passt me at the korner below, and awl unexpected enkountered hiz wife, and as natral as the bee tew the flower, tha flu together. Thare want enny thing sentimental about that kiss; thare want enny thing criminal about it. It rang out on the air as clear as the challenge ov a perlice offiser—it filled a whole block. Thare want mutch preliminary about it neither, for it smashed a 50 dollar bonnett, and muxed up a barricade ov edging and frizzled tucker. It want the fust one, it waz tew well did for that. It want the sipping ov two trembling lovers, afraid ov the echo; it want studdyed out nor stolen, but it wast full ov honest ripeness and chastened struggle which made me hanker for—for, one oph from the same peace. Jist one more remark and I am thru. Thare is one kind ov kissing that has alwus been deeemd extra hazardous (on akount ov fire) and that is kissing yure naber's wife. Gitting the wife's consent don't seem tew make the matter enny the less risky.

MORAL.—Don't eat onions during the kissing seazon unless yu chew them well.

JAMES THURBER

Conversation Piece: Connecticut

It was our couple's day off, and since my wife was across the road calling on a neighbor when I got up, I was alone in the house, or thought I was. I had gone out to the refrigerator for my glass of orange juice, and had come back to the living room with it, muttering to myself about something that annoyed me—the inertia of Longstreet at Gettysburg, or the assumption that the concept of eternal bliss is a reward rather than a cruel and unusual punishment of the kind proscribed by the Constitution of the United States, or the tendency of strangers to write to me in longhand, signing their names in a scrawl that looks like "Djimn Hovnbg"—when the voice of a man broke in on my dark thoughts. He was sitting in a chair in a far corner of the living room, and he began in the middle of his own thoughts.

"You seem to be unaware that everybody is crazy," he

313

said, "owing to a fallout of finely powdered fruitcake over the planet. In every office building, in every place where many people gather, there should be a sign reading, 'DANGER! 10,000 DOLTS.'"

"Good morning," I said, sitting on the edge of a chair and sipping my juice.

"I made myself a drink," said my uninvited visitor.

"There's a time for drinking," I told him.

"I am nutty, too, because of the fruitcake," he went on. "All I can think of is nervous ailments. Have you heard of the roofer who got shingles from Sears, Roebuck? Or the steeplechase horse with the galloping jumps, or the jittery cupbearer of the gods who had the Hebe Jeebies, or the three-legged descendant of Lassie afflicted with the collie wobbles?"

"No," I said. "What worries *me* is that 'thing' has developed a past tense, rare in any noun, you must admit. It has become 'thung'—'thing,' 'thang,' 'thung,' as in 'sing,' 'sang,' 'sung.' The way into the past tenses is downhill and gloomy, but fortunately the road goes uphill on the other side of the dark valley, and we climb out of thung into thing again. This is because of the cyclical nature of the species. We all go from thing to thung and back again, depending on our individual cycles. Right now, you seem to be thunger than I am. There is a ring in the very sound of 'thing,' but 'thung' is a fungus. At the low point of the cycle, one's fingers become fungers. Our fingers never actually become all thumbs. That is pure imprecision of definition. During the fungers phase, a surgeon should not be permitted to use a scalpel, jugglers drop what they are juggling, and everyone is a danger to himself and to others."

"You miss the point," said my guest irritably. "The trouble is that we allowed 'think' to become 'thought.' When man developed the tendency to end certain past tenses with the letters 'ught,' he slowed down his own think processes. It was all right when 'drink' became 'drank,' for the word and the act still had bounce, but—"

"What worries you," I said, "is what may yet happen. You are afraid the day will come when a woman, in reporting a winking man to a policeman, will say, 'I want to report a man who wought at me.'"

"What?" asked my strange guest.

"'Wought,'" I repeated.

"I'll ask the questions," he said petulantly. "I'll also answer them. If I'm wrong, I'll correct myself."

I made a gesture with my empty glass, indicating that this was my house, not his. "There was no reason for 'fight' to become 'fought,'" I said. "There was a time when a man was knighted for fighting, not knought because he had fought. The great good place, the lighted place, has become the lought place, so close to lost that our last link with light is—"

"You go around in tiny circles," he said, and he crossed to where I keep my liquor and made himself another highball. On his way back to his chair, he picked up a book from an end table and waved it at me. "This book was bought," he said. "Where did you bink it?"

"What makes you think I did bink it?" I demanded. "Maybe what I did was bight it."

"We are both wrong," my visitor said. "There's an inscription in this book, proving that you did not bink it or bight it. It was given to you."

"Logic is too big to apply to little matters, or mutters," I said. "We are getting into insemantics, or the meaninglessness of meaninglessness. There are three monsters one must avoid—the Loch Ness monster, the togetherness monster, and the meaninglessness monster. Any minute now you'll say that the hope of the world, or of the word, lies in turning everything that ends in 'ouse' into 'ice'—in the plural, that is."

"What are you yammering about now?" he demanded.

"I am referring to mouse and mice," I said stiffly. "Why, of all the hice in this town, did you have to wander into mine?"

"Not long ago," he began, paying no attention to what I had said, "you wrote, or wrought, an article—it sounded wrought to me—in which you said that 'evening' was a lovely word of two syllables, never three, and then a woman who proudly described herself as disagreeable wrought you a letter in which she maintained that if most people called it 'cat,' then 'evening' would properly *become* 'cat.' "

"I don't know how you know about the lady's letter," I said.

"I know you like a bought book, brother," he said impatiently. "You replied to her letter and then tore up your reply. Yet you made one excellent point. I refer to your bringing up the artillery of music and poetry, har-

monics and metre and melody, against those persons—
those monsters of mindlessness—who believe that
proper English usage should be determined by a majority vote, as in the elections of the late President Harding
and Governor Long, of Louisiana."

"Thank you," I said. "No, let me mix this one for you."
I took his glass and carried it to the bar. "I have the vanity to believe I did get over, in my letter to the lady, one
telling thrust. I wrote, 'Sunset and cat star, and one clear
scat for you.'"

"Excellent, excellent," he said jovially. "Why didn't
you send the letter?"

For answer, I quoted a line from Landor. "'I strove
with none, for none was worth my strife,'" I said.

"Don't brag," he told me. "It is mainly with those not
worth our strife that we strive. The chances of winning
are better. Why don't you put a record on your Magna-
vox there? Something instrumental, maybe. Get away
from words for a while."

"It's no use," I said. "When I play music, I think of music. I mean the word 'music.' Have you ever tried rearranging the letters of that word, in an effort to arrive at
a group that doesn't make you ill?"

"Why should I?" he asked uneasily. "Life is hard
enough when one is feeling well."

"The word is icsum and mucsi," I said. "It is also musci
and scumi. If you say 'Sicum!' your dog starts barking at
nothing, and if you say 'Sucim,' the pigs in the barnyard
begin squealing and grunting. 'Muics' is the cat's

miaow. Say 'miscu' and your fingers are fungers, say 'umsci' and the Russians are upon you. As for mucis— my God, are you ready for another drink already?"

"Yes, and make it double," he said. "When you turn words inside out, you turn your stomach upside down— don't you know that?"

"I know all about it," I said, fixing him a stiff one. "I often wish I could let words alone and not lie in bed rearranging 'Geneva' to get 'avenge,' or spelling 'repaid' backward, or—"

"Speaking of backward," he said, "you probably know that Red Grange becomes Der Egnarg. And which do you prefer for that Indian movie actress—Das Gupta or Sad Atpug?"

"I don't want any part of either one of them," I said sharply. I snatched his glass from him and took a long slug of the double Scotch just as my wife came into the room.

"Drinking already?" she demanded. "Do you realize it isn't noon yet?"

"I am trying to be a good host," I told her. "This gentleman fixed two drinks for himself, and then I made his next two."

"What gentleman?" she asked blankly.

I stood there a moment, holding my unexpected visitor's glass, and realized that he was no longer there. "He is gone," I said.

"You're the one that's gone," my wife retorted, "or will be if you finish that drink. Four drinks before breakfast! I'll scramble you a couple of eggs and make some

318

coffee right away." She whisked the glass away from me and hurried out into the kitchen.

"You dog," I said to the empty chair in the corner. "You got me into this."

I managed to eat a piece of toast and drink two cups of coffee, but I decided to skip the eggs. My wife shook her head at me. "It wasn't Scotch," I said defensively, "it was music." Then I went back to bed. I lay there for a while thinking of the Sesumarongi, a backward tribe but a tribe that is all around us.

MUNRO LEAF

Macbeth

Plenty of guys and dames have got themselves into jams by listening with too willing ears to phony fortunetellers. The stock market and the race tracks are piled high with the shirts, socks, and spare jewelry of these suckers, but this old-time, smash-hit play is about one block-headed Scotsman who tried to muscle his way up the ladder just 'cause three old hags put a bee in his best clan bonnet.

You'd think anybody named Mac-anything would be too canny to be taken in by any mumbo-jumbo boil-and-bubble what's-going-to-happen stuff, but I guess what threw him off was they didn't charge him any fee for their prophecy, and he couldn't let anything free go to waste.

Macbeth and his pal, Banquo, were walking home from a good battle they had just won for King Duncan of Scotland, when they stumbled across these three old witches. One of them sings out, "Hyah! Macbeth!" Number Two blabs up, "Boy, you're gonna get a new title and a raise in pay." And Number Three shakes a broomstick at him and says, "You ain't heard the half of it yet. You gonna be the head man himself. Big-shot King Macbeth. How you like them for prophecies?" Those weren't the exact words, but they're close enough for witch talk.

Macbeth he liked it fine, but old Banquo took his foot out of his mouth and said, "How 'bout me? Don't I get a piece of this?"

"You sure do, Brother Banquo," sing out the sisters. "You're gonna be the pappy, grandpappy, great-great-grandpappy, etc., of a whole fistful of kings."

Just then up pops a telegraph messenger boy from King Duncan, and Macbeth finds out that sure enough he's just been promoted the way Witch Two said he would. You could have blown him down with a bagpipe at first, but when he gets back to see King Dunc himself, he gets to thinking that that old gold crown would look pretty nice on his own bald spot and maybe them witches really had something there when they said he'd be next.

Well, time wagged its kilt and took a step forward to find King Duncan and his boys bedded down for the night in Macbeth's run-down castle. Mac's wife, Lady Macbeth, was really tough. She made a gangster's moll look like something off a daisy chain, and when she heard about what the witches said and there was old King Dunc pounding her best pillow, she starts in to

needle Mac into giving him the business. Mac didn't
think that would be hospitable-like, and she gets sore
and says, "O. K., you little wisp of highland heather. I'll
do it myself." But Mac gives in, and after she liquors up
the guards in the best B-Girl technique Mac goes in and
cools the king dead as a bowl of oatmeal.

Lady Mac smears the guards so they look as though
they done it.

Everybody wakes up in the morning and they all
screech, "Murder!" so Mac makes out he is so mad he
kills the guards himself personally, so they can't say
whether they did or didn't do it. Duncan's sons take it
on the lam, and the chiefs elect Mac the new king.

But don't you think he and Lady MacB. get any fun
out of it.

He invites his old pal Banquo to a party and hires a
couple of mobsters to rub him and his son out, so he
can't have all those king descendants the witches talked
about. The mobsters get Banquo, but they muff it on
the son and he scrams to safety. Mac sees Banquo's
ghost sitting in his chair, and from then on he has the
jitters bad.

Lady Mac starts walking in her sleep, washing her
hands all the time, and burbles about damned spots like
she was endorsing cleaning fluid, until she rubs herself
right out of this life.

Macbeth can't find any psychiatrists to help him, so
he bumps people off right and left just to quiet his
nerves, till all Scotland gets mad, and they finish him
and the play off in one swoop.

MORAL: *If you are worried about your future, stay out of drafts, get plenty of sleep, exercise, and green vegetables, but don't go around listening to gypsies or Rajpoo Swami, the Crystal Ball Gazer. It'll just tear you down.*

ARTHUR KOBER

Boggains in the Bronx

Bella looked at her watch, quickly drew her napkin across her mouth, pushed the plate away, and rose. Ma Gross saw her rise and frowned.

"Come on, Pa," said Bella. "Help me clear the table."

Mr. Gross had his newspaper propped up against a sugar bowl and was too deep in a news item to pay any attention to his daughter. The latter now started stacking the dishes.

"Come on, Ma," she said. "I'll wash the dishes and you can dry them."

"Look, look, how she rushes!" Mrs. Gross was obviously suspicious of such eager and unsolicited aid. "So who you rushing to see, Miss Hurry-Shmurry? Maybe you rushing to see President Rosenvelt, he's waiting donnstairs in the hall?"

Mrs. Gross's rasping voice managed to spear her husband. "Awways talk, talk, talk with the tongue," he shouted. "Give the poor tongue a couple minutes' rest!"

"Look who's talking!" Mrs. Gross curled her lip contemptuously as she addressed her husband. "He comes home fomm woik, puts by him the nose in newspaper, and now alluva sudden Mr. Boss, he's talking. Put better back the nose in newspaper, Mr. Boss."

"Aw, please help me with the dishes, will ya?" Bella pleaded. "Kitty Shapiro and her intended, Dr. Rappaport, they're coming here to pick me up. We're gonna take in a pickcha show."

Bella's parents suddenly came to life. Pa dropped the newspaper and began to empty the remains of the evening's dinner into one large platter. Ma carefully folded the napkins and placed them in the top drawer of the bureau.

"So is coming here Kitty's intendit, the docteh?" Mrs. Gross asked with great interest.

"The denttist!" Pa was more explicit.

"Where comes a fine boy like a denttist to Kitty Shapiro?" Ma wanted to know.

"What'sa metta with Kitty Shapiro?" Mr. Gross didn't like or dislike Kitty—he hardly knew her, but because he habitually challenged anything his wife said, he found himself in the position of defending his daughter's friend. "A nice girl, Kitty."

"Eh, she ain't so extra," his wife said, disparagingly. "She got no shape, she got no good looks, and still in all she's engaged. She got luck, that's all."

Bella removed the fruit bowl from the mantelpiece and took it into the kitchen. The bowl was a prize Mrs. Gross had captured on one of her vacations. It bore the inscription, burnt on the surface, "Souvenir of Flugelman Manor, Catskill Mts., Greene Co., N. Y." She found some oranges in the icebox and placed these in the bowl.

Mrs. Gross took advantage of her daughter's momentary absence to ask a question which had long disturbed her and which she asked with annoying regularity. "What is with our Bella? Such a nice girl can't catch a fine, steady boy who knows how to put by a dolleh? She got a good head on her," she added, listing her daughter's virtues. "She's ten times smott like Kitty Shapiro, and still in all Kitty, she can catch a nice boy, a docteh——"

"A denttist-docteh," Pa interrupted.

"Awright, a denttist-docteh, and our Bella can't find a steady boy who makes heavy wages."

"Oh, so you're off on that again!" said Bella, coming out of the kitchen. No subject annoyed her as much as this discussion of a future husband. She felt that there was no hurry about getting married—she was twenty-one; besides, she was waiting until "Mr. Right," as she put it, came along. "Can't you find anything else to talk about?" she exclaimed indignantly.

"Get awready engaged and I'll stop talking," Ma said.

"Don't worry," replied Bella, placing the bowl and its yellow contents in the center of the table, "you'll get rid of me soon enough."

"Sure! To a *schlemiel* like Mexie Fine, a collitch boy he can't even make a living yet!"

Bella turned toward her mother and, assuming a very

haughty air, said, "I'll have you unnastann, Ma, that Max Fine and I are not keeping company."

This subject was too familiar to Pa to be of any interest. He gathered his newspaper and wandered out toward the bathroom.

"Max and I," Bella added, "we just happen to be platonic friends."

"Tonic-shmonic! Believe me, all I say is when I see my dutter married, I'll be happy like anything. When——" The doorbell interrupted Mrs. Gross.

Bella admitted Kitty Shapiro and Dr. Rappaport.

"Hello, Kitty." Mrs. Gross's greeting was very warm. "How's the Mamma filling? She's filling good?"

"She's O.K., thank you. Oh, this here is my intended, Dr. Rappaport." She turned to her intended and took his hand. "Come here, Butchkie," she said. "Dr. Rappaport, this here is Mrs. Gross, Billie's mother."

"Pleasta meetchoo, Mrs. Gross." He extended a hand. This surprised Ma Gross, who quickly wiped her hand on her apron before shaking his.

"Likewise," she said. Suddenly her eye was caught by the engagement ring Kitty was wearing. "Say, that's some beyoodyful stone!" Kitty extended her hand so that Mrs. Gross could make a closer examination. "A stone like that must cust heavy money, believe me."

"Dr. Rappaport got it wholesale fomm a patient of his, a jewlerer," Kitty explained. "Dincha, Butchkie?" She gave her fiancé a smile which expressed profound admiration and affection.

Pa Gross came out of the bathroom, his suspenders dangling from his trousers, his newspaper in his hand. "Oh, hello, Kitty," he said, becoming aware of his guests.

"Hello, Mr. Gross. Come here, Butchkie." Again Kitty took her fiancé's hand. "This here is Mr. Gross, Billie's father. Mr. Gross, this here is my intended, Dr. Rappaport."

"Hoddeya do, Mr. Gross?"

"I can't complain, thenks," replied Mr. Gross.

"Pa! Look at you!" Bella's eyes flashed as she pointed to his trailing suspenders.

"Excuse me, Docteh," Pa apologized. "Bella don't like to see by me the pents falling donn. It ain't stylish by her."

"And by you it's stylish?" Mrs. Gross jumped to the defense of her daughter. "Listen to him awready!"

"Gee, Billie." Kitty was now examining Bella's dress. "That's some nifty outfit you got on. Turn arounn." Bella did so. "Very chick, Billie. Very! Is it new?"

"I just got it last week. Max Fine gave me a card to the wholesaler's. Really like it?"

"I should say. It's very chick, Billie. Wear it in good health."

"Thank you."

Pa had sidled up to Dr. Rappaport. He tapped him on the shoulder and said, "Listen, Docteh. If you don't mind, I'd like to esk you something."

"Sure, go ahead."

"I got by me here in mouth a britch——" Pa opened

328

his mouth and pulled his lip up with his finger. Bella turned and looked at her father in dismay.

"Pa!" she cried. "Waddeya doing?"

"Look at him! This is nice! This is refined!" It was Ma who was now indignant.

"What'sa metta?" Pa asked, closing his mouth. "What I done so terrible?"

"The Docteh is here a guest in house," Ma explained. "He didn't come here fa no visits fa two and a half dolless."

"Oh, that's awright," said Dr. Rappaport generously. "I don't mind."

"Give him one of your cards, Butchkie." Kitty turned to the others. "I better start getting my future hubby some business now."

"What pickcha we seeing?" asked Bella, looking into the bureau mirror as she got into her coat.

"Oh, there's one down the street where Herbert Moshill takes off a doctor. I thought it would be good fa Dr. Rappaport to see it. You know," Kitty explained, "because they got things in common. Well, goodnight."

Goodnights were exchanged. Ma waited until Bella and her friends had gone before she expressed herself.

"You seen the stone Kitty got on?" she asked her husband.

"No," he said.

"Such a stone!" She shrugged her shoulders. "Such stones I don't even wish my worst enemies. In five-and-ten-cent stores you get such stones. Believe me, before our Bella wears such a ring, betta she stick single."

"A nice boy, the Docteh," Pa said abstractedly, turning the pages of the newspaper.

"What's so nice? A shrimp! A skinny boy! Comes a good wind and blows him right away. Nice! Before our Bella marries such a shrimp, betta she stick single."

Pa looked up from his newspaper in surprise. "You want Bella to stay single?"

"God fabbid!" Ma quickly replied. "Oney such boggains like that denttist, Kitty Shapiro can kipp!"

FRANK SULLIVAN

The Cliché Expert Testifies on Baseball

Q—Mr. Arbuthnot, you state that your grandmother has passed away and you would like to have the afternoon off to go to her funeral.

A—That is correct.

Q—You are an expert in the clichés of baseball—right?

A—I pride myself on being well versed in the stereotypes of our national pastime.

Q—Well, we'll test you. Who plays baseball?

A—Big-League baseball is customarily played by brilliant outfielders, veteran hurlers, powerful sluggers, knuckle-ball artists, towering first basemen, key moundsmen, fleet base runners, ace southpaws, scrappy little shortstops, sensational war vets, ex-college stars, relief artists, rifle-armed twirlers, dependable mainstays, doughty right-handers, streamlined backstops, power-hitting batsmen, redoubtable infielders, erstwhile Dodgers, veteran sparkplugs, sterling moundsmen, aging twirlers, and rookie sensations.

Q—What other names are rookie sensations known by?

A—They are also known as aspiring rookies, sensational newcomers, promising freshmen, ex-sandlotters, highly touted striplings, and youngsters who will bear watching.

Q—What's the manager of a baseball team called?

A—A veteran pilot. Or youthful pilot. But he doesn't manage the team.

Q—No? What does he do?

A—He guides its destinies.

Q—How?

A—By the use of managerial strategy.

Q—Mr. Arbuthnot, please describe the average major-league-baseball athlete.

A—Well, he comes in three sizes, or types. The first type is tall, slim, lean, towering, rangy, huge, husky, big, strapping, sturdy, handsome, powerful, lanky, raw-boned, and rugged.

Q—Quite a hunk of athlete.

A—Well, those are the adjectives usage requires for the description of the Type One, or Ted Williams, ballplayer.

Q—What is Type Two like?

A—He is chunky or stocky—that is to say, Yogi Berra.

Q—And the third?

A—The third type is elongated and does not walk. He is Ol' Satchmo, or Satchel Paige.

Q—What do you mean Satchmo doesn't walk?

A—Not in the sports pages, he doesn't. He ambles.

Q—You mentioned a hurler, Mr. Arbuthnot. What is a hurler?

A—A hurler is a twirler.

Q—Well, what is a twirler?

A—A twirler is a flinger, a tosser. He's a moundsman.

Q—Moundsman?

A—Yes. He officiates on the mound. When the veteran pilot tells a hurler he is to twirl on a given day, that is a mound assignment, and the hurler who has been told to twirl is the mound nominee for that game.

Q—You mean he pitches?

A—That is right. You have cut the Gordian knot.

Q—What's the pitcher for the other team called?

A—He is the mound adversary, or mound opponent, of the mound nominee. That makes them rival hurlers, or twirlers. They face each other and have a mound duel, or pitchers' battle.

Q—Who wins?

A—The mound victor wins, and as a result he is a mound ace, or ace moundsman. He excels on the mound, or stars on it. He and the other moundsmen on his team are the mound corps.

Q—What happens to the mound nominee who loses the mound duel?

A—He is driven off the mound.

333

FRANK SULLIVAN

Q—What do you mean by that?

A—He's yanked. He's knocked out of the box.

Q—What's the box?

A—The box is the mound.

Q—I see. Why does the losing moundsman lose?

A—Because he issues, grants, yields, allows, or permits too many hits or walks, or both.

Q—A bit on the freehanded side, eh? Where does the mound victor go if he pitches the entire game?

A—He goes all the way.

Q—And how does the mound adversary who has been knocked out of the box explain his being driven off the mound?

A—He says, "I had trouble with my control," or "My curve wasn't working," or "I just didn't have anything today."

Q—What happens if a mound ace issues, grants, yields, allows, or permits too many hits and walks?

A—In that case, sooner or later, rumors are rife. Either that or they are rampant.

Q—Rife where?

A—In the front office.

Q—What's that?

A—That's the place where baseball's biggies—also known as baseball moguls—do their asking.

Q—What do they ask for?

A—Waivers on erratic southpaw.

Q—What are these baseball biggies further known as?

A—They are known as the Shrewd Mahatma or as

334

Horace Stoneham, but if they wear their shirt open at the neck, they are known as Bill Veeck.

Q—What do baseball biggies do when they are not asking for waivers?

A—They count the gate receipts, buy promising rookies, sell aging twirlers, and stand loyally by Manager Durocher.

Q—And what does Manager Durocher do?

A—He guides the destinies of the Giants and precipitates arguments with the men in blue.

Q—What men in blue?

A—The umpires, or arbiters.

Q—What kind of arguments does Durocher precipitate?

A—Heated arguments.

Q—And the men in blue do what to him and other players who precipitate heated arguments?

A—They send, relegate, banish, or thumb them to the showers.

Q—Mr. Arbuthnot, how do you, as a cliché expert, refer to first base?

A—First base is the initial sack.

Q—And second base?

A—The keystone sack.

Q—What's third base called?

A—The hot corner. The first inning is the initial frame, and an inning without runs is a scoreless stanza.

Q—What is one run known as?

A—A lone run, but four runs are known as a quartet of tallies.

Q—What is a baseball?

A—The pill, the horsehide, the old apple, or the sphere.

Q—And what's a bat?

A—The bat is the willow, or the wagon tongue, or the piece of lumber. In the hands of a mighty batsman, it is the mighty bludgeon.

Q—What does a mighty batsman do?

A—He amasses runs. He connects with the old apple. He raps 'em out and he pounds 'em out. He belts 'em and he clouts 'em.

Q—Clouts what?

A—Circuit clouts.

Q—What are they?

A—Home runs. Know what the mighty batsman does to the mighty bludgeon?

Q—No. What?

A—He wields it. Know what kind of orgies he fancies?

Q—What kind?

A—Batting orgies. Slugfests. That's why his team pins.

Q—Pins what?

A—All its hopes on him.

Q—Mr. Arbuthnot, what is a runner guilty of when he steals home?

A—A plate theft.

Q—And how many kinds of baseball games are there?

A—Five main classifications: scheduled tussles, crucial contests, pivotal games, drab frays, and arc-light tussles.

Q—And what does the team that wins—

A—Sir, a baseball team never wins. It scores a victory. or gains one, or chalks one up. Or it snatches.

Q—Snatches what?

A—Victory from the jaws of defeat.

Q—How?

A—By a ninth-inning rally.

Q—I see. Well, what do the teams that chalk up victories do to the teams that lose?

A—They nip, top, wallop, trounce, rout, down, subdue, smash, drub, paste, trip, crush, curb, whitewash, erase, bop, slam, batter, check, hammer, pop, wham, clout, and blank the visitors. Or they zero them.

Q—Gracious sakes! Now I know why ballplayers are old at thirty-five.

A—Oh, that isn't the half of it. They do other things to the visitors.

Q—Is it possible?

A—Certainly. They jolt them, or deal them a jolt. They also halt, sock, thump, larrup, vanquish, flatten, scalp, shellac, blast, slaughter, K.O., mow down, topple, whack, pound, rap, sink, baffle, thwart, foil, maul, and nick.

Q—Do the losers do anything at all to the victors?

A—Yes. They bow to the victors. And they taste.

Q—Taste what?

A—Defeat. They trail. They take a drubbing, pasting, or shellacking. They are in the cellar.

Q—What about the victors?

A—They loom as flag contenders. They're in the first division.

Q—Mr. Arbuthnot, what is the first sign of spring?

A—Well, a robin, of course.

Q—Yes, but I'm thinking of our subject here. How about when the ballplayers go south for spring training?

A—Ballplayers don't go south for the spring training.

Q—Why, they do!

A—They do *not*. They wend their way southward.

Q—Oh, I see. Well, do all ballplayers wend their way southward?

A—No. One remains at home.

Q—Who is he?

A—The lone holdout.

Q—Why does the lone holdout remain at home?

A—He refuses to ink pact.

Q—What do you mean by that?

A—He won't affix his Hancock to his contract.

Q—Why not?

A—He demands a pay hike, or salary boost.

Q—From whom?

A—From baseball's biggies.

Q—And what do baseball's biggies do to the lone holdout?

A—They attempt to lure him back into the fold.

Q—How?

A—By offering him new contract.

Q—What does lone holdout do then?

A—He weighs offer. If he doesn't like it, he balks at terms. If he does like it, he inks pact and gets pay hike.

Q—How much pay hike?

A—An undisclosed amount in excess of.

Q—That makes him what?

A—One of the highest-paid baseball stars in the annals of the game, barring Ruth.

Q—What if baseball's biggies won't give lone holdout pay hike?

A—In that case, lone holdout takes pay cut, old salary, or job in filling station in home town.

Q—Now, when baseball players reach the spring training camp and put on their uniforms—

A—May I correct you again, sir? Baseball players do not put on uniforms. They don them.

Q—I see. What for?

A—For a practice session or strenuous workout.

Q—And why must they have a strenuous workout?

A—Because they must shed the winter's accumulation of excess avoirdupois.

Q—You mean they must lose weight?

A—You put it in a nutshell. They must be streamlined, so they plunge.

Q—Plunge into what?

A—Into serious training.

Q—Can't get into serious training except by plunging, eh?

A—No. Protocol requires that they plunge. Training season gets under way in Grapefruit and Citrus Leagues. Casey Stengel bars night life.

Q—Mr. Arbuthnot, what is the opening game of the season called?

A—Let me see-e-e. It's on the tip of my tongue. Isn't that aggravating? Ah, I have it—the opener! At the opener, fifty-two thousand two hundred and ninety-three fans watch Giants bow to Dodgers.

Q—What do those fifty-two thousand two hundred and ninety-three fans constitute?

A—They constitute fandom.

Q—And how do they get into the ballpark?

A—They click through the turnstiles.

Q—Now, then, Mr. Arbuthnot, the climax of the baseball season is the World Series, is it not?

A—That's right.

Q—And what is the World Series called?

A—It's the fall classic, or crucial contest, also known as the fray, the epic struggle, and the Homeric struggle. It is part of the American scene, like ham and eggs or pumpkin pie. It's a colorful event.

Q—What is it packed with?

A—Thrills. Drama.

Q—What kind of drama?

A—Sheer or tense.

Q—Why does it have to be packed with thrills and drama?

A—Because if it isn't, it becomes drab fray.

Q—Where does the fall classic take place?

A—In a vast municipal stadium or huge ballpark.

Q—And the city in which the fall classic is held is what?

A—The city is baseball mad.

Q—And the hotels?

A—The hotels are jammed. Rooms are at a premium.

Q—Tickets, also, I presume.

A—Tickets? If you mean the cards of admission to the fall classic, they are referred to as elusive Series ducats, and they *are* at a premium, though I would prefer to say that they are scarcer than the proverbial hen's teeth.

Q—Who attends the Series?

A—A milling throng, or great outpouring of fans.

Q—What does the great outpouring of fans do?

A—It storms the portals and, of course, clicks through the turnstiles.

Q—Causing what?

A—Causing attendance records to go by the board. Stands fill early.

Q—What else does the crowd do?

A—It yells itself hoarse. Pent-up emotions are released. It rides the men in blue.

Q—What makes a baseball biggie unhappy on the morning of a Series tussle?

A—Leaden skies.

Q—Who is to blame for leaden skies?

A—A character known to the scribes as Jupiter Pluvius, or Jupe.

Q—What does rain dampen?

A—The ardor of the fans.

341

Q—If the weather clears, who gets credit for that?

A—Another character, known as Old Sol.

Q—Now, the team that wins the Series—

A—Again, I'm sorry to correct you, sir. A team does not win a Series. It wraps it up. It clinches it.

Q—Well, then what?

A—Then the newly crowned champions repair to their locker room.

Q—What reigns in that locker room?

A—Pandemonium, bedlam, and joy.

Q—Expressed how?

A—By lifting youthful pilot, or his equivalent, to the shoulders of his teammates.

Q—In the locker room of the losers, what is as thick as a day in—I mean so thick you could cut it with a knife?

A—Gloom. The losers are devoid.

Q—Devoid of what?

A—Animation.

Q—Why?

A—Because they came apart at the seams in the pivotal tussle.

Q—What happens to the newly crowned champions later?

A—They are hailed, acclaimed, and fêted. They receive mighty ovations, boisterous demonstrations, and thunderous welcomes.

Q—And when those are over?

A—They split the Series purse and go hunting.

A—Mr. Arbuthnot, if a powerful slugger or mighty

batsman wields a mighty bludgeon to such effect that he piles up a record number of circuit clouts, what does that make him?

A—That is very apt to make him most valuable player of the year.

Q—And that?

A—That makes the kids of America look up to him as their hero.

Q—If most valuable player of the year continues the batting orgies that make the kids of America worship him, what then?

A—Then he becomes one of Baseball's Immortals. He is enshrined in Baseball's Hall of Fame.

Q—And after that?

A—Someday he retires and becomes veteran scout, or veteran coach, or veteran pilot. Or sports broadcaster.

Q—And then?

A—Well, eventually a memorial plaque is unveiled to him at the opener.

Q—Thank you, Mr. Arbuthnot. You have been most helpful. I won't detain you any longer, and I hope your grandmother's funeral this afternoon is a tense drama packed with thrills.

A—Thanks a lot. Goodbye now.

Q—Hold on a moment, Mr. Arbuthnot. Just for my own curiosity—couldn't you have said "thanks" and "goodbye" and let it go at that, without adding that "lot" and "now" malarkey?

A—I could have, but it would have cost me my title as a cliché expert.

FRANK SULLIVAN

The Busy Cliché Expert

Q—Mr. Arbuthnot, as an expert in the use of the cliché, you are a pretty busy man, aren't you?

A—Mr. Todd, you never spoke a truer word. Half the time I don't know whether I'm coming or going. Why, taking care of my livestock is a man's-size job in itself.

Q—Your livestock?

A—Yes. At least once every day I have to beard the lion, keep the wolf from the door, let the cat out of the bag, take the bull by the horns, count my chickens before they are hatched, shoe the wild mare, and see that the horse isn't put behind the cart or stolen before I lock the barn door. You'd think I'd be rather fed up on dumb animals by this time, wouldn't you?

Q—It would seem likely, I must admit.

A—Well, I'm not. The more I see of men, the more I

like dogs. I dislike men, and do you know how I dislike them?

Q—No. How?

A—Cordially, to put it bluntly. Do you know how I treat men?

Q—No.

A—With the contempt they so richly deserve.

Q—I'll warrant, Mr. Arbuthnot, that when you abandon, you abandon lightly.

A—I do, and when cares weigh on me, they weigh heavily. But I go my way. I grin and bear it.

Q—Well, I should think the chores you mentioned would be exercise enough for any man, Mr. Arbuthnot.

A—Oh, that isn't my *exercise*. That's my work.

Q—What do you do for exercise?

A—I play the game. And hang up records. I sail a little.

Q—A skiff?

A—No, under false colors. I box some, too, hitting below the belt, and I go in for dancing.

Q—What do you dance?

A—Attendance. I am also pretty good at putting my shoulder to the wheel, sticking to my guns, pulling up stakes, and champing at the bit.

Q—Doesn't all that exercise do you in?

A—I should say it does. Do you know how I sleep?

Q—How?

A—Like a log. When I don't sleep like a log, I sleep the sleep of the just. In other words, I no sooner hit the hay than I'm in the arms of Morpheus.

Q—What do you strike, Mr. Arbuthnot?

A—I strike bargains. I take advantage of propositions. I get down to business. And to brass tacks. I enclose herewith, I beg to remain, I suit the action to the word, and I laud to the skies.

Q—What do you speed?

A—I speed the day.

Q—What is it you settle, and what do you coin?

A—I settle hash and coin phrases. I beggar description. I report progress. And I have quite a temper, too. Be careful, Mr. Todd. If you poke fun at me, I'll fly off the handle, run amuck, and hit the ceiling.

Q—In that case, I'll let well enough alone and not poke fun at you.

A—I shudder to think what would happen if you did.

Q—What else do you do, Mr. Arbuthnot?

A—Well, let me see. I take into account, I go far enough, I look for support, and I deem it a privilege. I put in an appearance, I get the upper hand of, I bring the matter up, and I let the matter drop. I keep things humming, and I speak in terms of. I boast a finer collection, and feel under the weather. I think things out, and have it on good authority.

Q—Mr. Arb—

A—No, hear me out, Mr. Todd. You asked for it. I take to task, I knuckle down, I buck up, I level criticism, I venture to predict, I inject a serious note, I lose caste, I am up to no good, I am down on my luck, I pass the time of day, I go down to posterity, I cast into the discard—that reminds me, do you realize why I am not wearing any pearls?

Q—Why not?

A—Swine got 'em. I steal marches, I beg the question, I stand my ground, I turn over a new leaf. Why, Mr. Todd, I'm so busy I haven't got a minute I can call my own. I'm on the go from the moment I put in an appearance at the crack o' dawn. When I'm not playing second fiddle, I'm off to Newcastle with coals, or burying the hatchet, or attending to my oil business.

Q—You are in the oil business?

A—Well, rather, the troubled-waters business. I pour every Tuesday from four to six. You must not fail to come to my show, Mr. Todd.

Q—You are having a show?

A—Yes, indeed. Advance showing of the autumn white feathers. On top of all these things I have to watch my stones with eternal vigilance, to see that none are left unturned. Then I have my bones to pick, and my blacksmith shop.

Q—Good heavens, a blacksmith shop, too?

A—Oh, yes. I strike while the iron is hot. I find favor. I look high and low. I stir my stumps. I nod approval. I bid farewell. I drop like flies, and I bend every effort. I pocket my pride and amass a fortune. If I don't pay the supreme penalty, I'll emerge unscathed.

Q—What is it you mince?

A—Words. I mark time. I face music. I fill the bill, answer the purpose, say the word, and give pause. Do you

347

wonder I have to have a girl come in by the day to mind my P's and Q's for me?

Q—No, I do not. But, Mr. Arbuthnot, in spite of your versatility, there remains one thing you cannot do.

A—I admit it freely. I cannot make head or tail. But I can stew in my own juice. You must grant me that. And I can shake a leg, and take a firm grip on myself. I can flatter myself, refresh my memory, bury my nose in a book, and put my best foot forward. I can gird my loins, give my right eye, save my face, elevate an eyebrow, wear a rapt expression, shoot a glance, use my head, knit my brows, fall down on my job, purse my lips, see eye to eye, keep a stiff upper lip, and a civil tongue in my head, without batting an eyelash. That's not doing so badly for a cliché expert, Mr. Todd.

Q—I should say not, Mr. Arbuthnot. I'd certainly like to see you sometime when you are doing all those things together.

A—You mean at one and the same time. Well, rest assured, I can do them. I speak the truth, the whole truth, and nothing but the truth. Good gracious, is that thunder I heard?

Q—Yes, I think that was a peal of thunder.

A—Then I must hurry. Good-by.

Q—But why not rest here until the storm has passed, Mr. Arbuthnot?

A—I can't do it. I must go.

Q—But why?

A—I've got to brave the elements. Oh, dear, I hope the lightning isn't forked or greased. Good-by.

W. C. SELLAR AND R. J. YEATMAN

1066 and All That

[EXCERPTS]

CÆSAR INVADES BRITAIN

The first date[1] in English History is 55 B.C. in which year
Julius Cæsar (the *memorable* Roman Emperor) landed,
like all other successful invaders of these islands, at
Thanet. This was in the Olden Days, when the Romans
were top nation on account of their classical education,
etc.

Julius Cæsar advanced very energetically, throwing his
cavalry several thousands of paces over the River Flu-
men; but the Ancient Britons, though all well over mili-
tary age, painted themselves true blue, or *woad*, and

[1] For the other date see Chapter XI, *William the Conqueror*.

fought as heroically under their dashing queen, Woadicea, as they did later in thin red lines under their good queen, Victoria.

Julius Cæsar was therefore compelled to invade Britain again the following year (54 B.C., not 56, owing to the peculiar Roman method of counting), and having defeated the Ancient Britons by unfair means, such as battering-rams, tortoises, hippocausts, centipedes, axes and bundles, set the memorable Latin sentence, "Veni, Vidi, Vici," which the Romans, who were all very well educated, construed correctly.

The Britons, however, who of course still used the old pronunciation, understanding him to have called them "Weeny, Weedy and Weaky," lost heart and gave up the struggle, thinking that he had already divided them All into Three Parts.

CULTURE AMONG THE ANCIENT BRITONS

The Ancient Britons were by no means savages before the Conquest, and had already made great strides in civilization, e.g. they buried each other in long round wheelbarrows (agriculture) and burnt each other alive (religion) under the guidance of even older Britons called Druids or Eisteddfods, who worshipped the Middletoe in the famous Druidical churchyard at Stoke Penge.

The Roman Conquest was, however, a *Good Thing*, since the Britons were only natives at that time.

THE ROMAN OCCUPATION

For some reason the Romans neglected to overrun the country with fire and the sword, though they had both of these; in fact, after the Conquest they did not mingle with the Britons at all, but lived a semi-detached life in villas. They occupied their time for two or three hundred years in building Roman roads and having Roman baths; this was called the Roman Occupation, and gave rise to the memorable Roman law, "HE WHO BATHS FIRST BATHS FAST," which was a Good Thing, and still is. The Roman roads ran absolutely straight in all directions and all led to Rome. The Romans also built towns wherever they were wanted, and, in addition, a wall between England and Scotland to keep out the savage Picts and Scots.

This wall was the work of the memorable Roman Emperor Balbus and was thus called Hadrian's Wall. The Picts, or painted men,[1] were so called to distinguish them from the Britons. (See *supra, woad.*)

BRITAIN CONQUERED AGAIN

The withdrawal of the Roman legions to take part in Gibbon's Decline and Fall of the Roman Empire (due to a clamour among the Romans for pompous amusements such as bread and circumstances) left Britain de-

---

[1] e.g. The Black Watch, The Red Comyn and Douglases of all colours.

fenceless and subjected Europe to that long succession of Waves of which History is chiefly composed. While the Roman Empire was overrun by waves not only of Ostrogoths, Vizigoths and even Goths, but also of Vandals (who destroyed works of art) and Huns (who destroyed everything and everybody, including Goths, Ostrogoths, Vizigoths and even Vandals), Britain was attacked by waves of Picts (and, of course, Scots) who had recently learnt how to climb the wall, and of Angles, Saxons and Jutes who, landing at Thanet, soon overran the country with fire (and, of course, the sword).

IMPORTANT NOTE

The Scots (originally Irish, but by now Scotch) were at this time inhabiting Ireland, having driven the Irish (Picts) out of Scotland; while the Picts (originally Scots) were now Irish (living in brackets) and *vice versa*. It is essential to keep these distinctions clearly in mind (and *verce visa*).

HUMILIATION OF THE BRITONS

The brutal Saxon invaders drove the Britons westward into Wales and compelled them to become Welsh; it is now considered doubtful whether this was a Good Thing. Memorable among the Saxon warriors were Hengist and his wife (? or horse), Horsa. Hengist made himself King in the South. Thus Hengist was the first English King and his wife (or horse), Horsa, the first

English Queen (or horse). The country was now almost entirely inhabited by Saxons and was therefore re-named England, and thus (naturally) soon became C. of E. This was a Good Thing, because previously the Saxons had worshipped some dreadful gods of their own called Monday, Tuesday, Wednesday, Thursday, Friday and Saturday. . . .

ALFRED THE CAKE

King Alfred was the first Good King, with the exception of Good King Wenceslas, who, though he looked 4th, really came first (it is not known, however, what King Wenceslas was King of). Alfred ought never to be confused with King Arthur, equally memorable but probably non-existent and therefore perhaps less important historically (unless he did exist).

There is a story that King Arthur once burnt some cakes belonging to Mrs. Girth, a great lady of the time, at a place called Atheling. As, however, Alfred could not have been an Incendiary King *and* a Good King, we may dismiss the story as absurd, and in any case the event is supposed to have occurred in a marsh where the cakes would not have burnt properly. Cf. the famous lines of poetry about King Arthur and the cakes:

"Then slowly answered Alfred from the marsh—"

ARTHUR, LORD TENNYSON. . . .

ETHELREAD THE UNREADY. A WEAK KING

Ethelread the unready was the first Weak King of England and was thus the cause of a fresh Wave of Danes.

He was called the Unready because he was never ready when the Danes were. Rather than wait for him the Danes used to fine him large sums called Danegeld, for not being ready. But though they were always ready, the Danes had very bad memories and often used to forget that they had been paid the Danegeld and come back for it almost before they had sailed away. By that time Ethelread was always unready again.

WILLIAM I. A CONQUERING KING

In the year 1066 occurred the other memorable date in English History, viz. *William the Conqueror, Ten Sixty-six*. This is also called *The Battle of Hastings,* and was when William I (1066) conquered England at the Battle of Senlac (*Ten Sixty-six*).

When William the Conqueror landed he lay down on the beach and swallowed two mouthfuls of sand. This was his first conquering action and was in the South; later he ravaged the North as well.

The Norman Conquest was a Good Thing, as from this time onwards England stopped being conquered and thus was able to become top nation.

DOOMSDAY BOOK AND THE FORESTS

William next invented a system according to which everybody had to belong to somebody else, and everybody else to the King. This was called the Feutile System, and in order to prove that it was true he wrote a book called the *Doomsday Book,* which contained an inventory of all the Possessions of all his subjects; after reading the book through carefully William agreed with it and signed it, indicating to everybody that the Possessions mentioned in it were now his.

William the Conqueror (1066) is memorable for having loved an old stag as if it was his father, and was in general very fond of animals: he therefore made some very just and conquering laws about the Forests. One of these laws said that *all the forests and places which were not already Possessions belonged to the King* and that anyone found in them should *have his ears and legs cut off*—(these belonged to somebody else under the Feutile System, anyway)—and (if this had not already been done) should have his *eyes put out with red-hot irons;* after this the offender was allowed to fly the country.

Another very conquering law made by William I said that everyone had to go to bed at eight o'clock. This was called the Curfew and was a Good Thing in the end since it was the cause of Gray's Energy in the country churchyard (at Stoke Penge).

Although in all these ways William the Conqueror (1066) was a very strong king he was eventually stumbled to death by a horse and was succeeded by his son Rufus.

BLUFF KING HAL

Henry VIII was a strong King with a very strong sense of humour and VIII wives, memorable amongst whom were Katherine the Arrogant, Anne of Cloves, Lady Jane Austin and Anne Hathaway. His beard was, however, red.

In his youth Henry was fond of playing tennis and after his accession is believed never to have lost a set. He also invented a game called *"Bluff King Hal"* which he invited his ministers to play with him. The players were blindfolded and knelt down with their heads on a block of wood; they then guessed whom the King would marry next.

Cardinal Wolsey, the memorable homespun statesman and inventor of the Wolsack, played this game with Henry and won. But his successor, Cromwell (*not to be confused with Cromwell*), aftering winning on points, was disqualified by the King (who always acted as umpire), and lost.

In the opinion of Shakespeare (the memorable playwriter and Top Poet) his unexpected defeat was due to his failure to fling away ambition.

THE RESTORATION

Henry wanted the Pope to give him a divorce from his first wife, Katherine. He wanted this because

(*a*) she was Arrogant.

(*b*) he had married her a very long time ago.

(*c*) when she had a baby it turned out to be Broody Mary, and Henry wanted a boy.

(*d*) he thought it would be a Good Thing.

The Pope, however, refused, and seceded with all his

followers from the Church of England. This was called the Restoration.

HENRY'S PLAN FAILS

Curiously enough Henry had all the time had an idea about a new wife for himself called Anne, who, he thought, looked as if she would be sure to have a son. So when the Divorce was all over (or nearly) he married her; but he was wrong about Anne, because she had a girl too, in a way (see Elizabeth).

After this Henry was afraid his reign would not be long enough for any more divorces, so he gave them up and executed his wives instead.[1] He also got less interested in his wives and gave himself up to Diplomacy, spending a great deal of his time playing tennis, etc., with the young King of France in a field called the Field of the Crock of Gold.

END OF WOLSEY

Cardinal Wolsey, although (as is well known) he had not thought to shed a tear about all this, did ultimately shed a memorable one. Having thus fallen from grace (indeed he had already been discovered entertaining some Papal Bulls) Wolsey determined to make a Pilgrimage to Leicester Abbey, saying to himself: "If I had served my God as I have served my King, I would have

---

[1] NOTE.—All except Anne of Cloves, whom he had on approval from Belgium and sent back on discovering that she was really not a queen at all but a "fat mare with glanders."

been a Good Thing." Having thus acknowledged that he was a Bad Man, and being in due course arrived at the Abbey, Wolsey very pluckily expired after making a memorable speech to the Prior, beginning, "Father Abbot, I come to lay my bones among you, Not to praise them . . ."

THE MONASTERIES

One of the strongest things that Henry VIII did was about the Monasteries. It was pointed out to him that no one in the monasteries was married, as the Monks all thought it was still the Middle Ages. So Henry, who, of course, considered marrying a Good Thing, told Cromwell to pass a very strong Act saying that the Middle Ages were all over and the monasteries were all to be dissolved. This was called the Disillusion of the Monasteries.

THE BOSTON TEA-PARTY

One day when George III was insane he heard that the Americans never had afternoon tea. This made him very obstinate and he invited them all to a compulsory tea-party at Boston; the Americans, however, started by pouring the tea into Boston Harbour and went on pouring things into Boston Harbour until they were quite Independent, thus causing the United States. These were also partly caused by Dick Washington who defeated the English at Bunker's Hill ("with his little mashie," as he told his father afterwards).

The War with the Americans is memorable as being the only war in which the English were ever defeated, and it was unfair because the Americans had *the Allies* on their side. In some ways the war was really a draw, since England remained top nation and had the Allies afterwards, while the Americans, in memory of George III's madness, still refuse to drink tea and go on pouring anything the English send them to drink into Boston Harbour.

After this the Americans made Wittington President and gave up speaking English and became U.S.A. and Columbia and 100%, etc. This was a Good Thing in the end, as it was a cause of the British Empire, but it prevented America from having any more History.

FANTASY

NELSON S. BOND

Mr. Mergenthwirker's Lobblies

That year instead of the raise I damn well deserved they handed me the resounding title of Assistant City Editor, which meant that in addition to all my regular duties I was now responsible for the boners of the leg men. The only good break I got—if you'd call it that—was a "private office" with my name on the door. A dingy little hole just off the City Room, littered with last year's papers, and elaborately furnished with three overflow files from the Morgue, a swivel chair with one missing caster, and a yellow oak desk neatly scalloped with cigarette scars.

The faint tap on the door gave me a chance to get my feet off the desk before I shouted, "Come in!" The door swung open hesitantly and I saw him.

"Yes?" I said.

363

He stood there, blinking at me apologetically. A tiny man, hardly more than five foot one, or maybe two, with sand-colored hair and eyes. His clothing was plain but neat. And he was nervous. His hands twitched and wriggled constantly; darting in and out of pockets, brushing imaginary pieces of lint from his lapels, fumbling at his watch chain—always on the move. He was restless on the hoof, too—shuffling and fidgeting like he had termites in his trousers.

"Are—are you the man who takes the news?" he said.

"Who, me?" I answered elaborately. "Hell, yes! I'm the whole damned newspaper. I write the front page, lay out the ads, draw the cartoons, dig up the dirt, and sell papers on the street. Why, me and Bill Hearst—say, what do you want, anyway?"

His meek, twidgety gaze needled me. He stood there gaping as though my every word was Gospel. He jerked when I shot the question at him, and his pale eyes grew a little frightened.

"Why, I—I just wanted to tell you," he faltered, "that there's going to be a murder. This afternoon."

You meet all kinds of crackpots in this racket. I grinned at him sort of cheerfully, and nodded.

"Nice going, Mr.——"

"Mergenthwirker," he supplied. "Henry Mergenthwirker."

"Nice going, Mr. Mergenthwirker," I said. "You socked it right on the button that time. There *is* going to be a nice little murder this afternoon. Blood and brains all over everything. I'm just writing the headlines now. 'D.A. SLAYS MATE IN——' "

"Oh, no!" gasped the little man. "Not the District Attorney! Nothing like that! It's a girl up in the Bronx. A secretary named Hazel Johnson. She's going to be killed with a hammer!"

Honestly, that stopped me for a minute. He looked so darned sincere, his tiny hands fluttering around his coat lapels like bewildered moths; his tawny eyes wide and horrified. I thought: "Perhaps this is one of those psychological cases. A potential murderer compelled to confess his crime before it happens. Perhaps it *has* happened already, and he is trying to establish an alibi." I looked at him sharply.

"What's the gag?" I said. "You know the girl?"

"Me?" he said. "No, I never saw her in my life."

"Then how do you know about the murder?"

He smiled beatifically.

"*They* told me," he said. He gestured vaguely toward the door with one hand.

"They? Who?"

"My lobblies," explained the little man patiently. He pointed, proudly, I thought, toward the doorway again. "The big one's name is Japheth, but the little one is named after me. They tell me everything."

"Now, wait a minute, buddy," I said. "Are you trying to tell me there's somebody in this room besides you and me?"

He rinsed his hands in a gesture of quick despair.

"Oh, *don't* tell me you can't see them!" he wailed. "So *few* people can!" He stamped his foot in sudden exasperation. "It's all because they *will* change color! If they'd only stay *put!* But, no! They're forever——"

This time I got it. I rose swiftly and grabbed the little fellow by the shirt front.

"Listen, Mr. Whatsis," I told him. "I've got things to do, but worrying about your D.T.'s isn't one of them. Now, scram! And on the way out, tell the boys in the City Room that it went over like a lead balloon."

I pushed him, indignantly protesting, through the door, and waited until the pit-a-pat of his footsteps disappeared down the hallway. Then I strolled out into the City Room, with one eye peeled for the grins. A couple of the boys were matching nickels over by Duff Godshall's desk. I sauntered over carelessly.

"O.K., boys," I said. "Let's have the wisecracks!"

"Tails!" said Duff. He took a nickel off the back of each of the other fellows' hands; then looked at me curiously. "Wisecracks?"

"I suppose none of you boys ever heard tell of a guy named Mergenthwirker?" I asked caustically.

Three heads shook in unison.

"It's a gag," guessed Bill McGhee. "Early in the day to start drinking, Len."

"Oh, skip it!" I said wearily. "Anyway, it didn't work, in case you're interested. Come on, who's matching who in this game?"

I had just pulled a couple of nickels from my vest

pocket when the boss shoved open his door and let out a blat to high heaven.

"Hawley! Godshall! Get Maguire and light out for the Bronx. There's a hammer killing up there! A broad named Johnson!"

The funny part about it was that there was no mystery connected with this hammer job. They caught the guilty man an hour after they found the body, and he confessed right off the bat. What I mean is, there wasn't one thing to connect my nutsack visitor with the case. So the affair bothered me. I looked up the name "Mergenthwirker" in the telephone book and the city directory, but it wasn't in either of them. I don't know just what I would have done if it *had* been. After all, you you can't go to the bobbies and say, "Look here, a guy named Mergenthwirker has two green familiars who told him there was going to be a murder." So I puzzled over the thing for a week or so, and then it gradually dropped out of my mind. It might never have occurred to me again if I hadn't dropped into Tony's joint one night for a drink.

Tony's bar, as usual, was jammed with half-lit reformers, solving national problems in three easy lessons, so I ducked for the back room. It's a dimly lit little hole, with only about four tables. As I entered, I saw this guy Mergenthwirker sitting at the best table—the one beneath the only light—with a beer glass before him. The places on his left and right had beer glasses, too, but no one was sitting there. The sandy little man looked up as I entered.

"Oh, hello!" he said in a pleased voice. Evidently he didn't bear me any ill will for kicking him out of my office. "Won't you join us?"

I would. I moved around to the chair on his left and started to pull it out. Mergenthwirker leaped up suddenly, slopping his beer all over the table.

"Oh, not there!" he cried. "You'll sit on Henry!"

I took the chair across from him. Tony came out with my beer, mopped up the mess on the table, and left. The little man smiled at me apologetically.

"It's so *dark* in here," he said. "I guess you didn't see Henry, did you?"

"No," I said bluntly, "I didn't. Listen, buddy, I've been looking for you. How did you know about the Johnson murder?"

There was an astonished, half-aggrieved look in his pale eyes.

"Why, my lobblies," he said. "My lobblies told me."

I jerked my head toward the empty chairs.

"Henry, here, and——"

"—and Japheth! Yes, certainly! They tell me all sorts of things. For instance"—he leaned far over the table eagerly—"did you know the Second National was going to be robbed Tuesday?"

"The Second National?"

"Yes!" he said excitedly. "Four men in a blue Olds will hold it up at 3:30 P.M. Only the police will catch them. They're going to smash up their car trying to escape!"

"Got all the details, haven't you?" I said.

"I *always* have all the details," he complained. "I had

all the details before, but you"—he smiled forgivingly
—"well, it doesn't matter. Will you call Tony, please?
Japheth wants more beer."

I gulped and stared at Japheth's glass . . . or maybe
I stared first and then gulped. The glass was empty! And
I would swear on a stack of proof sheets that I had been
watching the little man every instant since I came in.
And he did *not* drink that beer himself!

"Does he"—I began cautiously—"does he drink very
much beer?"

Mergenthwirker sighed.

"Barrels! Both he and Henry. But what can I do? If I
don't buy it for them, they make scenes."

"Scenes?" I repeated vaguely.

"Yes," he confided. "You know—pinch people on—on
busses, and whisper things to girls. Especially pretty
girls. *Young* girls." He smiled shyly, and a faint blush
crept over his colorless cheeks. "Henry's the worst. He
just doesn't seem to care *what* he says to young girls.
Once he even . . . I mean, there was that girl in At-
lantic City . . ."

Tony came just then with four glasses of beer. As he
renewed ours, I noted that now Henry's, as well as
Japheth's, glass was empty. And this time I *knew* Mergenthwirker had not touched the beer. I paid for the
round, and Tony waddled away.

"Mergenthwirker," I said seriously, "either you're nuts
or I am. You call Japheth and Henry 'lobblies.' What do
you mean by that?"

"Why, that's what they are, of course," he said, his eyes round with surprise.

"But how . . . or where . . . did you get them?"

"I've always had them," he said—proudly, this time. "Ever since—oh, since I was very young. Japheth came first, but he was lonely, so after a while the little one came, too. We named him Henry, after me. Of course, he was *very* young when he came, and he had some perfectly awful habits at first. But he's starting to get over them now."

"Habits?" I said. "What kind of habits?"

"Oh—lobbly habits!" said Mergenthwirker airily. "Things like pwidgeting and rikking trilks and . . . eh, what's that?" He leaned to his right, listened intently, then nodded.

"Japheth says you wouldn't understand," he told me. "Do you mind?"

"Not at all," I said. I was hot and cross and irritable and my watch told me it was time to grab some shuteye. "Say, Mergenthwirker," I said, "I've got to run along now, but I wish you'd drop in at the office again some day soon. Bring—bring the lobblies with you."

"Thank you, I will," said the little man. I rose from the table, reaching for my hat.

"Oh, Japheth and Henry say thank you for the drink," added my companion. I glanced at the table swiftly. Once more the beer glasses were empty. . . .

At three o'clock the next afternoon I hoked up a phony excuse to plant two of the boys and a cameraman in the

Second National Bank. At 3:30 on the dot a blue Olds sedan drew up, four men stepped out, whisked briskly into the bank, covered the joint with a tommy gun, scooped up the gravy, and moved along. At 3:57 their car, closely followed by my three men and the police, clipped an elevated post on Sixth. And at 4:10 my sheet pulled the first "beat" this burg has seen in the past six years—a complete pictorial account of the Second National robbery!

I had just finished receiving the boss's congratulations —*sans* bonus—when Mergenthwirker came in. He was beaming delightedly.

"So!" he said triumphantly.

"So!" I agreed slowly, "you were right. I don't know how or why—but you were."

"It's my lobblies," Mergenthwirker boasted. "They know everything."

"Man," I told him, "with Japheth and Henry to help you, you could be the richest guy this side of Hades. Do they know the results of horse races, lotteries, football games?"

"Why—why, I suppose so," said Mergenthwirker. "I never stopped to think——" His brows furrowed momentarily. "My *goodness!* I *could,* couldn't I!"

"Looks as if," I grunted. "Here, won't you and the boys sit down?"

The little man was dancing with nervousness.

"Oh, *no!*" he said excitedly. "Oh, *my!* I never even *thought* of using Henry and Japheth to—— Will you come over and have a drink with us? Talk it over?"

"Why not?" I said. We went down in the elevator, Mergenthwirker jabbering six to a dozen, to the vast amusement of the elevator boy. On the street he grabbed my arm and held me back.

"Let *them* go ahead," he whispered hoarsely. "Perhaps they wouldn't exactly like it if they knew I was planning to—to *use* them like that. I'll have to break it sort of gently, and see what they think. I wouldn't want to——"

His words were drowned in the belligerent squawk of one of those huge, lumbering trucks that the city still allows on its main thoroughfares. The traffic light had just turned red, holding us to the curb, but a few pedestrians ahead were still scrambling, with affronted awkwardness, for the safety zone. Mergenthwirker screamed shrilly, his tiny hands digging painfully into my arm.

"Henry!"

Suddenly he left me, and darted into the middle of the street with arms outthrust before him as though to push some slighter body out of danger. A horn growled, brakes squealed viciously, somewhere a whistle shrilled, and the spattering of many voices tightened into a murmuring knot in the center of the street. Suddenly numbed with fear, I elbowed my way through the crowd. Mergenthwirker, his body grotesquely twisted, lay crumpled on the asphalt. I leaned over him and lifted his head on my arm. His eyes fluttered open, recognized me.

"Henry—" he gasped. "Is he all right?" His head turned stiffly, his eyes searching the press of babbling bystanders. "Ah! There—I thought so. Then he *is* safe. . . ." He closed his eyes contentedly.

"Take it easy, guy," I said. "There'll be an ambulance here directly."

"Ambulance!" He stared at me; his tawny eyes were wide and then they were suddenly deep with growing fear. "For me? Oh, no—that can't be! I can't die! Japheth! Henry! What will they do without me? My lobblies —my lovely, beautiful lobblies! Nobody to talk with . . . nobody to buy them beer . . . and Henry is *so* young! What——"

"Listen," I said, "they'll be all right. I'll take care of them."

There was a slow ripple through the crowd. Far down the street I heard the wailing siren of an ambulance. The little man's eyes flickered briefly, and a great weariness pressed upon their lids.

"Thank you! Thank you very much," said Mr. Mergenthwirker. . . .

FRANK R. STOCKTON

A Tale of Negative Gravity

My wife and I were staying at a small town in northern
Italy; and on a certain pleasant afternoon in spring we
had taken a walk of six or seven miles to see the sun set
behind some low mountains to the west of the town.
Most of our walk had been along a hard, smooth highway, and then we turned into a series of narrower roads,
sometimes bordered by walls, and sometimes by light
fences of reed, or cane. Nearing the mountain, to a low
spur of which we intended to ascend, we easily scaled a
wall about four feet high, and found ourselves upon
pasture land, which led, sometimes by gradual ascents,
and sometimes by bits of rough climbing, to the spot we
wished to reach. We were afraid we were a little late,
and therefore hurried on, running up the grassy hills,
and bounding briskly over the rough and rocky places.

374

I carried a knapsack strapped firmly to my shoulders, and under my wife's arm was a large, soft basket of a kind much used by tourists. Her arm was passed through the handles, and around the bottom of the basket, which she pressed closely to her side. This was the way she always carried it. The basket contained two bottles of wine, one sweet for my wife, and another a little acid for myself. Sweet wines give me a headache.

When we reached the grassy bluff, well known thereabouts to lovers of sunset views, I stepped immediately to the edge to gaze upon the scene, but my wife sat down to take a sip of wine, for she was very thirsty; and then, leaving her basket, she came to my side. The scene was indeed one of great beauty. Beneath us stretched a wide valley of many shades of green, with a little river running through it, and red-tiled houses here and there. Beyond rose a range of mountains, pink, pale-green, and purple where their tips caught the reflection of the setting sun, and of a rich gray-green in shadows. Beyond all was the blue Italian sky, illumined by an especially fine sunset.

My wife and I are Americans, and at the time of this story were middle-aged people and very fond of seeing in each other's company whatever there was of interest or beauty around us. We had a son about twenty-two years old, of whom we were also very fond, but he was not with us, being at that time a student in Germany. Although we had good health, we were not very robust people, and, under ordinary circumstances, not much given to long country tramps. I was of medium size, without much muscular development, while my wife was quite stout, and growing stouter.

The reader may, perhaps, be somewhat surprised that a middle-aged couple, not very strong, or very good walkers, the lady loaded with a basket containing two bottles of wine and a metal drinking-cup, and the gentleman carrying a heavy knapsack, filled with all sorts of odds and ends, strapped to his shoulders, should set off on a seven-mile walk, jump over a wall, run up a hillside, and yet feel in very good trim to enjoy a sunset view. This peculiar state of things I will proceed to explain.

I had been a professional man, but some years before had retired upon a very comfortable income. I had always been very fond of scientific pursuits, and now made these the occupation and pleasure of much of my leisure time. Our home was in a small town; and in a corner of my grounds I built a laboratory, where I carried on my work and my experiments. I had long been anxious to discover the means, not only of producing, but of retaining and controlling, a natural force, really the same as centrifugal force, but which I called negative gravity. This name I adopted because it indicated better than any other the action of the force in question, as I produced it. Positive gravity attracts everything toward the center of the earth. Negative gravity, therefore, would be that power which repels everything from the center of the earth, just as the negative pole of a magnet repels the needle, while the positive pole attracts it. My object was, in fact, to store centrifugal force and to ren-

der it constant, controllable, and available for use. The
advantages of such a discovery could scarcely be described. In a word, it woud lighten the burdens of the
world.

I will not touch upon the labors and disappointments
of several years. It is enough to say that at last I discovered a method of producing, storing, and controlling
negative gravity.

The mechanism of my invention was rather compli-
cated, but the method of operating it was very simple.
A strong metallic case, about eight inches long, and half
as wide, contained the machinery for producing the
force; and this was put into action by means of the pressure of a screw worked from the outside. As soon as this
pressure was produced, negative gravity began to be
evolved and stored, and the greater the pressure the
greater the force. As the screw was moved outward,
and the pressure diminished, the force decreased, and
when the screw was withdrawn to its fullest extent, the
action of negative gravity entirely ceased. Thus this
force could be produced or dissipated at will to such
degrees as might be desired, and its action, so long as the
requisite pressure was maintained, was constant.

When this little apparatus worked to my satisfaction
I called my wife into my laboratory and explained to
her my invention and its value. She had known that I
had been at work with an important object, but I had
never told her what it was. I had said that if I
succeeded I would tell her all, but if I failed she need
not be troubled with the matter at all. Being a very sen-

sible woman, this satisfied her perfectly. Now I explained everything to her, the construction of the machine, and the wonderful uses to which this invention could be applied. I told her that it could diminish, or entirely dissipate, the weight of objects of any kind. A heavily loaded wagon, with two of these instruments fastened to its sides, and each screwed to a proper force, would be so lifted and supported that it would press upon the ground as lightly as an empty cart, and a small horse could draw it with ease. A bale of cotton, with one of these machines attached, could be handled and carried by a boy. A car, with a number of these machines, could be made to rise in the air like a balloon. Everything, in fact, that was heavy could be made light; and as a great part of labor, all over the world, is caused by the attraction of gravitation, so this repellent force, wherever applied, would make weight less and work easier. I told her of many, many ways in which the invention might be used, and would have told her of many more if she had not suddenly burst into tears.

"The world has gained something wonderful," she exclaimed, between her sobs, "but I have lost a husband!"

"What do you mean by that?" I asked, in surprise.

"I haven't minded it so far," she said, "because it gave you something to do, and it pleased you, and it never interfered with our home pleasures and our home life. But now that is all over. You will never be your own master again. It will succeed, I am sure, and you may make a great deal of money, but we don't need money.

What we need is the happiness which we have always had until now. Now there will be companies, and patents, and lawsuits, and experiments, and people calling you a humbug, and other people saying they discovered it long ago, and all sorts of persons coming to see you, and you'll be obliged to go to all sorts of places, and you will be an altered man, and we shall never be happy again. Millions of money will not repay us for the happiness we have lost."

These words of my wife struck me with much force. Before I had called her my mind had begun to be filled and perplexed with ideas of what I ought to do now that the great invention was perfected. Until now the matter had not troubled me at all. Sometimes I had gone backward and sometimes forward, but, on the whole, I had always felt encouraged. I had taken great pleasure in the work, but I had never allowed myself to be too much absorbed by it. But now everything was different. I began to feel that it was due to myself and to my fellow-beings, that I should properly put this invention before the world. And how should I set about it? What steps should I take? I must make no mistakes. When the matter should become known hundreds of scientific people might set themselves to work; how could I tell but that they might discover other methods of producing the same effect. I must guard myself against a great many things. I must get patents in all parts of the world. Already, as I have said, my mind began to be troubled and perplexed with these things. A turmoil of this sort did not suit my age or disposition. I could not but agree with my wife that the joys of a quiet and contented life were now about to be broken into.

"My dear," said I, "I believe, with you, that the thing will do us more harm than good. If it were not for depriving the world of the invention I would throw the whole thing to the winds. And yet," I added, regretfully, "I had expected a great deal of personal gratification from the use of this invention."

"Now, listen," said my wife, eagerly, "don't you think it would be best to do this: use the thing as much as you please for your own amusement and satisfaction, but let the world wait. It has waited a long time, and let it wait a little longer. When we are dead let Herbert have the invention. He will then be old enough to judge for himself whether it will be better to take advantage of it for his own profit, or simply to give it to the public for nothing. It would be cheating him if we were to do the latter, but it would also be doing him a great wrong if we were, at his age, to load him with such a heavy responsibility. Besides, if he took it up, you could not help going into it, too."

I took my wife's advice. I wrote a careful and complete account of the invention, and, sealing it up, I gave it to my lawyers to be handed to my son after my death. If he died first, I would make other arrangements. Then I determined to get all the good and fun out of the thing that was possible without telling any one anything about it. Even Herbert, who was away from home, was not to be told of the invention.

The first thing I did was to buy a strong leathern knap-sack, and inside of this I fastened my little machine, with a screw so arranged that it could be worked from the outside. Strapping this firmly to my shoulders, my wife gently turned the screw at the back until the upward tendency of the knapsack began to lift and sustain me. When I felt myself so gently supported and upheld that I seemed to weigh about thirty or forty pounds, I would set out for a walk. The knapsack did not raise me from the ground, but it gave me a very buoyant step. It was no labor at all to walk; it was a delight, an ecstasy. With the strength of a man and the weight of a child, I gayly strode along. The first day I walked half a dozen miles at a very brisk pace, and came back without feeling in the least degree tired. These walks now became one of the greatest joys of my life. When nobody was looking, I would bound over a fence, sometimes just touching it with one hand, and sometimes not touching it at all. I delighted in rough places. I sprang over streams. I jumped and I ran. I felt like Mercury himself.

I now set about making another machine, so that my wife could accompany me in my walks; but when it was finished she positively refused to use it. "I can't wear a knapsack," she said, "and there is no other good way of fastening it to me. Besides, everybody about here knows I am no walker, and it would only set them talking."

I occasionally made use of this second machine, but I will only give one instance of its application. Some repairs were needed to the foundation-walls of my barn, and a two-horse wagon, loaded with buildingstone, had been brought into my yard and left there. In the evening, when the men had gone away, I took my two machines and fastened them with strong chains, one on each side of the loaded wagon. Then, gradually turning the screws, the wagon was so lifted that its weight became very greatly diminished. We had an old donkey which used to belong to Herbert, and which was now occasionally used with a small cart to bring packages from the station. I went into the barn and put the harness on the little fellow, and, bringing him out to the wagon, I attached him to it. In this position he looked very funny, with a long pole sticking out in front of him and the great wagon behind him. When all was ready, I touched him up; and, to my great delight, he moved off with the two-horse load of stone as easily as if he were drawing his own cart. I led him out into the public road, along which he proceeded without difficulty. He was an opinionated little beast, and sometimes stopped, not liking the peculiar manner in which he was harnessed; but a touch of the switch made him move on, and I soon turned him and brought the wagon back into the yard. This determined the success of my invention in one of its most important uses, and with a satisfied heart I put the donkey into the stable and went into the house.

Our trip to Europe was made a few months after this, and was mainly on our son Herbert's account. He, poor fellow, was in great trouble, and so, therefore, were we. He had become engaged, with our full consent, to a young lady in our town, the daughter of a gentleman whom we esteemed very highly. Herbert was young to be engaged to be married, but as we felt that he would never find a girl to make him so good a wife, we were entirely satisfied, especially as it was agreed on all hands that the marriage was not to take place for some time. It seemed to us that in marrying Janet Gilbert, Herbert would secure for himself, in the very beginning of his career, the most important element of a happy life. But suddenly, without any reason that seemed to us justifiable, Mr. Gilbert, the only surviving parent of Janet, broke off the match; and he and his daughter soon after left the town for a trip to the West.

This blow nearly broke poor Herbert's heart. He gave up his professional studies and came home to us, and for a time we thought he would be seriously ill. Then we took him to Europe, and after a Continental tour of a month or two we left him, at his own request, in Göttingen, where he thought it would do him good to go to work again. Then we went down to the little town in Italy where my story first finds us. My wife had suffered much in mind and body on her son's account, and for this reason I was anxious that she should take outdoor exercise, and enjoy as much as possible the bracing air of the country. I had brought with me both my little machines. One was still in my knapsack, and the other I had fastened to the inside of an enormous family trunk. As one is obliged to pay for nearly every pound of his baggage on the Continent, this saved me a great deal of money. Everything heavy was packed into this great trunk,—books, papers, the bronze, iron, and marble relics we had picked up and all the articles that usu-

ally weigh down a tourist's baggage. I screwed up the
negative gravity apparatus until the trunk could be handled with great ease by an ordinary porter. I could
have made it weigh nothing at all, but this, of course, I
did not wish to do. The lightness of my baggage, however, had occasioned some comment, and I had over-
heard remarks which were not altogether complimen-
tary about people traveling around with empty trunks;
but this only amused me.

Desirous that my wife should have the advantage of
negative gravity while taking our walks, I had removed
the machine from the trunk and fastened it inside of the
basket, which she could carry under her arm. This assisted her wonderfully. When one arm was tired she
put the basket under the other, and thus, with one hand
on my arm, she could easily keep up with the free and
buoyant steps my knapsack enabled me to take. She
did not object to long tramps here, because nobody
knew that she was not a walker, and she always carried
some wine or other refreshment in the basket, not only
because it was pleasant to have it with us, but because
it seemed ridiculous to go about carrying an empty
basket.

There were English-speaking people stopping at the
hotel where we were, but they seemed more fond of
driving than walking, and none of them offered to accompany us on our rambles, for which we were very
glad. There was one man there, however, who was a
great walker. He was an Englishman, a member of an
Alpine Club, and generally went about dressed in a

knickerbocker suit, with gray woolen stockings covering an enormous pair of calves. One evening this gentleman was talking to me and some others about the ascent of the Matterhorn, and I took occasion to deliver in pretty strong language my opinion upon such exploits. I declared them to be useless, foolhardy, and if the climber had any one who loved him, wicked.

"Even if the weather should permit a view," I said, "what is that compared to the terrible risk to life? Under certain circumstances," I added (thinking of a kind of waistcoat I had some idea of making, which, set about with little negative gravity machines, all connected with a conveniently handled screw, would enable the wearer at times to dispense with his weight altogether), "such ascents might be divested of danger, and be quite admissible; but ordinarily they should be frowned upon by the intelligent public."

The Alpine Club man looked at me, especially regarding my somewhat slight figure and thinnish legs.

"It's all very well for you to talk that way," he said, "because it is easy to see that you are not up to that sort of thing."

"In conversations of this kind," I replied, "I never make personal allusions; but since you have chosen to do so, I feel inclined to invite you to walk with me tomorrow to the top of the mountain to the north of this town."

"I'll do it," he said, "at any time you choose to name." And as I left the room soon afterward I heard him laugh.

The next afternoon, about two o'clock, the Alpine Club man and myself set out for the mountain.

"What have you got in your knapsack?" he said.

"A hammer to use if I come across geological specimens, a field-glass, a flask of wine, and some other things."

"I wouldn't carry any weight, if I were you," he said.

"Oh, I don't mind it," I answered, and off we started.

The mountain to which we were bound was about two miles from the town. Its nearest side was steep, and in places almost precipitous, but it sloped away more gradually toward the north, and up that side a road led by devious windings to a village near the summit. It was not a very high mountain, but it would do for an afternoon's climb.

"I suppose you want to go up by the road," said my companion.

"Oh, no," I answered, "we won't go so far around as that. There is a path up this side, along which I have seen men driving their goats. I prefer to take that."

"All right, if you say so," he answered, with a smile; "but you'll find it pretty tough."

After a time he remarked:

"I wouldn't walk so fast, if I were you."

"Oh, I like to step along briskly," I said. And briskly on we went.

My wife had screwed up the machine in the knapsack more than usual, and walking seemed scarcely any effort at all. I carried a long alpenstock, and when we reached the mountain and began the ascent, I found that with the help of this and my knapsack I could go uphill at a wonderful rate. My companion had taken the lead, so as to show me how to climb. Making a *détour* over some rocks, I quickly passed him and went ahead. After that it was impossible for him to keep up with me. I ran up steep places, I cut off the windings of the path by lightly clambering over rocks, and even when I followed the beaten track my step was as rapid as if I had been walking on level ground.

"Look here!" shouted the Alpine Club man from below, "you'll kill yourself if you go at that rate! That's no way to climb mountains."

"It's my way!" I cried. And on I skipped.

Twenty minutes after I arrived at the summit, my companion joined me, puffing, and wiping his red face with his handkerchief.

"Confound it!" he cried, "I never came up a mountain so fast in my life."

"You need not have hurried," I said, coolly.

"I was afraid something would happen to you," he growled, "and I wanted to stop you. I never saw a person climb in such an utterly absurd way."

"I don't see why you should call it absurd," I said, smiling with an air of superiority. "I arrived here in a perfectly comfortable condition, neither heated nor wearied."

He made no answer, but walked off to a little distance, fanning himself with his hat and growling words which I did not catch. After a time I proposed to descend.

"You must be careful as you go down," he said. "It is

much more dangerous to go down steep places than to climb up."

"I am always prudent," I answered, and started in advance. I found the descent of the mountain much more pleasant than the ascent. It was positively exhilarating. I jumped from rocks and bluffs eight and ten feet in height, and touched the ground as gently as if I had stepped down but two feet. I ran down steep paths, and, with the aid of my alpenstock, stopped myself in an instant. I was careful to avoid dangerous places, but the runs and jumps I made were such as no man had ever made before upon that mountainside. Once only I heard my companion's voice.

"You'll break your——neck!" he yelled.

"Never fear!" I called back, and soon left him far above.

When I reached the bottom I would have waited for him, but my activity had warmed me up, and as a cool evening breeze was beginning to blow I thought it better not to stop and take cold. Half an hour after my arrival at the hotel I came down to the court, cool, fresh, and dressed for dinner, and just in time to meet the Alpine man as he entered, hot, dusty, and growling.

"Excuse me for not waiting for you," I said; but without stopping to hear my reason, he muttered something about waiting in a place where no one would care to stay and passed into the house.

There was no doubt that what I had done gratified my pique and tickled my vanity.

"I think now," I said, when I related the matter to my

388

wife, "that he will scarcely say that I am not up to that sort of thing."

"I am not sure," she answered, "that it was exactly fair. He did not know how you were assisted."

"It was fair enough," I said. "He is enabled to climb well by the inherited vigor of his constitution and by his training. He did not tell me what methods of exercise he used to get those great muscles upon his legs. I am enabled to climb by the exercise of my intellect. My method is my business and his method is his business. It is all perfectly fair."

Still she persisted:

"He *thought* that you climbed with your legs, and not with your head."

And now, after this long digression, necessary to explain how a middle-aged couple of slight pedestrian ability, and loaded with a heavy knapsack and basket, should have started out on a rough walk and climb, fourteen miles in all, we will return to ourselves, standing on the little bluff and gazing out upon the sunset view. When the sky began to fade a little we turned from it and prepared to go back to the town.

"Where is the basket?" I said.

"I left it right here," answered my wife. "I unscrewed the machine and it lay perfectly flat."

"Did you afterward take out the bottles?" I asked, seeing them lying on the grass.

"Yes, I believe I did. I had to take out yours in order to get at mine."

"Then," said I, after looking all about the grassy patch

on which we stood, "I am afraid you did not entirely
unscrew the instrument, and that when the weight of
the bottles was removed the basket gently rose into the
air."

"It may be so," she said, lugubriously. "The basket
was behind me as I drank my wine."

"I believe that is just what has happened," I said.
"Look up there! I vow that is our basket!"

I pulled out my field-glass and directed it at a little
speck high above our heads. It was the basket floating
high in the air. I gave the glass to my wife to look, but
she did not want to use it.

"What shall I do?" she cried. "I can't walk home without that basket. It's perfectly dreadful!" And she looked
as if she was going to cry.

"Do not distress yourself," I said, although I was a
good deal disturbed myself. "We shall get home very
well. You shall put your hand on my shoulder, while I
put my arm around you. Then you can screw up my
machine a good deal higher, and it will support us both.
In this way I am sure that we shall get on very well."

We carried out this plan, and managed to walk on
with moderate comfort. To be sure, with the knapsack
pulling me upward, and the weight of my wife pulling
me down, the straps hurt me somewhat, which they had
not done before. We did not spring lightly over the
wall into the road, but, still clinging to each other, we
clambered awkwardly over it. The road for the most
part declined gently toward the town, and with moderate ease we made our way along it. But we walked much

more slowly than we had done before, and it was quite dark when we reached our hotel. If it had not been for the light inside the court it would have been difficult for us to find it. A traveling-carriage was standing before the entrance, and against the light. It was necessary to pass around it, and my wife went first. I attempted to follow her, but strange to say, there was nothing under my feet. I stepped vigorously, but only wagged my legs in the air. To my horror I found that I was rising in the air! I soon saw, by the light below me, that I was some fifteen feet from the ground. The carriage drove away, and in the darkness I was not noticed. Of course I knew what had happened. The instrument in my knapsack had been screwed up to such an intensity, in order to support both myself and my wife, that when her weight was removed the force of the negative gravity was sufficient to raise me from the ground. But I was glad to find that when I had risen to the height I have mentioned I did not go up any higher, but hung in the air, about on a level with the second tier of windows of the hotel.

I now began to try to reach the screw in my knapsack in order to reduce the force of the negative gravity; but, do what I would, I could not get my hand to it. The machine in the knapsack had been placed so as to support me in a well-balanced and comfortable way; and in doing this it had been impossible to set the screw so that I could reach it. But in a temporary arrangement of the kind this had not been considered necessary, as my wife always turned the screw for me until sufficient lifting-power had been attained. I had intended, as I have said before, to construct a negative gravity waist-coat, in which the screw should be in front, and entirely under the wearer's control; but this was a thing of the future.

When I found that I could not turn the screw I began to be much alarmed. Here I was, dangling in the air, without any means of reaching the ground. I could not expect my wife to return to look for me, as she would naturally suppose I had stopped to speak to some one. I thought of loosening myself from the knapsack, but this would not do, for I should fall heavily, and either kill myself or break some of my bones. I did not dare to call for assistance, for if any of the simple-minded inhabitants of the town had discovered me floating in the air they would have taken me for a demon, and would probably have shot at me. A moderate breeze was blowing, and it wafted me gently down the street. If it had blown me against a tree I would have seized it, and have endeavored, so to speak, to climb down it; but there were no trees. There was a dim street lamp here and there, but reflectors above them threw their light upon the pavement, and none up to me. On many accounts I was glad that the night was so dark, for, much as I desired to get down, I wanted no one to see me in my strange position, which, to any one but myself and wife, would be utterly unaccountable. If I could rise as high as the roofs I might get on one of them, and, tearing off an armful of tiles, so load myself that I would be heavy enough to descend. But I did not rise to the eaves of any of the houses. If there had been a telegraph-pole, or anything of the kind that I could have clung to, I would have taken off the knapsack, and would have endeavored to scramble down as well as I could. But there was nothing I could cling to. Even the water-spouts, if I could have reached the face of the houses, were imbedded in the walls. At an open window, near which I was slowly blown, I saw two little boys going to bed by the light of a dim candle. I was dreadfully afraid that they would see me and raise an alarm. I actually came so near to the window that I threw out one foot and pushed against the wall with such force that I went nearly across the street. I thought I caught sight of a frightened look on the face of one of the boys; but of this I am not sure, and I heard no cries. I still floated, dangling, down the street. What was to be done? Should I call out? In that case, if I were not shot or stoned, my strange predicament, and the secret of my invention, would be exposed to the world. If I did not do this, I must either let myself drop and be killed or mangled, or hang there and die. When, during the course of the night, the air became more rarefied, I might rise higher and higher, perhaps to an altitude of one or two hundred feet. It would then be impossible for the people to reach me and get me down, even if they were convinced that I was not a demon. I should then expire, and when the birds of the air had eaten all of me that they could devour, I should forever hang above the unlucky town, a dangling skeleton, with a knapsack on its back.

Such thoughts were not re-assuring, and I determined that if I could find no means of getting down without assistance, I would call out and run all risks; but so long as I could endure the tension of the straps I would hold out and hope for a tree or a pole. Perhaps it might rain, and my wet clothes would then become so heavy that I would descend as low as the top of a lamp-post.

As this thought was passing through my mind I saw a spark of light upon the street approaching me. I rightly imagined that it came from a tobacco-pipe, and presently I heard a voice. It was that of the Alpine Club man. Of all people in the world I did not want him to discover me, and I hung as motionless as possible. The man was speaking to another person who was walking with him.

"He is crazy beyond a doubt," said the Alpine man. "Nobody but a maniac could have gone up and down that mountain as he did! He hasn't any muscles, and one need only look at him to know that he couldn't do any climbing in a natural way. It is only the excitement of insanity that gives him strength."

The two now stopped almost under me, and the speaker continued:

"Such things are very common with maniacs. At times they acquire an unnatural strength which is perfectly wonderful. I have seen a little fellow struggle and fight so that four strong men could not hold him."

Then the other person spoke:

"I am afraid what you say is too true," he remarked. "Indeed, I have known it for some time."

At these words my breath almost stopped. It was the voice of Mr. Gilbert, my townsman, and the father of

Janet. It must have been he who had arrived in the traveling-carriage. He was acquainted with the Alpine Club man, and they were talking of me. Proper or improper, I listened with all my ears.

"It is a very sad case," Mr. Gilbert continued. "My daughter was engaged to marry his son, but I broke off the match. I could not have her marry the son of a lunatic, and there could be no doubt of his condition. He has been seen—a man of his age, and the head of a family— to load himself up with a heavy knapsack, which there was no earthly necessity for him to carry, and go skipping along the road for miles, vaulting over fences and jumping over rocks and ditches like a young calf or a colt. I myself saw a most heart-rending instance of how a kindly man's nature can be changed by the derangement of his intellect. I was at some distance from his house, but I plainly saw him harness a little donkey which he owns to a large two-horse wagon loaded with stone, and beat and lash the poor little beast until it drew the heavy load some distance along the public road. I would have remonstrated with him on this horrible cruelty, but he had the wagon back in his yard before I could reach him."

"Oh, there can be no doubt of his insanity," said the Alpine Club man, "and he oughtn't to be allowed to travel about in this way. Some day he will pitch his wife over a precipice just for the fun of seeing her shoot through the air."

"I am sorry he is here," said Mr. Gilbert, "for it would be very painful to meet him. My daughter and I will retire very soon, and go away as early to-morrow morning as possible, so as to avoid seeing him."

And then they walked back to the hotel.

For a few moments I hung, utterly forgetful of my condition, and absorbed in the consideration of these revelations. One idea now filled my mind. Everything must be explained to Mr. Gilbert, even if it should be necessary to have him called to me, and for me to speak to him from the upper air.

Just then I saw something white approaching me along the road. My eyes had become accustomed to the darkness, and I perceived that it was an upturned face. I recognized the hurried gait, the form; it was my wife. As she came near me I called her name, and in the same breath entreated her not to scream. It must have been an effort for her to restrain herself, but she did it.

"You must help me to get down," I said, "without anybody seeing us."

"What shall I do?" she whispered.

"Try to catch hold of this string."

Taking a piece of twine from my pocket, I lowered one end to her. But it was too short; she could not reach it. I then tied my handkerchief to it, but still it was not long enough.

"I can get more string, or handkerchiefs," she whispered, hurriedly.

"No," I said; "you could not get them up to me. But, leaning against the hotel wall, on this side, in the corner, just inside of the garden gate, are some fishing-poles. I have seen them there every day. You can easily find them in the dark. Go, please, and bring me one of those."

The hotel was not far away, and in a few minutes my wife returned with a fishing-pole. She stood on tip-toe, and reached it high in air; but all she could do was to strike my feet and legs with it. My most frantic exertions did not enable me to get my hands low enough to touch it.

"Wait a minute," she said; and the rod was withdrawn.

I knew what she was doing. There was a hook and line attached to the pole, and with womanly dexterity she was fastening the hook to the extreme end of the rod. Soon she reached up, and gently struck at my legs. After a few attempts the hook caught in my trousers, a little below my right knee. Then there was a slight pull, a long scratch down my leg, and the hook was stopped by the top of my boot. Then came a steady downward pull, and I felt myself descending. Gently and firmly the rod was drawn down; carefully the lower end was kept free from the ground; and in a few moments my ankle was seized with a vigorous grasp. Then some one seemed to climb up me, my feet touched the ground, an arm was thrown around my neck, the hand of another arm was busy at the back of my knapsack, and I soon stood firmly in the road, entirely divested of negative gravity.

"Oh, that I should have forgotten," sobbed my wife, "and that I should have dropped your arms, and let you go up into the air! At first I thought that you had stopped below, and it was only a little while ago that the truth flashed upon me. Then I rushed out and began looking up for you. I knew that you had wax matches in your pocket, and hoped that you would keep on striking them, so that you would be seen."

"But I did not wish to be seen," I said, as we hurried to the hotel; "and I can never be sufficiently thankful that it was you who found me and brought me down. Do you know that it is Mr. Gilbert and his daughter who have just arrived? I must see him instantly. I will explain it all to you when I come upstairs."

I took off my knapsack and gave it to my wife, who carried it to our room, while I went to look for Mr. Gilbert. Fortunately I found him just as he was about to go up to his chamber. He took my offered hand, but looked at me sadly and gravely.

"Mr. Gilbert," I said, "I must speak to you in private. Let us step into this room. There is no one here."

"My friend," said Mr. Gilbert, "it will be much better to avoid discussing this subject. It is very painful to both of us, and no good can come from talking of it."

"You can not now comprehend what it is I want to say to you," I replied. "Come in here, and in a few minutes you will be very glad that you listened to me."

My manner was so earnest and impressive that Mr. Gilbert was constrained to follow me, and we went into a small room called the smoking-room, but in which people seldom smoked, and closed the door. I immediately began my statement. I told my old friend that I had discovered, by means that I need not explain at present, that he had considered me crazy, and that now the most important object of my life was to set myself right in his eyes. I thereupon gave him the whole history of my invention, and explained the reason of the actions that had appeared to him those of a lunatic. I said nothing about the little incident of that evening. That was a mere accident, and I did not care now to speak of it.

Mr. Gilbert listened to me very attentively.

"Your wife is here?" he asked, when I had finished.

"Yes," I said; "and she will corroborate my story in every item, and no one could ever suspect her of being crazy. I will go and bring her to you."

In a few minutes my wife was in the room, had shaken hands with Mr. Gilbert, and had been told of my suspected madness. She turned pale, but smiled.

"He did act like a crazy man," she said, "but I never supposed that anybody would think him one." And tears came into her eyes.

"And now, my dear," said I, "perhaps you will tell Mr. Gilbert how I did all this."

And then she told him the story that I had told.

Mr. Gilbert looked from the one to the other of us with a troubled air.

"Of course I do not doubt either of you, or rather I do not doubt that you believe what you say. All would be right if I could bring myself to credit that such a force as that you speak of can possibly exist."

"That is a matter," said I, "which I can easily prove to you by actual demonstration. If you can wait a short time, until my wife and I have had something to eat,

399

—for I am nearly famished, and I am sure she must be, —I will set your mind at rest upon that point."

"I will wait here," said Mr. Gilbert, "and smoke a cigar. Don't hurry yourselves. I shall be glad to have some time to think about what you have told me."

When we had finished the dinner, which had been set aside for us, I went upstairs and got my knapsack, and we both joined Mr. Gilbert in the smoking-room. I showed him the little machine, and explained, very briefly, the principle of its construction. I did not give any practical demonstration of its action, because there were people walking about the corridor who might at any moment come into the room; but, looking out of the window, I saw that the night was much clearer. The wind had dissipated the clouds, and the stars were shining brightly.

"If you will come up the street with me," said I to Mr. Gilbert, "I will show you how this thing works."

"That is just what I want to see," he answered.

"I will go with you," said my wife, throwing a shawl over her head. And we started up the street.

When we were outside the little town I found the starlight was quite sufficient for my purpose. The white roadway, the low walls, and objects about us, could easily be distinguished.

"Now," said I to Mr. Gilbert, "I want to put this knapsack on you, and let you see how it feels, and how it will help you to walk." To this he assented with some eagerness, and I strapped it firmly on him. "I will now turn this screw," said I, "until you shall become lighter and lighter."

"Be very careful not to turn it too much," said my wife earnestly.

"Oh, you may depend on me for that," said I, turning the screw very gradually.

Mr. Gilbert was a stout man, and I was obliged to give the screw a good many turns.

"There seems to be considerable hoist in it," he said directly. And then I put my arms around him, and found that I could raise him from the ground. "Are you lifting me?" he exclaimed in surprise.

"Yes; I did it with ease," I answered.

"Upon—my—word!" ejaculated Mr. Gilbert.

I then gave the screw a half turn more, and told him to walk and run. He started off, at first slowly, then he made long strides, then he began to run, and then to skip and jump. It had been many years since Mr. Gilbert had skipped and jumped. No one was in sight, and he was free to gambol as much as he pleased. "Could you give it another turn?" said he, bounding up to me. "I want to try that wall." I put on a little more negative gravity, and he vaulted over a five-foot wall with great ease. In an instant he had leaped back into the road, and in two bounds was at my side. "I came down as light as a cat," he said. "There was never anything like it." And away he went up the road, taking steps at least eight feet long, leaving my wife and me laughing heartily at the preternatural agility of our stout friend. In a

few minutes he was with us again. "Take it off," he said.
"If I wear it any longer I shall want one myself, and then
I shall be taken for a crazy man, and perhaps clapped
into an asylum."

"Now," said I, as I turned back the screw before un-
strapping the knapsack, "do you understand how I took
long walks, and leaped and jumped; how I ran uphill
and downhill, and how the little donkey drew the
loaded wagon?"

"I understand it all," cried he. "I take back all I ever
said or thought about you, my friend."

"And Herbert may marry Janet?" cried my wife.

"*May* marry her!" cried Mr. Gilbert. "Indeed he *shall*
marry her, if I have anything to say about it! My poor
girl has been drooping ever since I told her it could not
be."

My wife rushed at him, but whether she embraced
him or only shook his hands I can not say; for I had the
knapsack in one hand, and was rubbing my eyes with
the other.

"But, my dear fellow," said Mr. Gilbert directly, "if
you still consider it to your interest to keep your invention a secret, I wish you had never made it. No one
having a machine like that can help using it, and it is
often quite as bad to be considered a maniac as to be
one."

"My friend," I cried, with some excitement, "I have
made up my mind on this subject. The little machine in
this knapsack, which is the only one I now possess, has
been a great pleasure to me. But I now know it has also

402

been of the greatest injury indirectly to me and mine, not to mention some direct inconvenience and danger, which I will speak of another time. The secret lies with us three, and we will keep it. But the invention itself is too full of temptation and danger for any of us."

As I said this I held the knapsack with one hand while I quickly turned the screw with the other. In a few moments it was high above my head, while I with difficulty held it down by the straps. "Look!" I cried. And then I released my hold, and the knapsack shot into the air and disappeared into the upper gloom.

I was about to make a remark, but had no chance, for my wife threw herself upon my bosom, sobbing with joy.

"Oh, I am so glad—so glad!" she said. "And you will never make another?"

"Never another!" I answered.

"And now let us hurry in and see Janet," said my wife.

"You don't know how heavy and clumsy I feel," said Mr. Gilbert, striving to keep up with us as we walked back. "If I had worn that thing much longer, I should never have been willing to take it off!"

Janet had retired, but my wife went up to her room. "I think she has felt it as much as our boy," she said, when she rejoined me. "But I tell you, my dear, I left a very happy girl in that little bed-chamber over the garden."

And there were three very happy elderly people talking together until quite late that evening. "I shall write to Herbert to-night," I said, when we separated, "and tell him to meet us all in Geneva. It will do the young man no harm if we interrupt his studies just now."

"You must let me add a postscript to the letter," said Mr. Gilbert, "and I am sure it will require no knapsack with a screw in the back to bring him quickly to us."

And it did not.

There is a wonderful pleasure in tripping over the earth like a winged Mercury, and in feeling one's self relieved of much of that attraction of gravitation which drags us down to earth, and gradually makes the movement of our bodies but weariness and labor. But this pleasure is not to be compared, I think, to that given by the buoyancy and lightness of two young and loving hearts, reunited after a separation which they had supposed would last for ever.

What became of the basket and the knapsack, or whether they ever met in upper air, I do not know. If they but float away and stay away from ken of mortal man, I shall be satisfied.

And whether or not the world will ever know more of the power of negative gravity depends entirely upon the disposition of my son Herbert, when—after a good many years, I hope—he shall open the packet my lawyers have in keeping.

[NOTE.—It would be quite useless for any one to interview my wife on this subject, for she has entirely forgotten how my machine was made. And as for Mr. Gilbert, he never knew.]

404

ERIC KNIGHT

Never Come Monday

The first one to notice it was old Capper Wambley. And Capper was a very important man. He was the knocker-up in the village of Allerby Brig—that is to say, he got up early every morning and went round with his pole, tapping on the bedroom windows and waking up the people in time for them to get to work. And this particular morning old Capper knew there was something wrong.

He felt it first as he stepped outside his cottage and coughed in the dark to clear his lungs, and looked up at the sky to see what kind of weather it was. He felt that there was something wrong with the day, and then he decided what it was. It was still Sunday.

For a moment or two he felt fair flabbergasted at this, for he remembered that the day before had been Sunday, too.

"Ba gum," Capper said to himself. "This is a champion do, it is an' all. No doubt summat should be done."

Now old Capper Wambley was very old, so he sat down on the edge of the curb, and after a while he came to the conclusion that what ought to be done was to think about it. So he began thinking about the very strange event.

"Now," he said to himself, "it don't seem reasonable and proper that we should hev two Sundays in a row. Let us see if we can get it sorted out. Now the thing for a chap to do to prove it, is to decide what is the difference between a Sunday morning and a weekday morning."

Old Capper thought and thought, and he saw that the only difference between the two was that on a weekday morning he wakened the people up, and on a Sunday morning he didn't.

"So, if Ah doan't wakken the village up this morning, it *is* a Sunday morning," he said to himself.

Of course, it took old Capper a long time to figure this out, because you can see it was no light matter. Here was one man, as you might say, who was holding the calendar in his hands. It was a very important decision. But once Capper had decided, he knew he must be right, for he was a Yorkshireman.

"Because Ah'm net wakkening onybody, it maun be a Sunday morning. And because it's a Sunday morning, Ah maun't wakken onybody up. So no matter which way a lad looks at is, the answer cooms out that it's Sunday."

But now he had decided it was Sunday, Capper saw that not wakening people up might not be sufficient. "Some of them may wake up of their own accord," he thought, "and not knowing this is the second Sunday in a row, will go walking down to the mill. And God knows they have to get up early often enough, and it would be a tarrible shame not to let them have this extra piece of rest that is so miraculously sent."

So old Capper got up slowly from the curb, and went stomping down the street, and stopped at his first call, which was the home of John Willie Braithwaite, who was the fireman at the mill. Old Capper got his long pole with the trident of wire at the end and lifting it so that the wire rested against the upstairs window pane, began twirling and twisting the pole in the palms of his hands so that the wire clacked and chattered fit to wake the soundest sleeper.

Soon the window went up, and John Willie Braithwaite's head popped out of the window.

"Ah'm wakkened," John Willie said. "Whet time is't?"

Now old Capper could see that John Willie wasn't awake, but was just moving in his sleep the way men did from their tiredness and weariness of getting up before dawn. But he knew it didn't matter this morning.

"Ah just wakkened ye to tell ye it's another Sunday morning," old Capper said. "Soa tha c'n goa on back to bed an' sleep i' peace."

At this John Willie Braithwaite closed the window and went back to bed and got in beside his wife without ever having really wakened up. Meanwhile old Capper was on his rounds, busily going up and down the village in the not-yet-dawn, rapping and tapping on all his customers' windows, and telling them they needn't get up because it was still Sunday.

Naturally, the news caused quite a little bit of a fuss. Some people gladly went back to sleep, but others woke up and got dressed, remembering that the day before had been Sunday. They packed their breakfasts and put on their clogs and their smocks and their shawls and went clacking up the streets until they got by the Green, and there they saw old Capper Wambley.

"Now lad," they said, "whet's t'idea o' telling us this is another Sunday?"

"Well, it is," Capper said.

"How does'ta know it is?" Golliker Dilkes asked him.

"Ah can't explain it, but Ah'm full sure summat varry wonderful has happened, and it is," old Capper told them.

Some people were inclined to believe Capper, and some were not.

"Now lewk here, Capper," Golliker said, "Ah doan't but admit that it does seem Sundayish, like, but how are we off to be sure?"

Old Capper thought a while. Then he saw the answer.

"Well, here's the way us can tell," he said. "Now if this be a weekday, the mill whistle'll blaw the fifteen minutes, wean't it?"

"Aye," they agreed.

"But if it be a Sunday, like Ah say, the mill whistle wean't blaw the fifteen minutes, will it?"

They all agreed that was true. So they stood round old Capper, who had one of the few watches in the village, and they waited. They all looked at his watch, and saw it said twenty to six, then nineteen to six, then eighteen and seventeen and sixteen. And the second hand went round and finally it said quarter to six. But no whistle blew—largely because John Willie Braithwaite who was supposed to be there at five-thirty and get up steam and pull the whistle cord, was still home and sleeping warmly beside his wife.

"Well," old Capper says. "That shows it maun be a Sunday again, and now ye can all away hoam and get another hour's sleep."

So they all went home, glad to get another hour's sleep, and full of praises for old Capper because he had had the sense to perceive that it was another Sunday instead of a Monday morning.

Old Capper went off home himself, and was just making himself a little bit of breakfast, when Rowlie Helliwell came in.

"Capper," Rowlie said, "Ah hear that tha discovered this is another Sunday."

"Aye, that's soa," Capper replied.

"Well," Rowlie went on, "isn't heving two Sundays in a row just a varry little bit irregular, as tha maught say?"

"It is that, lad," Capper told him. "But tha maun remember us is living in varry unusual times."

"We are that," Rowlie agreed. "And Ah'm glad tha discovered it in time. For if tha hedn't, Ah would ha' gone and rung the school bell like a gert lummox, thinking it were a Monday. But now Ah know it's a Sunday, Ah maun goa and ring the church bell."

"Ah should say that all sounds right and proper to me," old Capper agreed.

"Me too," Rowlie said. "And Ah thank thee for saving me from a gert mistake.

"Eigh, it's nowt, lad," old Capper said modestly.

So away went Rowlie, and Capper settled down to his breakfast, but he was soon interrupted again. Some of the villagers, all dressed in their Sunday clothes, came up and told him that people from other villages who worked at the Allerby Brig mill were at the mill-gates insisting it was Monday. So Capper picked up a bit of bloater to eat on the way and went down there and told the people it was Sunday.

"But if it's Sunday in Allerby Brig, what day is it i' Wuxley Green?" someone asked.

"Aye, and i' Rombeck an' Tannerley?" someone else added.

"Well, happen it's Sunday theer, too," Capper told them. "Only you didn't notice it. When two Sundays come in a row ye could hardly blame a chap for mistaking the second one for Monday. Soa Ah advise ye to goa back and enjoy Sunday."

"Well," said Tich Mothersole, "Ah'm reight glad to hev another day o' rest; but Ah wish Ah'd known it afore Ah started, because ma Mary Alice allus brings me ma breakfast to bed o' Sunday morning."

"Nay, if tha hurries tha's still time enow to gate hoam and pop back into bed," the Capper pointed out. "Then the minute thy wife sees thee theer she'll knaw it's a Sunday and she'll up and hev a bit o' bacon o't' fire i' noa time."

They were just ready to move away when Mr. Bloggs arrived. Mr. Bloggs was late, but then that didn't matter, because he lived in another town, and Mr. Bloggs owned the mill.

" 'Ere, 'ere, 'ere, my good men," he said. "What's all this, 'ey? What's the idea you aren't all in the mill?"

So they explained to him that a second Sunday had arrived.

"Why, what nonsense," he said. "When I left 'ome it was a Monday. 'Ow can it be Sunday 'ere when it was a Monday in Puttersleigh?"

"Ah doan't knaw," old Capper said. "Unless," he added slowly, "it happens to be Sunday in Puttersleigh, too, and tha didn't realize it."

"It's Monday, I tell you. Come on in to work," Mr. Bloggs shouted. "How can it be two Sundays in a row?"

"It's Sunday," they said.

"It's not. It's Monday. And any man 'oo ain't in this mill in five minutes, is discharged."

"It's Sunday," they said.

"How can it be Sunday?" he shouted. "It's impossible."

411

He stared at them, and just then they heard the boom
—boom—boom, of the church bell ringing for Matins.
"That proves," they said, "it's a Sunday, and it'd be a
sin to work on Sunday."

So they all turned round and went back to their
homes, leaving Mr. Bloggs alone by his mill gates. He
stood there, shaking his head, and finally he clumped
upstairs and opened the office himself and sat down all
alone at his desk to think the whole matter out.

Meanwhile in the homes of the village the people
knew that since it was a Sunday, they would have to
do all the things that one does on a Sunday. The men
rested at home in comfortable chairs, and the women
started mixing Yorkshire puddings for the big noon-
time dinner. The children were dressed in their nicest
clothes and instead of going to school, they went up to
the church for Sunday School. Ethel Newligate, who
taught the Sunday School, went with them. Mr. Sims, the
schoolteacher, hearing the church bell, knew it must be
Sunday and off he went to play the organ. Rowlie Helliwell was already there to pump the bellows. The
church folk went up and stood in the pews. So the old
Reverend Mr. Stoninghorn put on his cassock and surplice. He was a little puzzled as to whether it should be
now the Fifth Sunday before Epiphany or the Fourth,
but he compromised by giving the same service as he
had done the day before, and preaching the same sermon. And many of the church folk said the sermon
sounded a right lot nicer the second time than the first,

because you could see just where it was going, in a manner of speaking.

All this time, of course, the mill was closed, but Mr. Bloggs wasn't idle. He picked up his telephone, which was the only one in the village, and asked the operator to get him the Greenwich Observatory. Mr. Bloggs always liked to be exact. When he got them he asked them what day it was, and they told him that it was Monday.

Armed with this fact, Mr. Bloggs went out and met the people just as they were coming out of church.

"Now see here," he said. "It's no use pretending. This is a Monday."

But they pointed out that they were just coming out of church, so how could it be Monday?

At this Mr. Bloggs got so angry that he shouted at them, and the noise brought the Rev. Mr. Stoninghorn to the church steps.

"You must not profane the Sabbath," he said, looking very handsome in his white surplice, and with his long white hair like a dandelion gone to seed.

Mr. Bloggs began to see he could get nowhere against Yorkshiremen by blustering, so he took another tack. He pointed out to the minister that while this may be Sunday, one would have to admit that it was a little bit unusual to have two Sundays in a row. Mr. Stoninghorn admitted this, and he agreed that a meeting ought to be called to look into the matter.

So it was announced through the village that a meeting was to be called at the school for four o'clock that afternoon. The Rev. Mr. Stoninghorn was asked to preside, but inasmuch as he was unsure whether or not it was the Sabbath, he declined. So Mr. Polkiby, the schoolmaster, agreed to take over the gavel and run a meeting in which everyone should have a chance to state his views on whether it was or wasn't Sunday.

At meeting time there wasn't a seat to be had, and after Mr. Polkiby rapped with the gavel, Mr. Bloggs got up and stated that it was Monday, and he could prove it because he had called up the Greenwich Observatory.

Then Taylor Huckle, the publican, got up and said it was Monday, because yesterday had been Sunday and the day after Sunday had always been Monday, for years and years, man and boy, as far back as he could remember.

After this there was a wait, because nobody liked to get up in front of so many people and put in their hap'orth; though a lot of people were dying to, because they knew Huckle was in favor of Monday for if it were Sunday he'd have to go on early closing hours.

So there was a long wait until somebody said: "Where's Sam Small?"

"Here Ah am," said a voice at the back of the hall, and they all spoke up and said: "Come on, Sam, let's hev thy opinion."

Now this Sam Small was a man whose word was worth listening to at any time, and on any subject. He was the inventor of the Sam Small Self-Doffing Spindle and had made a pile of brass from it, and was much traveled, not only having been to London and other parts, but to foreign lands as well on a cruise. So they waited politely as Sam walked down the aisle and clambered up on the stage.

"Well lads," he said, "it's this way. A day's a day, but then again, it ain't, in a manner of speaking. The time Ah went round t'world, one day it were Tuesday, and the next morning the captain said it were Thursday— and so it were, because Ah've nivver yet found that lost day. And on t'other hand, a lad on the ship told me if we'd gone round the world t'other way, we should of hed two Tuesdays. Now if we can have two Tuesdays when we're going round the world, Ah maintain we maught just as easy hev two Sundays when the world is going round us, which ivvery scientist knaws it is doing."

"Piffle," said Mr. Bloggs.

"Oh, aye?" asked Sam, his dander getting up. "Can tha tell me what day it is now i' Japan?"

"It's Monday," Mr. Bloggs said.

"Oh, pardon me, Mr. Bloggs," the schoolmaster said. "Just as a matter of academic accuracy . . ." and here he studied his watch carefully . . . "but in Japan now it is Tuesday."

"Tuesday?" roared Mr. Bloggs.

"There, tha sees," Sam said. "There don't seem to me to be noa sense to this day stuff. If it's Monday, as tha says, down i' Greenwich; and if it's Tuesday, as t'school-measter says, i' Japan; then Ah says it's just as liable to be Sunday up here."

"Nonsense," yelled Mr. Bloggs. "I know what the matter is. You're all lazy and you wanted another day off. So you call it Sunday."

"Nay lad," Sam replied. "There's six weekdays to one Sunday, so it seems to me like it were six to one i' thy favor that we'd hev an extra workday i'stead of an extra restday. Simply because tha lost, tha maun't be a bad sport about it."

At this the people applauded Sam, and seeing he was at a good place to stop, he got down off the platform.

"Fiddlesticks," Mr. Bloggs said, now thoroughly angry. "If this is Sunday, then what's tomorrow? Is it Monday or Tuesday? Or do we lose a day?"

"Happen Ah'm the man to clear that up," the Capper said, rising to his feet. "Us doesn't skip noa day at all. T'thing is that t'days o'to'week have gate tired o'turning, soa now they've stood still and wean't goa no further, they wean't."

"How ridiculous," Mr. Bloggs snorted. "If that were so we'd get no further and tomorrow would be Sunday, too, wouldn't it?"

The Capper scratched his head and thought a moment. Then he looked up quickly.

"Ba gum, lad," he said. "Tha's hit t'nail o't'yead. Tomorrow is off to be Sunday."

At this the meeting broke up, and everyone started for home. They crowded around old Capper and asked him about the next day.

"Ah'm reight sure it'll be Sunday, lads," old Capper said. "But when Ah coom round to wakken ye up, Ah'll tell ye."

"Nay, Ah gate a better idea," John Willie Braithwaite said. "If it's a Sunday, it'd be a fair shame to disturb a little bit o' good extra sleep. That'd mak' it as bad as a weekday 'most. So supposing, if it's another Sunday, just thee doan't bother to coom round—and when tha doesn't coom we'll knaw for sure that way it's Sunday."

"Aye, that's fine," old Capper said, "but Ah'll lose all me collections that way."

They all saw that was so, but they agreed that even if it kept on being Sunday, they would pay old Capper just the same as if it had become the rotation of week-days and he'd made his rounds.

"Nay, Ah couldn't tak' it," Capper protested.

"Nay, we'd like thee to," they protested.

"Well, if ye say," Capper agreed. "But how about lads i't'other villages. It's hard on them thinking it's a week-day and walking all the way here to find it's a Sunday."

"Well," John Willie said, "we'll form a committee, like, right now, and the members will each tak' a village and goa reight ovver theer and tell ivveryone that it's stay-ing Sunday these days—that the days o't'week is stuck, like."

Everyone thought it a good and orderly idea, and so it was done.

The next morning people in the village woke up, and they lay abed and listened. But they heard no trident of wire chattering in the greyness of the morning, nor old Capper's voice wheezing: " 'Awf pest fower, ist'a oop?" They waited but they heard no clogs clattering on the cobbles, and no whistle at the mill saying that if they didn't get there in fifteen minutes they'd be locked out.

So they knew it must be Sunday again, and they went back to sleep, and the next thing they knew was the church bell ringing once more. So that made it Sunday and they were sure of it.

And in the other towns roundabout, the people didn't go to work, and so they knew it was Sunday, too. They put on their best clothes, and did a bit of gardening and the men mended things about the house and the children didn't go to school, and everyone had a fine rest, so that their work-tired bodies began to grow glad and proud again.

The next day the news that the days of the week were stuck at Sunday had spread all over Yorkshire, and was percolating up to the Tyneside where the shipworkers were, and over into Lancashire where the youngsters worked before cotton mills and looms, and down into the black country where the men hauled at steel and went down into the mines, and down into Staffordshire where they toiled at the potteries and the car factories.

The newspapers sent men around to find out what had happened to the lost weekdays, and one of them came to the village and looked up old Capper. At first he laughed, until Ian Cawper came along. Ian Cawper was the biggest man in Yorkshire for sure, and happen the biggest and strongest man in all England without doubt. So he just asked the newspaper lad for a penny, and then he bent the penny in two, and the newspaper lad stopped laughing.

"Nah, lad," Ian said. "Happen tha'd better telly-phone thy paper that this is Sunday."

"Indeed I will," the young man said, very appreciatively.

Now although the wonderful thing that it was still Sunday found great gratification in the hearts of all the men who worked long hours handling steel and wood and cotton and iron and glass and fabric and paper and silk, at furnaces and forges and foundries and looms and jennies and sides and presses and drills and lathes and assembly belts, there were some men who were quite upset by the miraculous happening. And in spite of the fact that everyone else in the country now saw that a beautiful series of Sundays had happened, these men kept on trying to persuade everyone that they were just ordinary days of the week that people merely *thought* were Sundays.

These men soon saw that if it kept on being Sunday they'd never be able to make any more battleships and gasbombs and motor cars and airplanes and radios and badminton rackets and all the rest of the things that are civilizing influences upon the world. And, to go further, if they didn't make those things, they wouldn't be able to go on making more money than they had already.

This was quite an abhorrent state of affairs. So they went to the Prime Minister about it.

"I yield my reverence for religion, especially the Church of England, to no one," one of them said. "In fact, I am thoroughly in accord with religion—one day a week."

"Hear, hear," the others said.

"But, Mr. Prime Minister, think of my stockholders! Many are orphans. Many are widows. If my factory doesn't make money, these poor people will be destitute—because always having drawn dividends, they've never had to learn how to work. We cannot let them suffer."

"Gentlemen," said the Prime Minister, "you may rest assured that His Majesty's Government will do all within its power to safeguard that industry and commerce which is the backbone of our nation—indeed, of our Empire."

Then the Prime Minister went away and thought. Being a Prime Minister he didn't think as you or I would. You or I, in the same case, might have said to ourselves: "Come, come now. What we've got to decide is whether this is Sunday or isn't." Which is probably why you and I will never be Prime Ministers.

This Prime Minister thought of a lot of things all at once. Suddenly, he called his secretary and said:

"Carrington-Smaithe. It is a Sunday today, I hear, and it will be a Sunday again tomorrow. Pack my things. We're going away for the week end."

"But sir," said the secretary, "what about the International Crisis? We have two ultimatums which must be answered immediately."

"Dear me," said the Prime Minister. "That is a nuisance; but all the world knows the British week end is inviolate, and if this is Sunday, as it seems to me it must be, then I won't be able to answer till the week end is over."

"But when will it stop being Sunday, sir?"

"Well, Carrington-Smaithe, how long will it take our fastest cruiser squadron to get round to that troublesome part of the world?"

"Oh, about thirty-six more hours, sir."

"Hmmmph! Then I think it will stop being Sunday in about thirty-six more hours."

And with this the Prime Minister caught the five-fifteen train and went off to the country. And when the newspapers heard of it they printed it, and all the people in England—in fact, in all the world—knew that it was officially Sunday.

And back in Allerby Brig all the people were that proud of old Capper Wambley. For hadn't he been the first man in all the land to notice that the days of the week were stuck and every day kept turning up a Sunday.

And all over the land toil-weary people sighed with happiness at their escape from industrial chains. They rested their tired bodies. Some went to church every day. The men went walking with their dogs, or did odd jobs round the house, tinkering and gardening and cobbling and putting up shelves. In the cities people took busses out into the country and had picnics. The grownups lay in the sun and the children played in the fields, and the young men and women walked in the lanes and made love. There was only one flaw. Being Sundays, the pubs had to go on Sunday closing hours, which allows no man to buy a pint of beer unless he is a legal traveler who has come so many miles. But this

ERIC KNIGHT

did good in a way, because many men walked the legal
number of miles, and that way they saw parts of their
own country they never would have seen otherwise, and
they saw what other towns and villages looked like.

And all the time that went on, the Prime Minister sat
in his garden and read detective novels, or snoozed in
the sun with a couple of his favorite spaniels at his feet,
until there came a wireless message.

"Sign here," said the boy.

So the Prime Minister signed, and then he got a code
book and decoded the message. Immediately he had
done so, he called his secretary and said:

"Carrington-Smaithe! What day is today?"

"Sunday, sir," the secretary said.

"Nonsense," said the Prime Minister. "I am tired of
this blundering-through policy with its shilly-shallying.
If this goes on, we shall have a Constitutional Crisis!"

"A Constitutional Crisis, sir?"

"Yes, Carrington-Smaithe. So you'd better pack and
we'll get back to the City. We must act immediately. I
shall issue a statement that His Majesty's Government
hereby declares officially that today is Friday, and tomorrow shall be officially Saturday, and the days of the
week must now go on officially in their regular and accustomed order."

"But isn't this really Sunday, sir? Hasn't a miraculous thing happened that has stopped the days of the
week from arriving?"

"I don't know, my boy. But I do know this. Even if it

422

is Sunday, and we all, everywhere, decide to call it Monday or Tuesday, then it becomes Monday or Tuesday because we all believe it is Monday or Tuesday."

"Yes, I see, sir."

And so the secretary packed, and the Prime Minister went back to London where he now could answer his ultimatums quite forcefully, and all the newspapers of the land carried the news that today was Friday and tomorrow would be Saturday—officially.

It wasn't until the next morning that this news reached Allerby Brig where it had all started. Mr. Bloggs got the news first, of course, and so he ordered the siren blown at the mill. So everybody hurried off to the mill because if you weren't there fifteen minutes after the siren went you were locked out and lost half a day's pay.

But as they trooped into the yard, old Capper stopped them.

"Hold on, a minute, mates," he said. "Just what day is it?"

"Now come on in to work," Mr. Bloggs called. "It's Saturday."

"Nay," Capper said. "Yesterday were Sunday, so today maun be Monday, onless us's started slipping and now we're off to hev t'days backwards."

This remark of Capper's got everyone mixed up again and some said it was Saturday and some Monday while some still stuck to Sunday.

The upshot was that they decided to call Sam Small again to get his opinion. Sam arrived in about a half hour, and heard all sides. Then he looked around, and spoke in the voice of one who is used to handling such matters.

"There's nobbut one thing to dew, lads," he said. "And Ah'm the chap that's off to dew it."

With that he walked into the office, and picking up the telephone, he said:

"Connect me with His Majesty, the King."

Before you could wink the connection was made.

"Is this His Majesty, the King?" Sam asked.

"Why Sammywell Small, lad!" said the King, recognizing the voice. "If it doan't dew ma heart and sowl good to hear thy voice again. How's'ta been, Sam lad?"

"Reight nicely, Your Majesty," Sam said.

"And how's that reight bonnie wife o' thine, Dally?" asked the King, who, as you will have noticed, spoke the dialects fluently. It is things like that, that make a good king. Little things like passing laws can be left to lads who have nothing but brains.

"Dally's reight well," Sam said. "And how's thy missus and bairns, if tha doan't mind the question."

"Nay, Sam lad, Ah'm that glad tha axed ma," the king said. "My littlest 'un was a bit poorly last week. It's teethin' tha knaws. But she's feeling champion now."

"Well, Ah'm glad to hear that," Sam answered.

"Thanks," the King said. "Well, Sam, Ah doan't suppose tha called me oop just for idle barneying. Whet c'n Ah dew for thee, lad?"

"Well, it's this way, Your Majesty," Sam said. "Ah hoap

tha'll net think ma gormless for axing, but could ta tell me just whet day o' t'week it is for thee."

"Eigh Sam," the King said, "Ah doan't monkey wi' things like that. Ah leave all that to ma ministers and such. But Ah've just gate official infoormation from 'em that today's Sat'day."

"Your Majesty," said Sam, "if Sat'day's good enow for thee, then there's noa moar argyment. Thank you varry much."

"Net at all, Sam," the king said. "And by the way, Sam Small, it is our royal wish that tha doesn't wait soa long afore tha calls ma oop again. There's been sivveral things lately Ah would ha liked thy opinion on. When's'ta off to coom to Lunnon?"

"Nay, Your Majesty, Ah give oop traveling," Sam replied.

"Too bad, Sam. Too bad. Well, give me a ring soom time soon, will'ta?"

"That Ah will, lad."

"Well, so long," said the King.

"So long, Your Majesty," said Sam.

All during this conversation, of course, the people of the village had been crowding breathlessly round the door of the office, listening to Sam. And right in the forefront was Mr. Bloggs.

"Well, what did he say?" Mr. Bloggs breathed as Sam hung up.

"He said," said Sam, "that today was Sat'day."

"There, didn't I tell you," Mr. Bloggs shouted. "Now, doesn't that make it Saturday?"

Everyone thought it did, but they weren't quite sure. They thought the matter over quite a while, and then John Willie Braithwaite said:

"T'only trouble is, it doan't *feel* like Sat'day to me."

"But I tell you it is officially Saturday," Mr. Bloggs cried.

"Wait a minute, lads," Sam Small put in. "Now Ah doan't wark here, soa Ah play no favorites. But Ah c'n tell ye for sure how ye'll all knaw it's a Sat'day."

"How can we tell?" they asked.

"Why, it's that simple," Sam replied. "Ye'll knaw that ivvery Sat'day morning at a quarter to twelve, ye get paid a week's wages. Now if soa be this is Sat'day, Mr. Bloggs will begin paying each man a week's money exactly ten minutes from now. And, on t'other hand, then if he doan't start paying a week's brass i' ten minutes— it can't be Sat'day—and the chances are it's off to keep on being Sunday for a long time."

"Outrageous," Mr. Bloggs cried.

He argued and shouted, but they just stood and shook their heads and said that if it were a Saturday they'd draw a week's pay at exactly a quarter to twelve, as they always did on Saturday. And finally Mr. Bloggs, seeing no other way of getting the days of the week started properly again, gave in and paid off each man and woman and girl and boy.

By the time they were paid it was Saturday noon, and so they all trooped as usual down the stairs of the mill and into the yard to go home. And there old Capper stopped them.

"But if it's a Saturday today, lads and lasses, what day is it tomorrow?"

"It'll be Sunday," they all roared.

"Now ain't that champion," old Capper beamed. "If it's Sunday we'll all be able to lie abed late and get a bit o' extra sleep for a change."

S. J. PERELMAN

Acres and Pains

[EXCERPT]

According to recent figures compiled by trained statisticians working under filtered oatmeal, the first thing ninety-four per cent of the population does on acquiring a country place is to build some sort of swimming pool. The other six per cent instantly welshes on the deal and stops payment. I tried to, but the previous owner beat me to the bank. My checkbook had hardly ceased thrashing about in its final agony before I was out in whipcord breeches and cordovans, barking orders at a team of mules and a scoop shovel. I didn't want anything showy, just a fiord about the size of Lake Huron deep enough to float a yawl. In my overheated imagination I saw our anemic little creek transformed into a crystal mirror bordered by gay cabañas. I could almost hear the bevy of Powers models sighing with envy

431

as my tanned, muscular form flashed off the spring-board in a perfect swan dive. I even wired the Department of the Interior that if Grand Coulee proved insufficient, I could furnish water power to keep the wheels turning for a year or two.

What I had when the gang of workmen departed was a small, shrunken buffalo wallow infested with every variety of poisonous snake known to man, including several found only in the upper reaches of the Orinoco. Its surface was covered with an attractive green film dotted with decaying stumps and half-submerged oil cans. At night a dense mist shrouded the tarn; eerie lights flickered in the rushes, ghostly chuckles were audible, and if you ventured too close, you were liable to encounter a transparent citizen carrying his head under his arm. Thirteen families of ground hogs had set up light housekeeping in the dam itself, a massive affair of earth and logs that looked like the Union breastworks before Vicksburg. Every time it rained, the water boiled up, punching another hole in the structure, and I ran down the valley to pay the neighbors for the chickens it swept away. My children went hungry and unshod while I poured tons of cement into the coffers to make them hold. One morning I caught myself cackling hysterically and ramming an old mattress into the dam, and I knew I was licked. I called in the local dynamiter, indicated the project with a careless wave, and commanded him to erase it from the face of the earth.

The moment word was bruited about that Loch Wampum was doomed, the local savants gathered on the banks for a gleeful death watch. The man who had done the excavating was especially triumphant. "I could have told him it wouldn't work," he crowed. "By rights he should have dug out that gully where they dump the swill. Good stone bottom there." I asked him why he hadn't mentioned it earlier. "It don't pay to poke your nose in other people's business," he replied virtuously.

It took a day and a half for the dynamiter to drill the charges and string red flags across the township. On the appointed morning, the place was busier than New London during the Harvard-Yale regatta. Whole clans of Mennonites and Amish bearing box lunches arrived from the back country in ancient buckboards. Sight-seers wandered through the garden poking sly fun at our vegetables, and one bystander mimicked my gait and speech so cleverly that I could not help sharing the general merriment. When everything was ready, I retired to the tool shed with my family and made them lie flat on the floor. With a warning, "Stand clear, all!" the dynamiter threw his switch. The blast which followed tore the roof off the springhouse and broke windows in the county seat sixteen miles away. It's only effect on the dam, however, was to harden the cement in it. My specialist bit his lip in chagrin. "I must have cut her a bit too fine," he confessed; "I'll fix her tomorrow, by cracky."

He kept his word. When the dust finally settled, I had enough firewood for the next fifty years, most of it right inside the house where I could get at it. And when *I* finally settled, the man next door had a new front porch and a glass eye you couldn't tell from the other one. Of course it's a bit unwieldy for five people to take a bath in a washtub, particularly at one time, but at least you don't have to look out for copperheads.

ROBERT BENCHLEY

First—Catch Your Criminal

With the increase in crime during the past decade has come a corresponding increase in crime prevention. Or perhaps it is vice versa. At any rate, we are awfully busy down at our laboratory trying to find out who is a criminal and who isn't. (You can imagine the surprise of the head of our Research Department the other day when he reacted to one of his own tests, thereby proving himself to be a "lingoidphrensic" type, or man-eating shark. He immediately resigned his portfolio and gave himself up to the authorities; but as he is seventy-one years old, they didn't want him.)

Our theory of crime prevention has a strictly psychological basis, but we will listen to anything. It is our idea to take the criminal *before* he becomes a criminal and to chivvy him about the laboratory until he is too tired and disgusted to commit the crime. A great many times we have converted potential criminals into hermits and deep-sea divers by making them want to get away from it all and just be alone. The man who runs the lighthouse at Salt Mackerel Rock, Maine, is one of our graduates. He won't even let people bring him newspapers.

This man is a rather interesting case of a reformed "rhombusmanic," or "inverted nail-biter" type; that is, instead of wanting to bite his own nails he wanted to bite other people's. Perhaps I should say that his *tendencies* were in that direction, for we caught him before he had really started on anything that could be called a career in that field. Following was our course of experimentation: Mr. X, as we will call him (although his real name is Mr. Y), was a patient in the Nursing Home on City Island, having been brought there suffering from a three days' beard. He had been shaved, and was lying in his cot rubbing his chin with the tips of his fingers, when discovered by our Dr. Altschu, who was browsing about among the charity patients looking for types. Dr. Altschu immediately detected in Mr. X the indications of a rhombusmanic (low frontal elevation, pendent ear lobes, and absence of pupils in the eyes) and effected a transfer of the patient from the Nursing Home to the Crime Prevention laboratory. We gave a third baseman in exchange.

Once in the laboratory, Mr. X was put into a hot bath with a rubber walrus and told to get himself nice and clean. He was then dressed in a suit of blue denim and taken into the Chart Room, where he was seated in an easy-chair (or what he thought was an easy-chair) and told to watch the words that were thrown on the screen in front of him.

As a matter of fact, the chair was a special invention of Dr. Altschu's, with a delicate registering device concealed in the arms and an invisible wire stretching across the patient's neck, so that each fluctuation in his breathing and each quickening of his pulse was registered. Also the wire across his neck gradually choked him until he jumped up yelling: "Let's get the hell out of here!" At this point another registering device, which had in some unaccountable way become attached to his ankles to indicate ankle fluctuation, became suddenly rigid and threw him to the ground, where his weight and preference in flowers were taken simultaneously.

The room was then darkened and a series of jokes were flashed on the screen. It was the patient's reactions to these jokes, as indicated on a dial in the Control Room, which determined just which type of rhombusmanic he belonged to. (There are three types of rhombusmanic—the A type, or introvert; the B type, or extravert; and the D type, or Old Man River. There used to be a C type, or Life on the Oregon Trail; but we had to drop it, as it began to edge over into the lower thermodepressive type, which gets us into Juggling and Sleight of Hand.)

There was considerable confusion in the case of X, however, as he would not laugh at *any* of the jokes which were flashed on the screen. He just sat and asked when the news reel came on. We couldn't get him to react in the slightest degree, and the man in the Control Room kept popping his head out and saying: "O. K.! Start 'er up!" But X wouldn't start.

We tried the one about the man who had three daughters that he wanted to get married, the one about the Scotchman, the Irishman, and the Jew, and the one ending: "Lie down; do you want to make a fool out of the doctor?" But all that X would do was to keep asking about the news reel and saying: "I like Mickey Mouse." This in itself was significant, but we couldn't decide of what.

So we took Mr. X out of the Joke Registration Room and put him in the Blank-Filling-Out Clinic. We set great store by our blanks, or questionnaires, especially the pink ones. If we can get a patient to fill out one of our pink questionnaires, answering every question without once dashing it to the floor and screaming, "Of all the damned nonsense!" we feel that we have done a lot toward the preservation of Society. So far we haven't been able to find one patient who could keep his temper long enough to answer every question on the sheet. This makes it difficult to keep our records straight.

Mr. X was no exception to the rule, even though we began him on the blue questionnaire. His aversion to the questions, however, took the form of frivolity and sneering, which is even harder to cope with than rage. For example, the first question on the blue form was: "You are (a) Mohammed, (b) Disraeli, (c) Mussolini, (d) yourself. Cross out the wrong ones." On this the only name that X would cross out was Mussolini's, because he said that Mussolini was the only one who was wrong. To all the other questions he answered simply "Yes" or else drew a thumb-nail sketch of a sailboat and labeled it, "My vacation sport."

It was obvious that X was no ordinary rhombusmanic, but it was equally obvious that he ought not to be allowed at large with as many questionnaires as are being put out today. Here was a man who was evidently in a way to become either a menace to Society or else darned good company. We couldn't decide which, so we subjected him to further tests. By this time we had him in the Cutting and Binding Room.

Here he had little electric bulbs flashed before his eyes and was told to say the first word which popped into his mind at each flash. All he would say was "Ooops!" every time. He was told to shut his eyes and twirl around on his heel three times and then walk straight ahead and place his finger on the center of a wall chart. He shut his eyes as we told him, but kept on twirling round and round without stopping, maintaining that he liked it. When he was finally persuaded to stop, he walked forward and stuck his finger in Dr. Altschu's mouth, keeping on until Dr. Altschu gagged.

He was shown cards of different colors and asked to explain what they reminded him of; but on the first card (which was green) he launched forth into such a long reminiscence that we finally had to stop him and hide the rest of the cards.

By this time the patient was beginning to get restless, and we of the examining staff were frankly upset. So we came right out and asked him if he didn't think that he might possibly be a criminal in the making, and he said that he was sure of it. In fact, he said it was only a question of minutes before he killed us all.

It was then that he asked us if we thought that we could get him a job as a lighthouse keeper where he wouldn't have to see anyone ever again, and the position at Salt Mackerel Rock was found for him.

It is along these lines that we are trying to build our system of crime prevention, on the theory that, if we can catch the criminal before he commits the crime, there will be no crime. What we need right now, however, are more experimental chairs and lots more colored bulbs.

ROBERT BENCHLEY

The King and the Old Man

BEING A WHIMSICAL LEGEND, WRITTEN WITHOUT APOLOGIES
TO THE LONDON CHRISTIAN WEEKLIES

For you must know that in those days there was a King
ruling in the land who was very great, so great even that
he was called "Pepin Glabamus," or "Pepin Flatfoot,"
and there were in his kingdom anywhere from twenty-
and-four to twenty-and-eight maidens who were in sore
distress and concerning whom no one, not even the
youth of the university, had any interest whatsoever.
Now the King grieved greatly at this, and so great was
his grief that he became known far and wide as "Pepin
Glubabo" or "Pepin Red-Eye." He was also known as
"That Old Buzzard."

Now there came to the castle one night an Old Man,
who begged admittance on the grounds that he represented the Fuller Brush Company and would like to
show the King a thing or two about brushing. But the

King, who was still in high dudgeon (the low dudgeons being full of paynims and poor white trash left over from the Fifth, or Crucial, Crusade), sent out word that he had already been brushed and to get the hell out from under that portcullis. But the Old Man paid no heed to the King's command, but instead sent back word that he had some very nice mead which was guaranteed to make the drinker's ears fly out and snap back, all to the count of "one-two-one-two." So the King, it being Christmas Eve and being sorely troubled in spirit, sent down word, "Oh, well." And so the Old Man came up.

And so the Old Man came up. (A very medieval and mystic effect is gained by repeating the same sentence twice, as you will find out by reading farther in this tale, you sucker.) And when he had reached the King's chamber, he encountered the Chamberlain who, lest the Queen should take to prowling of a night, was always stationed by the door in possession of a loud gong and a basket of red fire. And, at the sound of the gong and the sight of the red fire over the transom, the King was accustomed to open a secret passageway like a flash, and into this secret passageway could dart any business friends who might be sharing a friendly nightcap with His Majesty. Only one night, being sore confused and in something of a daze, the King himself had darted into the secret passageway, leaving the business friend behind on top of the silken canopy, very uncomfortable from the pointed spearheads which held the canopy in place. It was from this unhappy incident, or so said the jester and court winchell, that the Royal Museum acquired its rare collection of golden tresses and slightly damaged neck ornaments, listed in the catalogue under the head of "Or Else."

At last the Old Man came into the presence of the King and, what with opening his sack of mead and testing it himself (the King being no fool), and what with giving of it to the King for him to taste, and what with trying it first with juice of half a lemon and then with effervescent waters to see which way it went best, it was no time at all before both the King and the Old Man were going through the King's supply of neckties to see which ones they should send to the Pope for Christmas.

"Here is one that I have worn only once," said the King.

"How did you ever happen to do that?" asked the Old Man, looking at its tapestry design and screaming with laughter.

And the King screamed, too, not once but eleven times —and the evening was on. The evening was on, and the night was on, and the morning, up until ten-thirty, was on, and, by that time, the Queen was on and had packed up and gone to her mother's.

And so it happened that late on Christmas Day the King rolled over and, finding his head where it had bounced under the bed, replaced it on one shoulder and rubbed his eyes, which he found in the pocket of his waistcoat, and then said:

"Old Man, who *are* you?"

But the Old Man had gone on, rather, it looked to the

King as if he had gone, but he was all the time in the open bureau drawer with the neckties.

And so, to this day, no one ever found out who the Old Man really was, but there are those who say that he was the West Wind, and there are those who say that he was the Down from a Thistle, but there are older and wiser ones who say that he was just a naughty Old Man.

STEPHEN LEACOCK

Sorrows of a Super Soul: or, The Memoirs of Marie Mushenough

(TRANSLATED, BY MACHINERY, OUT OF THE ORIGINAL
RUSSIAN.)

Do you ever look at your face in the glass?

I do.

Sometimes I stand for hours and peer at my face and wonder at it. At times I turn it upside down and gaze intently at it. I try to think what it means. It seems to look back at me with its great brown eyes as if it knew me and wanted to speak to me.

Why was I born?

I do not know.

I ask my face a thousand times a day and find no answer.

At times when people pass my room—my maid Nitnitzka, or Jakub, the serving-man—and see me talking to my face, they think I am foolish.

But I am not.

At times I cast myself on the sofa and bury my head in the cushions. Even then I cannot find out why I was born.

I am seventeen.

Shall I ever be seventy-seven? Ah!

Shall I ever be even sixty-seven, or sixty-seven even? Oh!

And if I am both of these, shall I ever be eighty-seven?

I cannot tell.

Often I start up in the night with wild eyes and wonder if I shall be eighty-seven.

Next Day.

I passed a flower in my walk to-day. It grew in the meadow beside the river bank.

It stood dreaming on a long stem.

I knew its name. It was a Tchupvskja. I love beautiful names.

I leaned over and spoke to it. I asked it if my heart would ever know love. It said it thought so.

On the way home I passed an onion.

It lay upon the road.

Someone had stepped upon its stem and crushed it. How it must have suffered. I placed it in my bosom. All night it lay beside my pillow.

Another Day.

My heart is yearning for love! How is it that I can love no one?

I have tried and I cannot. My father—Ivan Ivanovitch —he is so big and so kind, and yet I cannot love him; and my mother, Katoosha Katooshavitch, she is just as big, and yet I cannot love her. And my brother, Dimitri Dimitrivitch, I cannot love him.

And Alexis Alexovitch!

I cannot love him. And yet I am to marry him. They have set the day. It is a month from to-day. One month. Thirty days. Why cannot I love Alexis? He is tall and strong. He is a soldier. He is in the Guard of the Czar, Nicholas Romanoff, and yet I cannot love him.

Next Day but one.

How they cramp and confine me here—Ivan Ivanovitch my father, and my mother (I forget her name for the minute), and all the rest.

I cannot breathe.

They will not let me.

Every time I try to commit suicide they hinder me.

Last night I tried again.

I placed a phial of sulphuric acid on the table beside my bed.

In the morning it was still there.

It had not killed me.

They have forbidden me to drown myself.

Why!

I do not know why? In vain I ask the air and the trees why I should not drown myself? They do not see any reason why.

And yet I long to be free, free as the young birds, as the very youngest of them.

I watch the leaves blowing in the wind and I want to be a leaf.

Yet here they want to make me eat!

Yesterday I ate a banana! Ugh!

Next Day.

To-day in my walk I found a cabbage.

It lay in a corner of the hedge. Cruel boys had chased it there with stones.

It was dead when I lifted it up.

Beside it was an egg.

It too was dead. Ah, how I wept—

This Morning.

How my heart beats. To-day A MAN passed. He passed: actually passed.

From my window I saw him go by the garden gate and out into the meadow beside the river where my Tchupvskja flower is growing!

How beautiful he looked! Not tall like Alexis Alexovitch, ah, no! but so short and wide and round—shaped like the beautiful cabbage that died last week.

He wore a velvet jacket and he carried a camp stool and an easel on his back, and in his face was a curved pipe with a long stem, and his face was not red and rough like the face of Alexis, but mild and beautiful and with a smile that played on it like moonlight over putty.

Do I love him? I cannot tell. Not yet. Love is a gentle plant. You cannot force its growth.

As he passed I leaned from the window and threw a rosebud at him.

But he did not see it.

Then I threw a cake of soap and a toothbrush at him. But I missed him, and he passed on.

Another Day.

Love has come into my life. It fills it. I have seen HIM again. I have spoken with him. He sat beside the river on his camp stool. How beautiful he looked, sitting on it: how strong he seemed and how frail the little stool on which he sat.

Before him was the easel and he was painting. I spoke to him.

I know his name now.

His name—. How my heart beats as I write it—no, I cannot write it, I will whisper it—it is Otto Dinkelspiel.

Is it not a beautiful name? Ah!

He was painting on a canvas—beautiful colours, red and gold and white, in glorious opalescent streaks in all directions.

I looked at it in wonder.

Instinctively I spoke to him. "What are you painting?" I said. "Is it the Heavenly Child?"

"No," he said, "it is a cow!"

Then I looked again and I could see that it was a cow.

I looked straight into his eyes.

"It shall be our secret," I said; "no one else shall know."
And I knew that I loved him.

A Week Later.

Each morning I go to see Otto beside the river in the
meadow.

He sits and paints, and I sit with my hands clasped
about my knees and talk to him. I tell him all that I think,
all that I read, all that I know, all that I feel, all that I do
not feel.

He listens to me with that far-away look that I have
learned to love and that means that he is thinking
deeply; at times he almost seems not to hear.

The intercourse of our minds is wonderful.

We stimulate one another's thought.

Otto is my master. I am his disciple!

Yesterday I asked him if Hegel or Schlegel or Whegel
gives the truest view of life.

He said he didn't know! My Otto!

To-day.

Otto touched me! He touched me!

How the recollection of it thrills me!

I stood beside him on the river bank, and as we
talked the handle of my parasol touched the bottom button of his waistcoat.

It seemed to burn me like fire!

To-morrow I am to bring Otto to see my father.

But to-night I can think of nothing else but that Otto
has touched me.

Next Day.

Otto has touched father! He touched him for ten roubles. My father is furious. I cannot tell what it means.

I brought Otto to our home. He spoke with my father, Ivan Ivanovitch. They sat together in the evening. And now my father is angry. He says that Otto wanted to touch him.

Why should he be angry?

But Otto is forbidden the house, and I can see him only in the meadow.

Two Days Later.

To-day Otto asked me for a keepsake.

I offered him one of my hatpins. But he said no. He has taken instead the diamond buckle from my belt.

I read his meaning.

He means that I am to him as a diamond is to lesser natures.

This Morning.

Yesterday Otto asked me for another keepsake. I took a gold rouble from my bag and said that he should break it in half and that each should keep one of the halves.

But Otto said no. I divined his thought. It would violate our love to break the coin.

He is to keep it for both of us, and it is to remain unbroken like our love.

Is it not a sweet thought?

Otto is so thoughtful. He thinks of everything.

To-day he asked me if I had another gold rouble.

Next Day.

To-day I brought Otto another gold rouble.

His eyes shone with love when he saw it.

He has given me for it a bronze kopek. Our love is to be as pure as gold and as strong as bronze.

Is it not beautiful?

Later.

I am so fearful that Alexis Alexovitch may return.

I fear that if he comes Otto might kill him. Otto is so calm, I dread to think of what would happen if he were aroused.

Next Day.

I have told Otto about Alexis. I have told him that Alexis is a soldier, that he is in the Guards of the Czar, and that I am betrothed to him. At first Otto would not listen to me. He feared that his anger might overmaster him. He began folding up his camp stool.

Then I told him that Alexis would not come for some time yet, and he grew calmer.

I have begged him for my sake not to kill Alexis. He has given me his promise.

Another Day.

Ivan Ivanovitch, my father, has heard from Alexis. He will return in fourteen days. The day after his return I am to marry him.

And meantime I have still fourteen days to love Otto.

My love is perfect. It makes me want to die. Last night

I tried again to commit suicide. Why should I live now that I have known a perfect love? I placed a box of cartridges beside my bed. I awoke unharmed. They did not kill me. But I know what it means. It means that Otto and I are to die together. I must tell Otto.

Later.

To-day I told Otto that we must kill ourselves, that our love is so perfect that we have no right to live.

At first he looked so strange.

He suggested that I should kill myself first and that he should starve himself beside my grave.

But I could not accept the sacrifice.

I offered instead to help him to hang himself beside the river.

He is to think it over. If he does not hang himself, he is to shoot himself. I have lent him my father's revolver. How grateful he looked when he took it.

Next Day.

Why does Otto seem to avoid me? Has he some secret sorrow that I cannot share? To-day he moved his camp stool to the other side of the meadow. He was in the long grass behind an elderberry bush. At first I did not see him. I thought that he had hanged himself. But he said no. He had forgotten to get a rope. He had tried, he said, to shoot himself. But he had missed himself.

Five Days Later.

Otto and I are not to die. We are to live; to live and

love one another for ever! We are going away, out into the world together! How happy I am!

Otto and I are to flee together.

When Alexis comes we shall be gone; we shall be far away.

I have said to Otto that I will fly with him, and he has said yes.

I told him that we would go out into the world together; empty-handed we would fare forth together and defy the world. I said that he should be my knight-errant, my paladin!

Otto said he would be it.

He has consented. But he says we must not fare forth empty-handed. I do not know why he thinks this, but he is firm, and I yield to my lord. He is making all our preparations.

Each morning I bring to the meadow a little bundle of my things and give them to my knight-errant and he takes them to the inn where he is staying.

Last week I brought my jewel-case, and yesterday, at his request, I took my money from the bank and brought it to my paladin. It will be so safe with him.

To-day he said that I shall need some little things to remember my father and mother by when we are gone. So I am to take my father's gold watch while he is asleep. My hero! How thoughtful he is of my happiness.

Next Day.

All is ready. To-morrow I am to meet Otto at the meadow with the watch and the rest of the things.

To-morrow night we are to flee together. I am to go down to the little gate at the foot of the garden, and Otto will be there.

To-day I have wandered about the house and garden and have said good-bye. I have said good-bye to my Tchupvskja flower, and to the birds and the bees.

To-morrow it will be all over.

Next Evening.

How can I write what has happened! My soul is shattered to its depths.

All that I dreaded most has happened. How can I live! Alexis has come back. He and Otto have fought.

Ah God! it has been terrible.

I stood with Otto in the meadow. I had brought him the watch, and I gave it to him, and all my love and my life with it.

Then, as we stood, I turned and saw Alexis Alexovitch striding towards us through the grass.

How tall and soldierly he looked! And the thought flashed through my mind that if Otto killed him he would be lying there a dead, inanimate thing.

"Go, Otto," I cried, "go, if you stay you will kill him."

Otto looked and saw Alexis coming. He turned one glance at me: his face was full of infinite meaning.

Then, for my sake, he ran. How noble he looked as he ran. Brave heart! he dared not stay and risk the outburst of his anger.

But Alexis overtook him.

Then beside the river bank they fought. Ah! But it was

455

terrible to see them fight. Is it not awful when men fight together?

I could only stand and wring my hands and look on in agony!

First, Alexis seized Otto by the waistband of his trousers and swung him round and round in the air. I could see Otto's face as he went round: the same mute courage was written on it as when he turned to run. Alexis swung Otto round and round until his waistband broke, and he was thrown into the grass.

That was the first part of the fight.

Then Alexis stood beside Otto and kicked him from behind as he lay in the grass, and they fought like that for some time. That was the second part of the fight. Then came the third and last part. Alexis picked up the easel and smashed the picture over Otto's head. It fastened itself like a collar about his neck. Then Alexis picked Otto up with the picture round his neck and threw him into the stream.

He floated!

My paladin!

He floated!

I could see his upturned face as he floated onwards down the stream, through the meadow! It was full of deep resignation.

Then Alexis Alexovitch came to me and gathered me up in his arms and carried me thus across the meadow— he is so tall and strong—and whispered that he loved me, and that to-morrow he would shield me from the world. He carried me thus to the house in his arms among the grass and flowers; and there was my father, Ivan Ivanovitch, and my mother, Katoosha Katoosha-vitch. And to-morrow I am to marry Alexis. He had brought back from the inn my jewels and my money, and he gave me again the diamond clasp that Otto had taken from my waist.

How can I bear it? Alexis is to take me to Petersburg, and he has bought a beautiful house in the Prospekt, and I am to live in it with him, and we are to be rich, and I am to be presented at the Court of Nicholas Romanoff and his wife. Ah! Is it not dreadful?

And I can only think of Otto floating down the stream with the easel about his neck. From the little river he will float into the Dnieper, and from the Dnieper into the Bug, and from the Bug he will float down the Volga, and from the Volga into the Caspian Sea. And from the Caspian Sea there is no outlet, and Otto will float round and round it for ever.

Is it not dreadful?

STEPHEN LEACOCK

Hannah of the Highlands: or,
The Laird of Loch Aucherlocherty

"Sair maun ye greet, but hoot awa!
There's muckle yet, love isna' a'—
Nae more ye'll see, howe'er ye whine
The bonnie breeks of Auld Lang Syne!"

The simple words rang out fresh and sweet upon the morning air.

It was Hannah of the Highlands. She was gathering lobsters in the burn that ran through the glen.

The scene about her was typically Highland. Wild hills rose on both sides of the burn to a height of seventy-five feet, covered with a dense Highland forest that stretched a hundred yards in either direction. At the foot of the burn a beautiful Scotch logch lay in the hollow of the hills. Beyond it again, through the gap of the hills, was the sea. Through the Glen, and close beside the burn where Hannah stood, wound the road that rose again to follow the cliffs along the shore.

The tourists in the Highlands will find no more beautiful spot than the Glen of Aucherlocherty.

Nor is there any spot which can more justly claim to be historic ground.

It was here in the glen that Bonnie Prince Charlie had lain and hidden after the defeat of Culloden. Almost in the same spot the great boulder still stands behind which the Bruce had lain hidden after Bannockburn; while behind a number of lesser stones the Covenanters had concealed themselves during the height of the Stuart persecution.

Through the Glen Montrose had passed on his fateful ride to Killiecrankie; while at the lower end of it the rock was still pointed out behind which William Wallace had paused to change his breeches while flying from the wrath of Rob Roy.

Grim memories such as these gave character to the spot.

Indeed, most of the great events of Scotch history had taken place in the Glen, while the little logch had been the scene of some of the most stirring naval combats in the history of the Grampian Hills.

But there was little in the scene which lay so peaceful on this April morning to recall the sanguinary history of the Glen. Its sides at present were covered with a thick growth of gorse, elderberry, egg-plants, and ghillie flower, while the woods about it were loud with the voice of the throstle, the linnet, the magpie, the jack-daw, and other song-birds of the Highlands.

It was a gloriously beautiful Scotch morning. The rain fell softly and quietly, bringing dampness and moisture, and almost a sense of wetness to the soft moss underfoot. Grey mists flew hither and thither, carrying with them an invigorating rawness that had almost a feeling of dampness.

It is the memory of such a morning that draws a tear from the eye of Scotchmen after years of exile. The Scotch heart, reader, can be moved to its depths by the sight of a raindrop or the sound of a wet rag.

And meantime Hannah, the beautiful Highland girl, was singing. The fresh young voice rose high above the rain. Even the birds seemed to pause to listen, and as they listened to the simple words of the Gaelic folk-song, fell off the bough with a thud on the grass.

The Highland girl made a beautiful picture as she stood.

Her bare feet were in the burn, the rippling water of which laved her ankles. The lobsters played about her feet, or clung affectionately to her toes, as if loath to leave the water and be gathered in the folds of her blue apron.

It was a scene to charm the heart of a Burne-Jones, or an Alma Tadema, or of anybody fond of lobsters.

The girl's golden hair flowed widely behind her, gathered in a single braid with a piece of stovepipe wire.

"Will you sell me one of your lobsters?"

Hannah looked up. There, standing in the burn a few yards above her, was the vision of a young man.

The beautiful Highland girl gazed at him fascinated.

He seemed a higher order of being.

He carried a fishing-rod and basket in his hand. He was dressed in a salmon-fishing costume of an English gentleman. Salmon-fishing boots reached to his thighs, while above them he wore a fishing-jacket fastened loosely with a fishing-belt about his waist. He wore a small fishing-cap on his head.

There were no fish in his basket.

He drew near to the Highland girl.

Hannah knew as she looked at him that it must be Ian McWhinus, the new laird.

At sight she loved him.

"Ye're sair welcome," she said, as she handed to the young man the finest of her lobsters.

He put it in his basket.

Then he felt in the pocket of his jacket and brought out a sixpenny-piece.

"You must let me pay for it," he said.

Hannah took the sixpence and held it a moment, flushing with true Highland pride.

"I'll no be selling the fush for money," she said.

Something in the girl's speech went straight to the young man's heart. He handed her half a crown. Whistling lightly, he strode off up the side of the burn. Hannah stood gazing after him spell-bound. She was aroused from her reverie by an angry voice calling her name.

"Hannah, Hannah," cried the voice, "come away ben; are ye daft, lass, that ye stand there keeking at a Mc-Whinus?"

Then Hannah realized what she had done.

She had spoken with a McWhinus, a thing that no McShamus had done for a hundred and fifty years. For nearly two centuries the McShamuses and the McWhinuses, albeit both dwellers in the Glen, had been torn asunder by one of those painful divisions by which the life of the Scotch people is broken into fragments.

It had arisen out of a point of spiritual belief.

It had been six generations agone at a Highland banquet, in the days when the unrestrained temper of the time gave way to wild orgies, during which theological discussions raged with unrestrained fury. Shamus McShamus, an embittered Calvinist, half crazed perhaps with liquor, had maintained that damnation could be achieved only by faith. Whimper McWhinus had held that damnation could be achieved also by good works. Inflamed with drink, McShamus had struck McWhinus across the temple with an oatcake and killed him. McShamus had been brought to trial. Although defended by some of the most skilled lawyers of Aucherlocherty, he had been acquitted. On the very night of his acquittal, Whangus McWhinus, the son of the murdered man, had lain in wait for Shamus McShamus, in the hollow of the Glen road where it rises to the cliff, and had shot him through the bagpipes. Since then the feud had raged with unquenched bitterness for a century and a half.

With each generation the difference between the two families became more acute. They differed on every possible point. They wore different tartans, sat under different ministers, drank different brands of whisky, and upheld different doctrines in regard to eternal punishment.

To add to the feud the McWhinuses had grown rich, while the McShamuses had become poor.

At least once in every generation a McWhinus or a McShamus had been shot, and always at the turn of the Glen road where it rose to the edge of the cliff. Finally, two generations gone, the McWhinuses had been raised to sudden wealth by the discovery of a coal mine on their land. To show their contempt for the McShamuses they had left the Glen to live in America. The McShamuses, to show their contempt for the McWhinuses, had remained in the Glen. The feud was kept alive in their memory.

And now the descendant of the McWhinuses had come back, and bought out the property of the Laird of Aucherlocherty beside the Glen. Ian McWhinus knew nothing of the feud. Reared in another atmosphere, the traditions of Scotland had no meaning for him. He had entirely degenerated. To him the tartan had become only a piece of coloured cloth. He wore a kilt as a masquerade costume for a Hallowe'en dance, and when it rained he put on a raincoat. He was no longer Scotch. More than that, he had married a beautiful American wife, a talcum-powder blonde with a dough face and the exquisite rotundity of the packing-house district of the Middle-West. Ian McWhinus was her slave. For her sake he had bought the lobster from Hannah. For her sake, too, he had scrutinized closely the beautiful Highland girl, for his wife was anxious to bring back a Scotch housemaid with her to Chicago.

And meantime Hannah, with the rapture of a new love in her heart, followed her father, Oyster McOyster McShamus, to the cottage. Oyster McOyster, even in advancing age, was a fine specimen of Scotch manhood. Ninety-seven years of age, he was approaching the time when many of his countrymen begin to show the ravages of time. But he bore himself straight as a lath, while his tall stature and his native Highland costume accentuated the fine outline of his form. This costume consisted of a black velvet beetle-shell jacket, which extended from the shoulder half-way down the back, and was continued in a short kilt of the tartan of the McShamuses, which extended from the waist half-way to the thigh. The costume reappeared again after an interval in the form of rolled golf stockings, which extended half-way up to the knee, while on his feet a pair of half shoes were buckled half-way up with a Highland clasp. On his head half-way between the ear and the upper superficies of the skull he wore half a Scotch cap, from which a tall rhinoceros feather extended half-way into the air.

A pair of bagpipes were beneath his arm, from which, as he walked, he blew those deep and plaintive sounds which have done much to imprint upon the characters of those who hear them a melancholy and resigned despair.

At the door of the cottage he turned and faced his daughter.

"What said Ian McWhinus to you i' the burnside?" he said fiercely.

" 'Twas nae muckle," said Hannah, and she added, for the truth was ever more to her than her father's wrath, "he gi'ed me saxpence for a fush."

"Siller!" shrieked the Highlander. "Siller from a Mc-Whinus!"

Hannah handed him the sixpence. Oyster McOyster dashed it fiecely on the ground, then picking it up he dashed it with full force against the wall of the cottage. Then, seizing it again, he dashed it angrily into the pocket of his kilt.

They entered the cottage.

Hannah had never seen her father's face so dour as it looked that night.

Their home seemed changed.

Hannah and her mother and father sat down that night in silence to their simple meal of oatmeal porridge and Scotch whisky. In the evening the mother sat to her spinning. Busily she plied her work, for it was a task of love. Her eldest born, Jamie, was away at college at Edinburgh, preparing for the ministry. His graduation day was approaching, and Jamie's mother was spinning him a pair of breeches against the day. The breeches were to be a surprise. Already they were shaping that way. Oyster McShamus sat reading the Old Testament in silence, while Hannah looked into the peat fire and thought of the beautiful young Laird. Only once the Highlander spoke.

"The McWhinus is back," he said, and his glance turned towards the old flint-lock musket on the wall. That night Hannah dreamed of the feud, of the Glen and the burn, of love, of lobsters, and of the Laird of Loch Aucherlocherty. And when she rose in the morning there was a wistful look in her eyes, and there came no song from her throat.

The days passed.

Each day the beautiful Highland girl saw the young Laird, though her father knew it not.

In the mornings she would see him as he came fishing to the burn. At times he wore his fishing-suit, at other times he had on a knickerbocker suit of shepherd's plaid with a domino pattern *négligé* shirt. For his sake the beautiful Highland girl made herself more beautiful still. Each morning she would twine a Scotch thistle in her hair, and pin a spray of burdock at her heart.

And at times he spoke to her. How Hannah treasured his words. Once, catching sight of her father in the distance, he had asked her who was the old sardine in the petticoats, and the girl had answered gladly that it was her father, for, as a fisherman's daughter, she was proud to have her father mistaken for a sardine.

At another time he had asked her if she was handy about the work of the house. How Hannah's heart had beat at the question. She made up her mind to spin him a pair of breeches like the ones now finishing for her brother Jamie.

And every evening as the sun set Hannah would watch in secret from the window of the cottage waiting for the young Laird to come past in his motor-car, down the Glen road to the sea. Always he would slacken the car at the sharp turn at the top of the cliff. For six generations no McWhinus had passed that spot after nightfall with his life. But Ian McWhinus knew nothing of the feud.

At times Oyster McOyster would see him pass, and standing at the roadside would call down Gaelic curses on his head.

Once, when her father was from home, Hannah had stood on the roadside, and Ian had stopped the machine and had taken her with him in the car for a ride. Hannah, her heart beating with delight, had listened to him as he explained how the car was worked. Had her father known that she had sat thus beside a McWhinus, he would have slain her where she sat.

The tragedy of Hannah's love ran swiftly to its close.

Each day she met the young Laird at the burn.

Each day she gave him the finest of her lobsters. She wore a new thistle every day.

And every night, in secret as her mother slept, she span a new concentric section of his breeches.

And the young Laird, when he went home, said to the talcum blonde, that the Highland fisher-girl was not half such a damn fool as she seemed.

Then came the fateful afternoon.

He stood beside her at the burn.

"Hannah," he said, as he bent towards her, "I want to take you to America."

Hannah had fallen fainting in his arms.

Ian propped her against a tree, and went home.

An hour later, when Hannah entered her home, her father was standing behind the fireplace. He was staring fixedly into the fire, with the flint-lock musket in his hands. There was the old dour look of the feud upon his face, and there were muttered curses on his lips. His wife Ellen clung to his arm and vainly sought to quiet him.

"Curse him," he muttered, "I'll e'en kill him the night as he passes in his deil machine."

Then Hannah knew that Oyster McShamus had seen her with Ian beside the burn. She turned and fled from the house. Straight up the road she ran towards the manor-house of Aucherlocherty to warn Ian. To save him from her father's wrath, that was her one thought. Night gathered about the Highland girl as she ran. The rain clouds and the gathering storm hung low with fitful lightning overhead. She still ran on. About her was the rolling of the thunder and the angry roaring of the swollen burn. Then the storm broke upon the darkness with all the fury of the Highland gale. The sky was rent with the fierce play of the elements. Yet on Hannah ran. Again and again the lightning hit her, but she ran on still. She fell over the stones, tripped and stumbled in the ruts, butted into the hedges, cannoned off against the stone walls. But she never stopped. She went quicker and quicker. The storm was awful. Lightning, fire, flame, and thunder were all about her. Trees were falling, hurdles were flying, birds were being struck by lightning. Dogs, sheep, and even cattle were hurled through the air.

She reached the manor-house, and stood a moment at the door. The storm had lulled, the rain ceased, and for a brief moment there was quiet. The light was streaming from the windows of the house. Hannah paused. Suddenly her heart misgave her. Her quick ear had caught the sound of a woman's voice within. She approached the window and looked in. Then, as if rooted to the spot, the Highland girl gazed and listened at the pane.

Ian lay upon a sofa. The *négligé* dressing-gown that he wore enhanced the pallid beauty of his face. Beside him sat the talcum-powder blonde. She was feeding him with chocolates. Hannah understood. Ian had trifled with her love. He had bought her lobsters to win her heart, only to cast it aside.

Hannah turned from the window. She plucked the thistle from her throat and flung it on the ground. Then, as she turned her eye, she caught sight of the motor standing in the shed.

"The deil machine!" she muttered, while the wild light of Highland frenzy gathered in her eye; then, as she rushed to it and tore the tarpaulin from off it, "Ye'll no be wanting of a mark the night, Oyster McShamus," she cried.

A moment later, the motor, with Hannah at the wheel,

was thundering down the road to the Glen. The power was on to the full, and the demented girl clung tight to the steering-gear as the machine rocked and thundered down the descent. The storm was raging again, and the thunder mingled with the roar of the machine as it coursed madly towards the sea. The great eye of the motor blazed in front. The lurid light of it flashed a second on the trees and the burn as it passed, and flashed blinding on the eyes of Oyster as he stood erect on the cliff-side below, musket in hand, and faced the blazing apparition that charged upon him with the old Highland blood surging in his veins.

It was all over in a moment—a blinding flash of lightning, the report of a musket, a great peal of thunder, and the motor bearing the devoted girl hurled headlong over the cliff.

They found her there in the morning. She lay on her side motionless, half buried in the sand, upturned towards the blue Highland sky, serene now after the passing of the storm. Quiet and still she lay. The sea-birds seemed to pause in their flight to look down on her. The little group of Scotch people that had gathered stood and gazed at her with reverential awe. They made no attempt to put her together. It would have been useless. Her gasoline tubes were twisted and bent, her tank burst, her sprockets broken from their sides, and her steering-gear an utter wreck. The motor would never run again.

After a time they roused themselves from their grief and looked about for Hannah. They found her. She lay among the sand and seaweed, her fair hair soaked in gasoline. Then they looked about for Oyster McShamus. Him, too, they found, lying half buried in the grass and soaked in whisky. Then they looked about for Ellen. They found her lying across the door of the cottage half buried in Jamie's breeches.

Then they gathered them up. Life was not extinct. They chafed their hands. They rubbed their feet. They put hot bricks upon their stomachs. They poured hot whisky down their throats. That brought them to.

Of course.

It always does.

They all lived.

But the feud was done for. That was the end of it. Hannah had put it to the bad.

ABOUT THE EDITOR

HART DAY LEAVITT was born in 1909 at Concord, New Hampshire. His great interest, literature, was aroused at Phillips Exeter Academy, and he went on to major in English at Yale University. After graduating in 1932, he tried a number of odd jobs—selling children's clothes, playing in a jazz band, and writing for a newspaper— but eventually settled on teaching English, and has been an instructor at Phillips Andover Academy for the past twenty-three years. As a free-lance photographer and writer, he has contributed to newspapers and magazines and is the editor of *The Looking Glass Book of Stories*. In 1938 he married Caroline Williams Parker of Concord, New Hampshire, and they have three children, Sally, Ned and Judy.

LOOKING GLASS LIBRARY

The publishers of the Looking Glass Library are Jason Epstein, Clelia Carroll, and Edward Gorey. The consulting editors are W. H. Auden, Phyllis McGinley, and Edmund Wilson.

The following titles are available in the series: